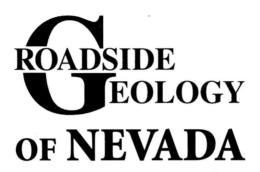

ROADSIDE GEOLOGY OF NEVADA

FRANK DeCOURTEN AND NORMA BIGGAR

2017
Mountain Press Publishing Company
Missoula, Montana

Geological maps for the road guides are based on the
2007 *Geologic Map of Nevada* by A. E. Crawford

The maps and illustrations in this volume were
constructed by Chelsea Feeney (cmcfeeney.com).

Photographs by authors unless otherwise credited.

Roadside Geology is a registered trademark
of Mountain Press Publishing Company.

Library of Congress Cataloging-in-Publication Data

Names: DeCourten, Frank. | Biggar, Norma.
Title: Roadside geology of Nevada / Frank DeCourten and Norma Biggar.
Description: Missoula, Montana : Mountain Press Publishing Company, [2017] |
  Series: Roadside geology series | Includes bibliographical references and index.
Identifiers: LCCN 2016051729 | ISBN 9780878426720 (pbk. : alk. paper)
Subjects: LCSH: Geology—Nevada—Guidebooks. | Nevada—Guidebooks.
Classification: LCC QD137 .D43 2017 | DDC 557.93—dc23
LC record available at https://lccn.loc.gov/2016051729

Printed in the United States of America

MP **Mountain Press**
PUBLISHING COMPANY
P.O. Box 2399 • Missoula, MT 59806 • 406-728-1900
800-234-5308 • info@mtnpress.com
www.mountain-press.com

To the memory of Norma Biggar.

Acknowledgments

Land of space and sunshine, rock and sky
—Woody Paul

Anyone who travels the landscape of Nevada quickly comes to understand why Woody Paul (Paul Chrisman) used those lyrics to praise the Silver State in the 1980s tune recorded by Riders in the Sky. The spaces in Nevada are *really* wide and *really* open, and rock is everywhere, illuminated by the brilliant desert sunshine and largely undraped by vegetation. Armies of scientists have swarmed the bold rock exposures, seeking to understand the deep history of one of North America's most magnificent natural regions. Their collective efforts have resulted in a literal mountain of research reports and geological maps that provide the foundation for our current understanding of Nevada geology. In addition, new imaging and analytical techniques are allowing us to explore the rock record and geologic structures of the state in ways that were unimaginable only a few decades ago. Unraveling the tangled geological history of Nevada is a continuing quest, an on-going adventure in reconstructing a tale of landscape evolution encompassing billions of years.

When you drive Nevada's highways in search of interesting geology, be sure to fill your vehicle's tank with gas, bring plenty of food and water, and tell someone where you are going.

Any book describing Nevada's geology is, of necessity, a collaborative effort. It is beyond the capacity of any individual, or pair of them, to see every rock exposure in the state and absorb every detail of Nevada's intricate geologic history. In compiling the information for this volume, we have utilized heavily the resources of the DeLaMare Science and Engineering Library at the University of Nevada, Reno, and the Earth Sciences and Map Library at the University of California, Berkeley. In addition, the Great Basin Science Sample and Records Library in Reno served as a center for information and guidance during the early stages of library and field research. There, the staff of the Nevada Bureau of Mines and Geology (Jim Faulds, director) was consistently helpful in sharing their resources, expertise, and knowledge. Laura Ruud, executive manager of the Geological Society of Nevada, also provided both enthusiastic encouragement of our project and access to the excellent GSN field guides and symposia proceedings. Jennifer Carey at Mountain Press Publishing Company provided skillful editing of the original manuscript along with project oversight, all with a generous portion of patience. The graphic illustrations in this book were produced by Chelsea Feeney, whose extraordinary technical skills and creative talents are evident throughout the volume. Finally, we owe a debt of gratitude to those innumerable colleagues, friends, and family members who patiently tolerated our obsession with Nevada geology as this project progressed from a tenuous idea to a printed volume.

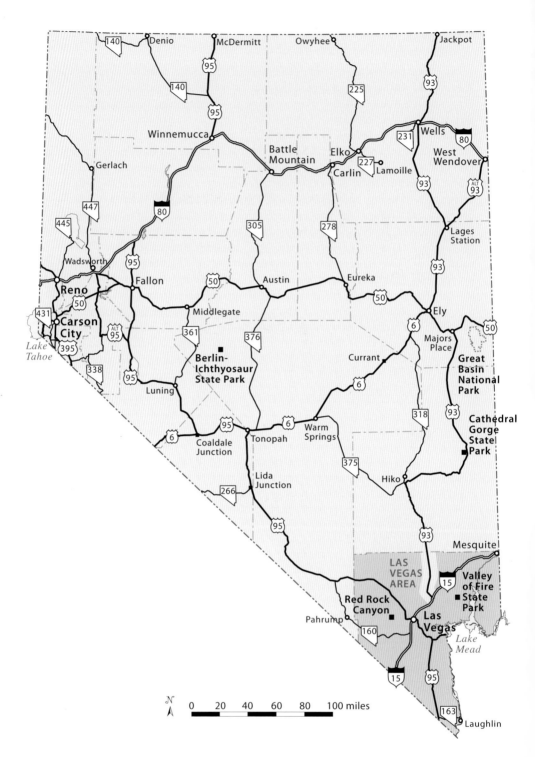

Roads and sections of Roadside Geology of Nevada.

CONTENTS

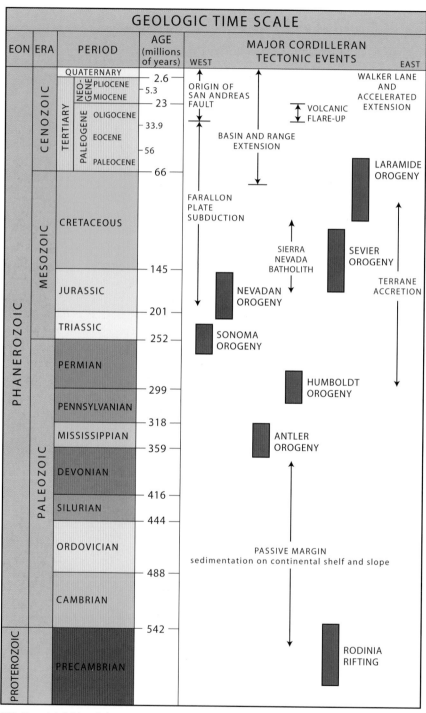

GEOLOGIC TIME SCALE

EON	ERA	PERIOD	AGE (millions of years)	MAJOR CORDILLERAN TECTONIC EVENTS

WEST   EAST

QUATERNARY
PLIOCENE — 2.6
MIOCENE — 5.3
— 23
OLIGOCENE — 33.9
EOCENE — 56
PALEOCENE — 66

— 145

— 201

— 252

— 299

— 318

— 359

— 416

— 444

— 488

— 542

CENOZOIC · TERTIARY · NEOGENE · PALEOGENE

MESOZOIC · CRETACEOUS · JURASSIC · TRIASSIC

PALEOZOIC · PERMIAN · PENNSYLVANIAN · MISSISSIPPIAN · DEVONIAN · SILURIAN · ORDOVICIAN · CAMBRIAN

PHANEROZOIC

PROTEROZOIC · PRECAMBRIAN

ORIGIN OF SAN ANDREAS FAULT

WALKER LANE AND ACCELERATED EXTENSION

VOLCANIC FLARE-UP

BASIN AND RANGE EXTENSION

LARAMIDE OROGENY

FARALLON PLATE SUBDUCTION

SIERRA NEVADA BATHOLITH

SEVIER OROGENY

TERRANE ACCRETION

NEVADAN OROGENY

SONOMA OROGENY

HUMBOLDT OROGENY

ANTLER OROGENY

PASSIVE MARGIN
sedimentation on continental shelf and slope

RODINIA RIFTING

NOTE: Nevada's fold and thrust structures formed during the Antler through Laramide Orogenies. Fault-block structures were superimposed on these during the Basin and Range extension.

Introduction to Nevada's Magnificent Landscape

Though it is commonly known for its bright lights and frenzied urban centers, Nevada is a land of wide-open spaces with rugged desert mountains and broad arid valleys. More than three hundred named mountain ranges, some with snow-capped peaks soaring to elevations exceeding 13,000 feet, rise from the dry plains like an armada of rocky ships sailing north through a boundless sagebrush ocean. Nevada's rocks are well exposed and document an incredible story encompassing more than 2 billion years of geological evolution along the western edge of North America. Exploring the rocks and landscape features of Nevada gives deeper meaning to the modern landscapes, provides a framework for understanding the extraordinary mineral wealth of the state, and establishes the context for current phenomena, such as earthquakes, geothermal activity, and landslides. Nevada is, without exaggeration, a geological paradise, and exploring it offers endless intrigue and wonder to those who seek to understand the story beneath the scenery.

One way to explore Nevada geology is to travel its roads with eyes tuned to the natural features and rock exposures. Though there are probably fewer paved roads per square mile in Nevada than in most other states, dozens of well-maintained roads cross the state in every direction. But before we begin exploring the roadside geology along more than thirty of Nevada's roads, we'll describe the broader physiographic and geologic setting of the state, the nature of its rock record, the tectonic history of the western edge of our continent, and how the desert landscape has been affected by climate change in the recent geological past.

THE BASIN AND RANGE PROVINCE

Nearly all of Nevada lies within the physiographic region of western North America known as the Basin and Range Province. This vast area encompasses more than 300,000 square miles, stretching from Oregon and Idaho in the north southward through Nevada and Utah to eastern California, southern Arizona, and Mexico. As the name suggests, this area is characterized by a repetitive pattern of alternating mountain ranges and intervening valleys that define a distinctive corrugated, or wrinkled, landscape. Much of the Basin and Range Province either lies in the rain shadow cast by the Sierra Nevada and Cascades range to the west or is located in latitudes that receive minimal rainfall, so that desert conditions prevail throughout most of it. Within the Nevada portion of the Basin and Range, the ranges are typically less than 50 miles long and 10 to

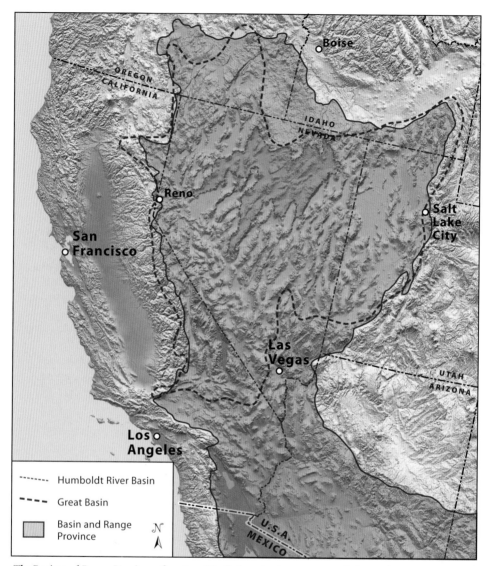

The Basin and Range Province of western North America is a vast area of alternating mountains and valleys. The dashed purple line delineates the Great Basin, a region of internal drainage where rivers carry water from high watersheds to enclosed basins. The shaded blue area is the drainage basin of the Humboldt River, the largest internally drained river basin in the Great Basin. —Modified from the National Park Service and the Geological Society of America

25 miles wide, rise a few thousand feet above the adjacent lowlands, and are generally aligned to the north or northeast. The intervening valleys are generally much broader than the adjacent mountains, but with comparable lengths and a parallel north-south alignment. Many of the two hundred or so named valleys in Nevada are completely enclosed, with no drainage into adjacent

valleys or river systems. Dry lakebeds, or playas, are very common features of the intermountain basins in Nevada.

The northern portion of the Basin and Range, which encompasses nearly all of Nevada, is distinct from the rest of the province by virtue of its internal drainage. The few rivers that exist in this dry expanse, known as the Great Basin, carry water from adjacent highlands to terminal sinks, where it collects in lakes, seeps into the ground, or evaporates into the dry desert air. In the eastern Great Basin, several rivers flowing from the Wasatch Range of Utah deliver water to the Great Salt Lake. In northern Nevada, the Humboldt River, the largest river entirely within the province, flows more than 300 miles from its source near the East Humboldt Range to the Humboldt Sink, southwest of Lovelock, Nevada. On the western side of the Great Basin, rivers draining the Sierra Nevada flow short distances before terminating in enclosed basins or sinks. Among these streams are the Truckee, Carson, and Walker Rivers, which end, respectively, in Pyramid Lake, the Carson Sink, and Walker Lake. Though most of Nevada lies in the Great Basin, there are exceptions. Small areas in extreme northern Nevada drain into the Snake River via the Jarbidge, Owyhee, and Bruneau Rivers, while parts of southeast Nevada are drained by tributaries of the Colorado River such as the White and Virgin Rivers.

The mountain ranges of Nevada are typically bounded by great fractures in the crust, known as normal faults, which are characterized by the downward movement of the block of rock above the inclined fracture. The basins between the mountains generally represent this sunken block, while the mountain ranges are formed from masses of rock lifted relative to the downfaulted basin blocks. Sediment, such as sand, silt, and gravel derived from erosion of the mountain bedrock, accumulates in the basins, sometimes to depths exceeding 10,000 feet. This arrangement of elevated blocks and subsided basins creates the distinctive landscape described by geologists as horst-and-graben topography, and Nevada provides one of the best examples in the world of this pattern.

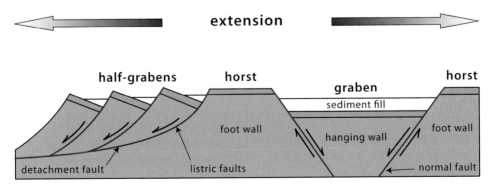

Normal faulting elevates mountain blocks while simultaneously downfaulting the basin blocks, forming horst-and-graben topography. Half-grabens result from listric normal faults that cause tilting of the blocks above the fault plane as they are displaced downward. Many listric faults in the Basin and Range merge in the subsurface into a nearly horizontal plane known as a detachment fault.

The horsts (German for "heap") are defined as the elevated bedrock blocks bounded on each side by a normal fault, and the sediment-filled valleys correspond to the grabens (German for "trench").

While many of Nevada's mountain ranges are true horsts, some of them have prominent normal faults on only one side, which produces a tilted mountain range with asymmetric slopes. A steep escarpment forms on the actively faulted side, while the opposing slope gently descends into the adjacent lowland. The flanking valley, bordered by a normal fault on one side only, is known as a half-graben. The sediment that collects in the half-graben is usually much thicker on one side of the valley than the other. The geological structure of Nevada's basins, and whether they are grabens or half-grabens, strongly influences the slope and dimensions of the valleys, the amount and distribution of subsurface water and sediment, and the location of geothermal activity.

Normal faults result from tension, a stretching force that fractures Earth's crust into numerous blocks and allows the terrain to be lengthened in a direction perpendicular to the trend of the faults. The north-south trending mountain ranges of Nevada, along with the valleys that separate them, have developed because geological forces are stretching the crust in an east-west direction. Geologists studying the subsurface structure of Basin and Range normal faults have discovered that many of them flatten as they descend beneath the surface, becoming nearly horizontal planes at depths of 3 or 4 miles. Such normal faults that flatten with depth are known as listric normal faults. The block of rock that moves down a curved listric fault must rotate as it descends. This explains why rock layers in many of Nevada's mountain ranges appear to be tilted in one direction or another. It is not uncommon for several listric normal faults to flatten into the same horizontal plane in the subsurface, creating a regional detachment fault, which can result in even greater extension of the crust as the blocks above slide farther apart from each other on this buried plane.

THE TECTONIC FORCES TEARING NEVADA APART

The extension of the Nevada portion of the Basin and Range Province began approximately 40 to 30 million years ago, and since that time the region's crust has been stretched by as much as 100 percent. This means that the current sites of Reno and Salt Lake City are now twice as far apart as they were prior to the onset of normal faulting. The Basin and Range Province is an extended land, a portion of North America that is being stretched to the west relative to the more stable parts of the continent to the east, such as the Rocky Mountains and Colorado Plateau. Powerful tectonic forces are behind this stretching.

The interaction of tectonic plates on Earth's surface generates these forces. The plates are made of lithosphere, which consists of all the crust, along with an underlying slab of rigid dense rock of the uppermost mantle. The lithosphere is about 60 miles thick and rests on the asthenosphere, a zone of soft, semisolid rock in the upper mantle. The crust constitutes the upper skin on this thick slab and may be composed of relatively dense basalt of the oceanic crust, or less dense and generally thicker granitic crust of the continents. Heat flowing from the deep interior of Earth causes slow currents to form in the asthenosphere

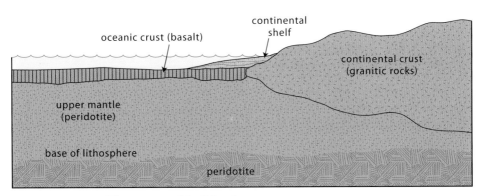

The structure of the lithosphere. —Adapted from Alt and Hyndman, 1984

which, in turn, creates stress in the rigid lithosphere. The lithosphere is broken into plates, which collide with each other, are carried apart in opposite directions, or simply slide past each other. The interactions between these plates are responsible for all global-scale geological phenomena such as mountain-building, volcanoes, and earthquakes.

In western North America, several plates interact with one another in a somewhat complicated fashion, a situation that has developed over the past 30 million years, a relatively brief span of geologic time. Today, the western margin of North America at the latitude of Nevada is dominated by the boundary between the Pacific Plate moving to the northwest and the North American Plate sliding slowly to the southwest. The relative motion between the two plates is mostly lateral, or side by side, as the Pacific Plate slides northwest along the leading edge of North America with a displacement of about 2 inches per year, comparable to the rate of human fingernail growth. Such plate interactions, where two plates slide past each other, define what is known as a transform fault boundary. The famous San Andreas fault system in California is the transform fault boundary between the North American and Pacific Plates.

The entire western edge of North America inland from the San Andreas fault system is being slowly sheared from the stable parts of the continent to the east. A large fragment of the edge of the continent, from the Coast Ranges of California to the eastern edge of the Sierra Nevada, appears to be moving as a coherent block. This mass has been called the Sierra Nevada–Great Valley microplate, and it represents a fragment of western North America being torn away from the rest of the continent by the northwesterly motion of the Pacific Plate. Together, the Pacific Plate and the Sierra Nevada–Great Valley microplate drag the lithosphere behind them, pulling and stretching the crust in Nevada to the west and northwest. These plate tectonic forces are the primary reason why the Basin and Range Province, and hence the magnificent mountain ranges of Nevada, have formed in the recent geologic past. There may be other sources of tensional stress in the Basin and Range lithosphere, such as flow in the underlying asthenosphere or gravitational collapse of former highlands, but it is probably no coincidence that the Basin and Range pattern is best developed inland

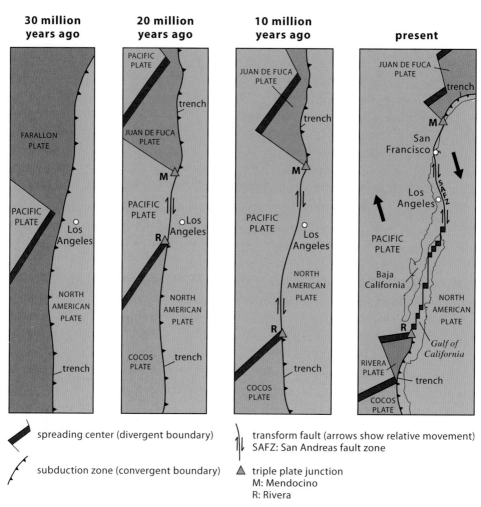

| 30 million years ago | 20 million years ago | 10 million years ago | present |

The San Andreas fault system originated about 30 million years ago as a consequence of the interaction between the North American and Pacific Plates. North of the San Andreas fault system, a smaller oceanic slab, the Juan de Fuca plate is moving obliquely toward the North American Plate in what geologists refer to as a convergent plate boundary. This kind of interaction results in the descent of the oceanic lithosphere beneath the continent in a process known as subduction. —Wallce, R. E. 1990. US Geological Survey Professional Paper 1515

from the transform plate boundary. To the north, where a convergent boundary between the Juan de Fuca and North American Plates prevails, the physiographic and geologic patterns that typify the Basin and Range are either less prominent or nonexistent.

Measurement of crustal movements in western North America utilizing very precise GPS stations reveal that the rate and direction of stretching varies across the Basin and Range Province. In Nevada, the eastern portion of the state is being stretched to the west at a rate of about 1 to 2 millimeters (about 0.05 inch) per year. In western Nevada, the rate increases to as much as 12 millimeters (0.5 inch) per year, and the direction shifts slightly to the north-west because of northwest-directed shear stresses along the western edge of the region. This interesting pattern reflects the rapid movement of the Pacific Plate to the northwest relative to the edge of the North American Plate.

In western Nevada, the characteristic normal faults of the Basin and Range are associated with many strike-slip faults, which involve lateral, rather than vertical displacement of the rock masses. Strike-slip faults result from shear stresses that rip the crust apart and propel the blocks past each other later-ally. Strike-slip faults are especially prominent in a 50-mile-wide zone, known as the Walker Lane, that extends parallel to the California border through

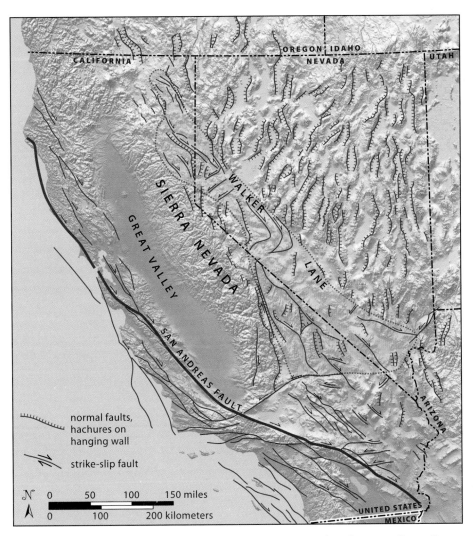

The Walker Lane along the California-Nevada border is a zone of northwest trending strike-slip faults that accommodates shear stress between the Pacific and North American Plates.
—Based on Henry, Faulds, and dePolo, 2007

western Nevada from north of Reno to Las Vegas. About 25 percent of the relative motion between the Pacific and North American Plates is accommodated by the strike-slip faults in the Walker Lane, while the remainder is distributed across the San Andreas fault system.

Earthquakes in Nevada

Nevada is one of the most seismically active regions in North America. Because earthquakes result from the energy released as rocks rupture under tectonic forces, it is not very surprising that the highly faulted crust in Nevada experiences continuous seismic activity. Nevada residents have felt thousands of earthquakes since the 1850s, when most of the towns and settlements were established. Among these earthquakes are some powerful events, such as three temblors, the largest with an estimated magnitude of 7.75, in Pleasant Valley in 1915; a magnitude 7.3 event in west-central Nevada in 1932; and a series of

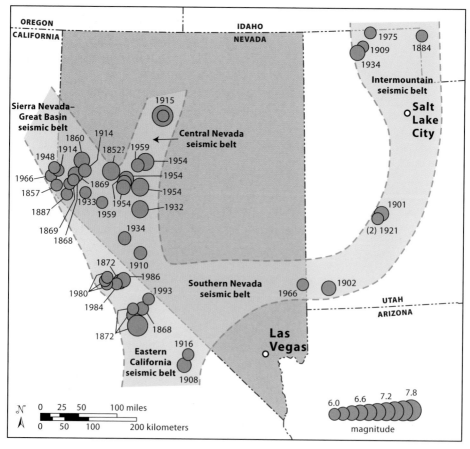

Seismic zones in Nevada, with dates and locations of major historic earthquakes.
—Modified from dePolo and dePolo, 1999

strong events in Fairview Valley in western Nevada in 1954 that caused ground ruptures still visible today. Earthquakes are a serious hazard to Nevada residents and visitors and serve as a constant reminder that the geological processes that have shaped the Nevada landscape remain active today.

Seismic activity is not randomly distributed in Nevada. The majority of Nevada's moderate earthquakes occur in the Sierra Nevada–Great Basin seismic belt, which is approximately aligned with the Walker Lane, the region of numerous northwest-trending strike-slip faults in western Nevada. Branching off this zone is a northeast-aligned belt of earthquake activity known as the Central Nevada seismic belt, a zone of significant seismicity that has produced some of Nevada's most powerful historic earthquakes. The least well-defined of Nevada's earthquake zones is the east-west-trending Southern Nevada seismic belt, which links the seismically active regions of the Mojave Desert with the Intermountain seismic belt in Utah. In this region, some of the small to moderate earthquakes may be related the nuclear weapons testing at Yucca Mountain or to the filling of Lake Mead behind Hoover Dam, but the level of natural seismicity in this broad zone is still above average. In several places in Nevada, historic earthquakes have produced ground ruptures and exposed fault surfaces, known as scarps, that are clearly visible. The abrupt escarpments that typify the rugged mountains of the Basin and Range are the result of a long history of incremental displacement along normal faults, some of which must have produced strong prehistoric earthquakes.

ROCKS OF NEVADA

Prior to 30 million years ago, a long series of earlier plate interactions shaped the western edge of North America, including the part that eventually became Nevada. We will briefly review these plate tectonic events later, but one of the overall consequences of Nevada's extraordinary geologic history is its incredibly varied and complex rock assemblages. Nearly every kind of rock known to geologists can be found somewhere in Nevada, and some minerals occur nowhere else. Exploring the geology of Nevada's roadsides is rather like twisting a geological kaleidoscope: every bend in the road brings new rocks into view. While it is impossible in a modest book to describe all the rocks and minerals that can be encountered on Nevada's roads, a few basic ideas will be helpful in learning the most from your travels through the state.

Rocks are aggregates of minerals, naturally occurring inorganic solid compounds. Thus, quartz, a common mineral, is a relatively pure compound consisting of silicon (Si) and oxygen (O) atoms bonded in a ratio of 1 to 2 . We can write the chemical formula as SiO_2. Other common minerals include feldspar (a common form is composed of silicon, oxygen, potassium, and aluminum or $KAlSi_3O_8$), hematite (an iron oxide, Fe_2O_3), and calcite (a calcium carbonate, $CaCO_3$). The composition of rocks, because they are aggregates of different minerals, cannot be expressed with chemical formulas. Granite, for example, generally consists of five or six different minerals, each with its own unique formula. Worldwide, geologists have cataloged more than four thousand different minerals, while the rocks composed of these are arranged into igneous,

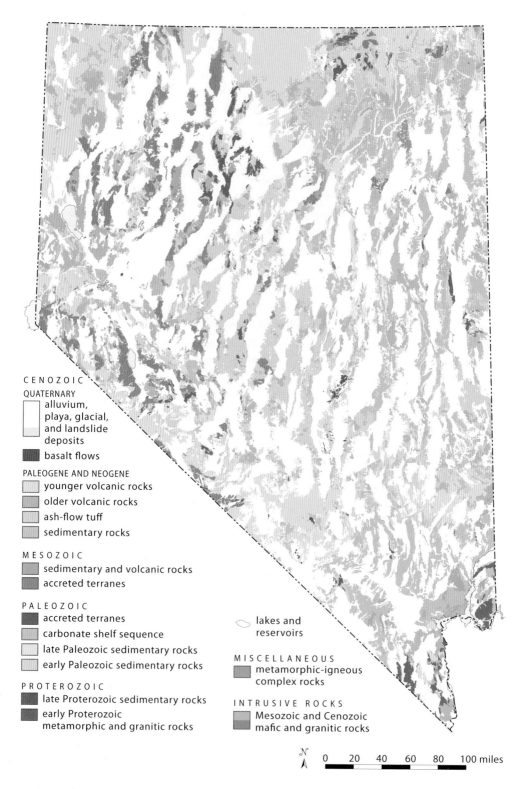

CENOZOIC

QUATERNARY
- alluvium, playa, glacial, and landslide deposits
- basalt flows

PALEOGENE AND NEOGENE
- younger volcanic rocks
- older volcanic rocks
- ash-flow tuff
- sedimentary rocks

MESOZOIC
- sedimentary and volcanic rocks
- accreted terranes

PALEOZOIC
- accreted terranes
- carbonate shelf sequence
- late Paleozoic sedimentary rocks
- early Paleozoic sedimentary rocks

PROTEROZOIC
- late Proterozoic sedimentary rocks
- early Proterozoic metamorphic and granitic rocks

- lakes and reservoirs

MISCELLANEOUS
- metamorphic-igneous complex rocks

INTRUSIVE ROCKS
- Mesozoic and Cenozoic mafic and granitic rocks

N

0 20 40 60 80 100 miles

The diversity of rock types in Nevada is clearly represented by the somewhat complicated pattern of colors on the state geologic map. —From Nevada Bureau of Mines and Geology, 1999

sedimentary, and metamorphic categories, depending on the manner in which the mineral aggregates formed.

Igneous rocks form from molten magma that cools and crystallizes into a solid mass of minerals. The magma may cool quickly on the surface following volcanic eruption, in which case the igneous rocks is said to be extrusive, or volcanic. With minimal time to grow, mineral crystals in extrusive rocks are mostly invisible, giving the rock a dull, even surface appearance. Extrusive igneous rocks often have gas bubbles, or vesicles, preserved in them. Common extrusive rocks in Nevada include basalt, andesite, dacite, latite, and rhyolite, depending on what minerals the rocks contain. When magma cools instantly, a glassy rock known as obsidian is the result. Pumice, another glassy-textured extrusive rock, contains numerous vesicles that give it a characteristic bubbly appearance.

Another type of igneous rock forms during violent volcanic explosions when hot particles and rock fragments collect on the surface following the blast. These rocks, known as pyroclastic rocks, may consist of microscopic ash particles (tuff) or larger chunks and pieces (agglomerate). Tuffs are extremely widespread in Nevada, and sometimes the tiny ash particles are welded into a dense, glassy rock known as an ignimbrite, formed when hot, glowing ash blown from an erupting volcano accumulates and hardens on the surface.

When magma cools slowly deep underground, a mass of igneous rock forms with large, easily visible, intergrown crystals. Such rocks are known as intrusive, or plutonic, and can be identified by the sparkling flash and glitter resulting from the intergrowth of larger crystals. There are many types of intrusive igneous rocks in Nevada, but the most common are granite, granodiorite, quartz monzonite, diorite, and gabbro. The distinctions between these rocks reflect the variable identity and proportions of minerals in each type.

Sedimentary rocks consist of particles such as sand, or chemicals such as salt, that accumulate in layers and become hardened, or lithified, over time. Sandstone, perhaps the most well-known example of a sedimentary rock, is composed mostly of sand-sized grains less than about 0.1 inch in size. Smaller particles make up siltstone and shale, while the larger, rounded particles making up gravel deposits are known as conglomerate after they become lithified into solid rock. The term *breccia* denotes a sedimentary rock consisting of large fragments similar to those in conglomerate, but with an angular form defined by sharp edges and corners. Some sedimentary rocks consist mostly of chemicals precipitated from water as mineral crystals, rather than rock particles. Examples of chemical sedimentary rocks that are especially common in Nevada include limestone (composed of calcite), dolomite, chert (microcrystalline quartz), gypsum, and rock salt (consisting of halite). Sometimes sedimentary rocks are given names that identify special types of sediments that collected under specific circumstances. For example, tillite is composed of nonstratified sand and gravels deposited from melting glacial ice. Evaporites are mixed assemblages of minerals such as salt and gypsum left behind after large bodies of water evaporate. Fanglomerate is mass of sand, gravel, and larger blocks that accumulated in an alluvial fan at the base of a mountain range prior to lithification.

Metamorphic rocks are igneous or sedimentary rocks that have been altered from their original state by heat, pressure, or chemical activity in the geological environment. Because of Nevada's tortuous geological history and widespread occurrence of igneous rocks, metamorphic rocks are very common in the state. Some well-known varieties include banded gneiss, platy slate, schist (characterized by shiny flakes of crinkled mica), marble (metamorphosed limestone or dolomite), and quartzite (the result of sandstone metamorphism). Along fault planes, metamorphic rocks called mylonites are produced when rock is crushed, sheared, and compacted during episodes of fault slip or seismic events. Jasperoid is a hard and dense, reddish-black rock that typically forms along fault planes in masses of limestone and dolomite.

Throughout Nevada, many rocks have been altered in and around hot springs. The combination of high temperature, acidic solutions, and reactive vapors results in a form of metamorphism known as hydrothermal alteration. This process produces soft clay and vividly colored metal oxide minerals along with sulfur-bearing minerals such as pyrite, or fool's gold. Hydrothermal alteration has been extremely important in the development of the valuable ores of gold, silver, copper, and other metallic elements in many of Nevada's famous mining districts.

Formations are packages of rock with more or less uniform characteristics. A formation is a sequence of rock layers, or a body of unstratified rock, that has similar characteristics, such as grain size, texture, composition, and bedding thickness. The combination of such features serves to distinguish the rock in a particular formation from other sequences of rock adjacent to it. Because the rocks that make up a formation are more or less uniform in their characteristics, they represent rocks that originated under similar conditions in similar environments. The boundaries between successive formations are placed where the characteristics of the rocks change, for example where coarse sandstone is overlain by a sequence of fine mudstone layers. Such shifts represent changes in the nature of sediment accumulation, which, in turn, suggest changes in the environment of deposition. Formations, then, represent chapters or phases of more or less constant conditions in the overall continuum of environmental change recorded by successive formations.

Formations are generally named for the locality where the rock unit is particularly well exposed or was first studied and defined. Vinini Creek, for example, flows from the eastern Roberts Mountains about 25 miles north of Eureka. In 1942, geologists named a sequence of rock layers exposed along this creek the Vinini Formation. That name is now used for this unique assemblage of rocks no matter where it is exposed in north-central Nevada. On occasion, when a particular type of rock composes nearly all of a formation, the word *formation* is replaced with an epithet reflective of that dominant lithology, or rock type. Such is the case in Nevada for formations like the Eureka Quartzite and the Pioche Shale.

More than eight hundred different formations are recognized in the state. In addition, many of these formations are subdivided into members, as in the Bartine Member of the McColley Canyon Formation. Members are also normally designated by geographic names, adding even more terms to the lexicon of Nevada geology. Finally, formations of similar rock types, age, and origin can be grouped together as a formal group. The Star Peak Group of the Humboldt Range region of northwest Nevada, for example, consists of the Prida Formation and the overlying Natchez Pass Formation.

MINERALS AND MINING

Few regions of comparable size anywhere on Earth are endowed with such extensive and varied mineral resources as Nevada. From gold and silver to limestone and lithium, dozens of different mineral commodities are currently produced from seventy major mining and processing centers in Nevada. Miners have been extracting ore for more than 150 years, and nearly eight hundred localities have been identified in Nevada where significant concentrations of valuable minerals occur, though not all of these proved feasible for mining. It is impossible to overstate the importance of mining and mineral processing in the history, economics, and culture of Nevada. In 2012, for instance, the total value of all mined commodities in Nevada was just under $10.5 billion, and the mining industry directly employed 15,400 people while providing jobs for another 65,000 people in mining-related work. In a geological province with such pervasive mineralization, it is little wonder that evidence of mining can be seen almost everywhere when traveling the roads and highways of Nevada.

Although Nevada is known as the Silver State, the most valuable mineral commodity produced in the state today is gold. In 2012, Nevada produced more than 5 million ounces of gold, making it the leading gold-producing state in the

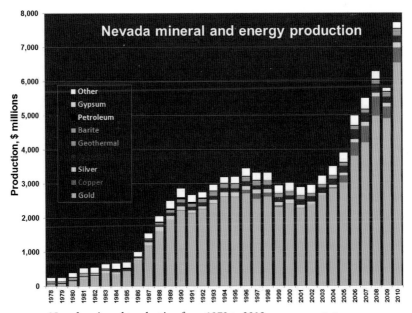

Nevada mineral production from 1978 to 2010. —From Price and others, 2011

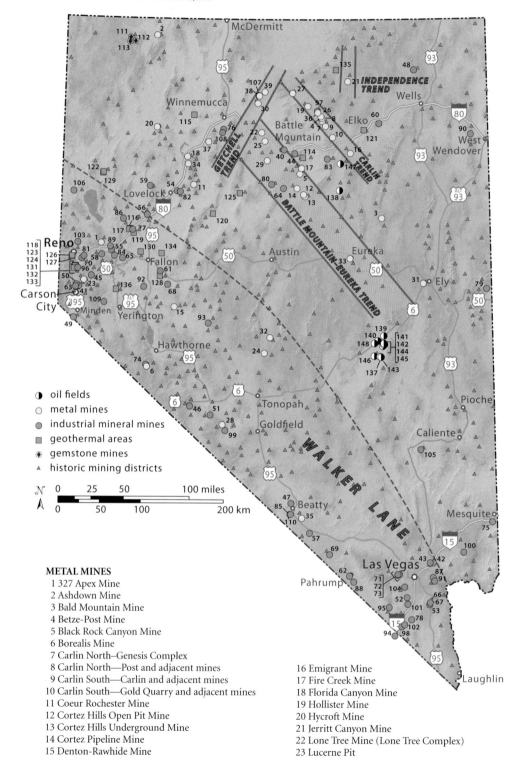

Historic mining districts, metal mines, industrial mineral mines, oil fields, gemstone mines, and geothermal areas of Nevada. Many are concentrated along trends.
—Modified from Muntean and Davis, 2014

- ◐ oil fields
- ○ metal mines
- ● industrial mineral mines
- ▪ geothermal areas
- ◆ gemstone mines
- ▲ historic mining districts

METAL MINES

1 327 Apex Mine
2 Ashdown Mine
3 Bald Mountain Mine
4 Betze-Post Mine
5 Black Rock Canyon Mine
6 Borealis Mine
7 Carlin North–Genesis Complex
8 Carlin North—Post and adjacent mines
9 Carlin South—Carlin and adjacent mines
10 Carlin South—Gold Quarry and adjacent mines
11 Coeur Rochester Mine
12 Cortez Hills Open Pit Mine
13 Cortez Hills Underground Mine
14 Cortez Pipeline Mine
15 Denton-Rawhide Mine

16 Emigrant Mine
17 Fire Creek Mine
18 Florida Canyon Mine
19 Hollister Mine
20 Hycroft Mine
21 Jerritt Canyon Mine
22 Lone Tree Mine (Lone Tree Complex)
23 Lucerne Pit

24 Manhattan Gulch Mine
25 Marigold Mine
26 Meikle Mine
27 Midas Mine
28 Mineral Ridge Mine
29 Phoenix Mine
30 Pinson Mine
31 Robinson Mine
32 Round Mountain Mine
(Smoky Valley Common Operation)
33 Ruby Hill Mine
34 Standard Mine
35 Sterling Mine
36 Storm Mine
37 Sunrise Gold Placer Mine
38 Turquoise Ridge Joint Venture
39 Twin Creeks Mine

INDUSTRIAL MINERAL MINES
40 3D Pit
41 Adams Claim Gypsum Mine
42 Apex Landfill Pit
43 Apex Quarry
44 Argenta Mine
45 Basalite Dayton Pit
46 Basalt Mine
47 Beatty (D and H Mining) Quarry
48 Big Ledge Mine
49 Bing Materials Pit
50 Black and Red Cinder Pits
51 Blanco Mine
52 Blue Diamond Pit
53 Boulder Ranch Quarry
54 Buff-Satin Mine
55 Celite Plant
56 Churchill Limestone Project
57 Cinder Cone Pit
58 Clark Mine
59 Colado Mine
60 Elburz Pit
61 Fallon Bentonite Project
62 Gamebird Pit
63 Goni Pit
64 Greystone Mine
65 Hazen Pit
66 Henderson Community Pit
67 Henderson Community Pit
68 Huck Salt
69 IMV Pits
70 Lockwood Quarry
71 Lone Mountain
72 Lone Mountain
73 Lone Mountain Community Pit
74 Lucky Boy Quarry
75 Mesquite Community Pit
76 MIN-AD Mine
77 Moltan Mine
78 Money Pit
79 Mt. Moriah Quarry
80 Mountain Springs Mine
81 Mustang Pit
82 Nassau (Section 8) Mine
83 Nevada Barth Iron Mine
84 Nevada Cement Mine
85 New Discovery Mine
86 Nightingale Pit
87 PABCO Gypsum-Apex Pit

88 Pahrump Community Pit
89 Paiute Pit
90 Pilot Peak Quarry
91 Pioneer Gypsum Mine
92 Popcorn Mine
93 Premier Chemicals, LLC
94 Primm Quarry
95 Rainbow Quarries
96 Rilite Aggregate
97 Rossi Mine
98 Sierra Ready Mix Quarry
99 Silver Peak Operations
100 Simplot Silica Products Pit
101 Sloan Quarry
102 South Jean Pit
103 Spanish Springs Quarry
104 Spring Mountain Pit
105 Tenacity Perlite Mine
106 Terraced Hill Clay Mine
107 Turquoise Ridge Quarry
108 W. Glen Sexton Family Trust
109 Wabuska Iron Mine
110 White Caps Mill

GEMSTONE MINES
111 Bonanza Opal Mine
112 Rainbow Ridge Opal Mine
113 Royal Peacock Opal Mine

GEOTHERMAL AREAS
114 Beowawe
115 Blue Mountain
116 Bradys
117 Bradys
118 Burdette (Galena 1)
119 Desert Peak
120 Dixie Valley
121 Elko Hot Springs
122 Empire
123 Galena 2
124 Galena 3
125 Jersey Valley
126 Moana Hot Springs
127 Moana Hot Springs
128 Salt Wells
129 San Emidio
130 Soda Lake No. 1, 2
131 Steamboat 1-A
132 Steamboat 2, 3
133 Steamboat Hills
134 Stillwater 2
135 Tuscarora
136 Wabuska

OIL FIELDS
137 Bacon Flat
138 Blackburn
139 Currant
140 Duckwater Creek
141 Eagle Springs
142 Ghost Ranch
143 Grant Canyon
144 Kate Spring
145 Sand Dune
146 Sans Spring
147 Tomera Ranch
148 Trap Spring

United States and one of the most important gold mining regions in the world. Nevada also produces significant amounts of copper, silver, gypsum, barite, lithium, magnesite, clays, and sand and gravel. The origin of this rich array of varied mineral resources involves multiple geological processes and events that have occurred over hundreds of millions of years. No two of the many mining districts in Nevada are identical in terms of ore-forming processes, geological setting, or distribution and concentration of valuable metals. In some, the ore bodies have developed in young (Cenozoic-age) igneous rocks, while in others, ancient sedimentary rocks of Paleozoic age are host materials for rich ores. In many Nevada mining districts, multiple ore bodies formed at different times, in different rocks, through different geological processes. Nonetheless, every mining region in Nevada is the consequence of the long history of plate interactions along the western edge of North America.

Most metals useful to humans, such as gold, silver, iron, copper, tungsten, zinc, and others, exist in rocks at extremely low concentrations. For example, the natural abundance of gold in Earth's crust is only about 0.00000031 percent by weight. Silver makes up about 0.00000079 percent of Earth's crust, while zinc and copper occur at abundances of about 0.007 percent. At such low concentrations, it would require the processing of tens of thousands of tons of average rock to produce even a single ounce of these metals. However, the concentrations of metals in rock can be increased dramatically through a variety of geological mechanisms that generally involve the intrusion of magma into masses of deformed and chemically reactive rock such as limestone, dolomite, or shale. The trace metals contained in both the magma and the rock it interacts with can be mobilized by the hot gases and fluids and transported through deformed rock masses until they resolidify in the highly concentrated form known as ore. Whether a body of rock can be considered ore or not depends on the concentration of the valuable mineral, its accessibility from the surface, the costs associated with extracting the target material from the rock, and the market price of the commodity.

In one way or another, magma is involved in the formation of most but not all types of ore. Volcanic and plutonic igneous rocks, which form from magma, are widespread across Nevada, with ages spanning a period of time exceeding 200 million years. The magma was erupted through, or crystallized within, older rock, mostly oceanic, that was mangled and deformed by earlier tectonic events. These general conditions set the stage for the formation of many kinds of ore bodies through a variety of specific geologic processes.

Hydrothermal ore bodies form when gases and fluids associated with the magma interact with and alter surrounding rock masses. Substances such as water, carbon dioxide, sulfurous compounds, and acids make the gases and fluids highly reactive in the geologic environment. Hot, briny and acidic magmatic fluids act as powerful solvents, capable of dissolving metals and minerals and carrying them along as they migrate through subsurface rock. Chemical reactions between the magmatic fluids and surrounding rock, sometimes involving groundwater from the surface or water released from mineral crystals, can lead to the development of hydrothermal ore bodies in which otherwise

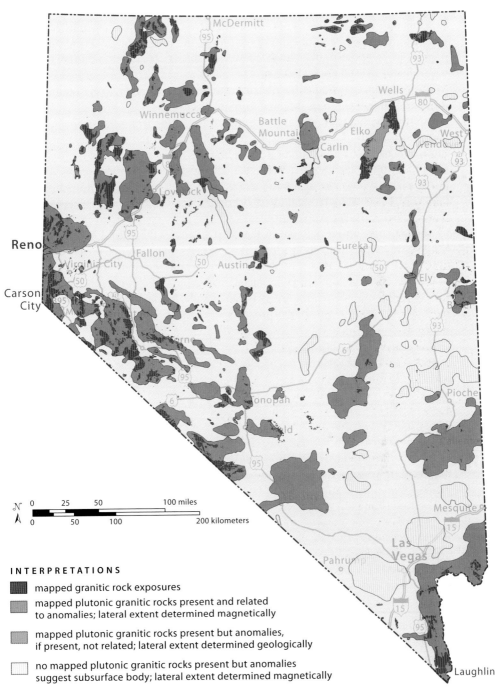

INTERPRETATIONS

■ mapped granitic rock exposures

■ mapped plutonic granitic rocks present and related
to anomalies; lateral extent determined magnetically

■ mapped plutonic granitic rocks present but anomalies,
if present, not related; lateral extent determined geologically

□ no mapped plutonic granitic rocks present but anomalies
suggest subsurface body; lateral extent determined magnetically

The distribution of granitic plutonic igneous rocks based on surface exposures and magnetic surveys. Volcanic igneous rocks formed on the surface (not shown) are even more widespread.
—Modified from Ludington and others, 1996

rare minerals are precipitated in more concentrated masses. The chemistry of the fluids, their temperature, and the nature of the rock through which they migrate are extremely important in influencing the size, location, and mineralogy of hydrothermal ore bodies.

Hydrothermal ore bodies formed near the surface are known as epithermal deposits. Vapors and fluids escaping from underground bodies of magma can rise toward the surface carrying metals in solution, along with acidic sulfurous compounds. Within a few thousand feet of the surface, the rising magmatic fluids may interact with groundwater and boil due to the reduction in pressure accompanying their ascent. These metal-rich fluids can dissolve certain minerals, creating a spongy, or vuggy, rock with many small cavities. When the hydrothermal fluids cool, metals and metal-bearing minerals such as gold, argentite (silver sulfide), chalcopyrite (copper iron sulfide), and arsenopyrite (iron arsenic sulfide) may be precipitated in the open spaces in the altered host rock. While most epithermal deposits form at depths less than about 3,000 feet and at temperatures of around 500°F, there is considerable variation in chemistry of the hydrothermal fluids, types of metals and minerals deposited, and size of the ore bodies in various mining districts in Nevada. In many cases, preexisting

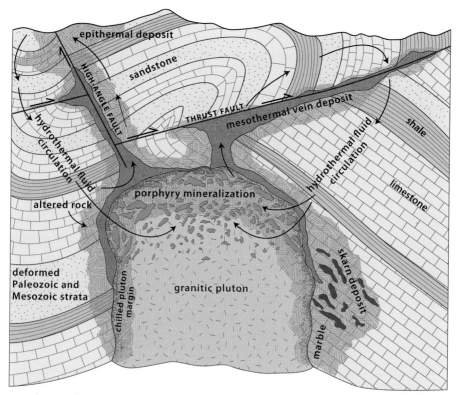

Diagram showing the various types of ore deposits associated with plutons. The magma represented by the granitic rock was the source of the heat, volatile gases, and sulfurous compounds that reacted with the surrounding rock to form the ore bodies.

faults or other planes of weakness help confined the flow of epithermal fluids, resulting in mineralized vein deposits.

Hydrothermal deposits formed at somewhat greater depths are known as mesothermal ore bodies. Mesothermal ore bodies typically form at depths of 3,000 to 12,000 feet below the surface, where interactions with groundwater are not involved and where boiling fluids are less likely due to the higher pressures.

Porphyry deposits are another kind of ore deposit associated with igneous rocks. The primary metal present in porphyry deposits is usually identified by geologists when describing it, as in the porphyry copper deposit near Yerington, or the porphyry molybdenum deposit at Mt. Hope, northwest of Eureka. Porphyry deposits generally form deep underground in association with plutons, masses of plutonic igneous rock representing bodies of magma that cooled and crystallized below the surface. Hence, porphyry deposits are typically formed at a greater depth than hydrothermal deposits but can be exposed at the surface following uplift and erosion. As magma crystallizes underground, many metals and volatile gases are left behind, concentrated in the residual fluids. The magma crystallizes first near the outer edges of the future pluton where the molten liquid is in contact with solid rock surrounding it. The remaining magma crystallizes inward from the chilled margin of the pluton, continuously concentrating metals and volatile gases. When the pressure within the residual fluids reaches a critical threshold, the surrounding shell of rock, both the igneous rock of the pluton and the metamorphic rock that surrounds it, is ruptured and the pressurized fluids escape violently through the shattered rock. When the exploding gases and fluids cool, the minerals and metals carried by them can precipitate as tiny grains of metals and metallic minerals (usually metal sulfides) scattered through the rock along the edges of the pluton. Such ore deposits are of relatively low grade, but the volume of mineralized rock can be significant. Where it is feasible to mine and process great volumes of ore near the surface, porphyry deposits can sustain mining operations for many decades. The primary minerals in most porphyry ore deposits are usually chalcopyrite and bornite (both copper iron sulfides), pyrite (iron sulfide), and molybdenite (molybdenum sulfide). About 65 percent of the world copper supply comes from the mining of porphyry ore deposits, and significant amounts of gold are commonly found accompanying the copper.

Skarns are another type of ore deposit associated with plutons. A skarn is a mineralized mass of rock composed of calcium silicate minerals, such as garnet, epidote, and pyroxene. Skarns form when carbonate sedimentary rocks, such as limestone or dolomite, are intruded by magma. Silica (silicon and oxygen), aluminum, and sulfurous compounds escape from the magma and recrystallize the carbonate host rocks through a chemical process known as metasomatism. This chemical alteration is facilitated by the heat from the magma and can lead to the precipitation of ore minerals such as pyrrhotite (iron sulfide), sphalerite (zinc sulfide), arsenopyrite (iron arsenic sulfide), and scheelite (calcium tungsten oxide). Skarns can have significant concentrations of elemental gold, copper, and other metals. Many of the gold-producing mines of the Battle Mountain region of northern Nevada target gold-bearing skarn deposits.

Polymetallic vein deposits are also associated with intrusive igneous rock bodies, forming when volatiles released from magma travel significant distances along fractures, faults, or other planes of weakness in the surrounding rock. As they cool, these fluids react with the surrounding rock and precipitate quartz as veins in the enclosing rock. The quartz veins commonly carry valuable sulfide ore minerals such as tetrahedrite (copper iron antimony sulfide), sphalerite (zinc sulfide), galena (lead sulfide), and jamesonite (a lea iron antimony sulfide). Many different metals can be extracted from polymetallic vein deposits if they are sufficiently rich. At least 265 polymetallic vein deposits are known in Nevada, and these are associated with intrusive igneous rocks ranging in age from Triassic to mid-Cenozoic. Historically, the most productive polymetallic veins in Nevada were those mined near Austin along US 50. The mines of the Reese River district have produced silver, gold, lead, copper, zinc, uranium, molybdenum, antimony, and arsenic since their discovery in the late 1800s. No place in Nevada better illustrates the polymetallic nature of these types of ore deposits.

Carlin-type gold deposits. Not all ore deposits are directly associated with igneous rocks. Perhaps the most distinctive type of ore deposits in Nevada are the Carlin-type gold deposits, named for the extensive gold ore bodies first discovered in 1961 near Carlin in Elko County. In Carlin-type ores, the host rock is generally impure, or dirty, limestone containing clay and silt in addition to normal carbonate minerals, such as calcite. Extensive tracts of limestone, some of it containing clay, formed in Paleozoic time in eastern Nevada as part of the continental shelf of western North America. In particular, the Silurian and Devonian strata of northern and eastern Nevada appear to be the prime hosts for Carlin-type ores. Gold in such Carlin-type deposits is widely disseminated through the host limestone as minute microscopic particles associated with pyrite, orpiment and realgar (arsenic sulfides), and the siliceous rock known as jasperoid. The richest ores tend to be associated with faults and folds in the Paleozoic sedimentary rocks, suggesting that the geologic structures played a role in the mineralization process. Because the gold particles are so small, Carlin-type ore looks very much like normal deformed and mildly altered limestone. However, the mostly low-grade gold mineralization extends through such an enormous mass of rock that impressive amounts of gold can be processed from the ore, provided that it is feasible to mine large quantities. In Nevada, more than one hundred sites of Carlin-type gold deposits have been discovered, collectively containing some 200 million ounces of gold. Where these deposits were found at the surface or in the shallow subsurface, some of the largest-scale mining operations in the world have been in progress for many decades. So much mineralized rock exists in these deposits that approximately 70 percent of the gold currently produced in the United States comes from the Nevada Carlin-type deposits alone.

The origin of the gigantic Carlin-type ore bodies is still not completely understood. The age of mineralization in most of these deposits is Eocene, a time frame that coincides with a surge of magma moving upward into Paleozoic rocks across northern Nevada. However, the Carlin-type gold deposits are not directly associated with igneous rocks. Carlin-type ores are also dissimilar from normal epithermal ores in that the gold they contain was not precipitated as a consequence of mineralizing fluids boiling or cooling. The large magma masses that moved into the crust during the Eocene Epoch may have provided heat (and possibly some fluids) to drive the mineralizing process, but the silty nature of the limestone host rock, patterns of faulting and folding, and possibly deeper crustal structures appear to also have been important in the formation of Carlin-type ores.

Barite (barium sulfate) is a valuable industrial mineral used in oil-drilling mud (due to its high density), ceramics and glass making, medical applications, and paints. Nevada is the leading producer of barite in the United States, and the Greystone Mine in Lander County is generally the most productive site in the state. The barite deposits occur in a belt about 50 miles wide that runs diagonally through Nevada, approximately coincident with the Antler orogenic belt of mid-Paleozoic age. Within this belt, the barite occurs in deep-sea sediments, such as black shales and argillites, that were thrust eastward during the Antler Orogeny. Such masses of barite are thought to precipitate on deep ocean floors when hot, metal-rich water and gases from submarine hot springs are discharged into cold seawater. Chemical reactions adjacent to the deep-sea hydrothermal vents can concentrate barium (and other metals) in the form of sulfates and sulfides that accumulate in the deep sediments. These ores most likely originated hundreds of millions of years ago when much of western Nevada was the bottom of a deep ocean basin.

Mineral Trends

Ore deposits, and hence formal mining districts, are not randomly distributed in Nevada. As Nevada's mining legacy unfolded, it did not take geologists long to realize that pockets of mineralized rock tended to occur in linear belts that became known as trends. Several such zones of mineralization have been recognized and given names descriptive of their general location. The Carlin trend, a northwest-trending zone of mostly Carlin-type gold deposits, extends from the Piñon Range south of Carlin to the Tuscarora Mountains to the northwest. This zone is about 70 miles long and 10 miles wide, though its total extent is still uncertain. The Carlin trend is the largest and most productive gold mining region in North America, with more than forty sites of significant mineralization and a cumulative gold production of nearly 100 million ounces since the early 1960s.

The Battle Mountain–Eureka trend lies roughly parallel to the Carlin trend but southwest of it. This belt of mineralization extends for more than 150 miles, from the northern White Pine Range in the southeast to the Battle Mountain region to the northwest. Within this roughly 25-mile zone, more than one hundred ore bodies have been identified, most of them clustered near Battle Mountain. Carlin-type gold deposits are common within this belt, but other types of mineral deposits, including epithermal systems, skarns, and veins, also yield copper, zinc, lead, and other metals. In 2011, the Barrick Cortez Mine in the Battle Mountain–Eureka trend was Nevada's single most productive gold mine, yielding more than 1.4 million ounces in that year.

The Getchell trend, named for the Getchell Mine in the Osgood Mountains northeast of Winnemucca, is oriented in a northeast-southwest alignment, transverse to the trend of the Carlin and Battle Mountain–Eureka trends. About twenty-five different ore bodies are known from the Getchell trend, most of them of the Carlin-type, consisting of deformed early Paleozoic sedimentary rocks containing microscopic particles of disseminated gold. Many of the mines in the Getchell trend are associated with plutons of Cretaceous granitic rock and dikes related to them. Some skarn and epithermal deposits also occur in this zone, mostly associated with Cenozoic igneous bodies.

The Independence trend is named for the Independence Mountains in Elko County, where major Carlin-type ores bodies occur, most notably at the Jerritt Canyon Mine, which has produced over 8 million ounces of gold since 1981. In this region, deformed silty and carbonaceous limestones of Ordovician age contain fine particles of disseminated gold. In the northern portion of the Independence trend some sites of epithermal gold mineralization are associated with Cenozoic igneous rocks.

The Walker Lane trend is composed of several mining districts generally aligned along the broad zone of right-lateral strike-slip faulting in western Nevada. Famous mining areas within this trend include the Round Mountain and Manhattan districts in the Toquima Range, the historic Goldfield area of Esmeralda County, and the famous Comstock Lode of the Virginia Range. Most of the mines within the Walker Lane trend target epithermal gold, silver, or polymetallic ores contained in volcanic rocks of Cenozoic age.

Geologists are still working to fully understand the alignment of mineral trends in Nevada, and no single interpretation for these zones of mineralization is adequate to explain all the geologic details in them. What is certain is that few regions of comparable size anywhere on Earth have been so intensely mineralized or produced such a varied array of mineral commodities as the Silver State.

OVERVIEW OF NEVADA'S PLATE TECTONIC HISTORY

———— PROTEROZOIC EON ————
2,500 to 542 million years ago

Earth's plate tectonic system has operated for about 4 billion years, developing soon after the embryonic planet cooled sufficiently for rigid rocks to form on the exterior of the planet while internal heat kept deeper material partially molten. Slow, heat-driven movement of the semisolid asthenosphere beneath the lithosphere fractured the outer shell of rock to create the twenty or so lithospheric plates that exist in the modern world. It is important to remember that the plates we know today have not always existed. Through their interactions with each other over geologic time, plates can break apart into smaller slabs, collide to create larger masses of lithosphere, or disappear completely in subduction zones, where they descend into the hotter regions of the inner Earth. As the configuration of plates constantly changes on Earth, the interactions between them evolve as well. Each shift in the nature of a plate boundary leaves a semipermanent geological signature in the rock record of the region affected. The rock record of Nevada, with its almost bewildering complexity and variety, records more than 2 billion years of changing plate interactions along the western margin of North America.

The oldest rocks in Nevada occur in the East Humboldt Range in the northeastern part of the state. Though there is some uncertainty about the precise ages of the high-grade metamorphic rocks in this area, the ratios of lead isotopes in some of the mineral grains suggest ages as old as 2.5 billion years. This falls near the boundary of the Archean Eon, one of the earliest subdivisions of geologic time, and the Proterozoic Eon. Rocks similar to those of the East Humboldt Range occur to the north in the Grouse Creek Mountains of Utah and in several mountain ranges in southern Wyoming. Farther south, in eastern Clark County and adjacent areas, metamorphic and igneous rocks as old as 1.7 billion years are known. These somewhat younger rocks originated in the Proterozoic Eon and are distinct from the older metamorphic complex to the north.

The Proterozoic and Archean basement rocks of Nevada were part of an ancient supercontinent known as Rodinia about 1 billion years ago. The construction of Rodinia involved the collision of numerous smaller fragments of continental crust during a period of several hundred million years. The Archean basement rocks of northern Nevada and the younger Proterozoic materials to the south may represent two different masses that collided during the assembly of this ancient supercontinent. Some of the metamorphism and deformation seen in Nevada's oldest rocks may be the result of these collisions.

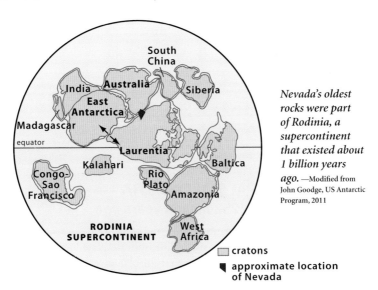

Nevada's oldest rocks were part of Rodinia, a supercontinent that existed about 1 billion years ago. —Modified from John Goodge, US Antarctic Program, 2011

Rodinia was situated along the equator in Proterozoic time and was surrounded by an enormous global ocean. Near the end of the Proterozoic Eon, about 700 to 600 million years ago, Rodinia was affected by continental rifting, a plate tectonic process that breaks a large plate into smaller ones. As numerous fragments were rifted from the supercontinent, narrow seaways opened between them and became progressively wider through the process of seafloor spreading. In the modern world, similar events are in progress around Africa, where the Arabian Plate has recently been rifted from northeast Africa, opening the narrow Red Sea. One of the prominent fragments of Rodinia was Laurentia, the predecessor to modern North America. The zone of rifting along the western edge of Laurentia ran through the center of what is now Nevada. To the west of this zone, fragments of Rodinia were carried farther from Laurentia and are now embedded in the cores of Siberia and possibly Antarctica and Australia. Because the rift zone slashed diagonally from northeast to southwest Nevada, no continental rock older than about 700 million years exists in western Nevada. Such ancient basement rocks are only present in the eastern parts of the state, though they are usually deeply buried under younger materials and only seen at the surface in a few places.

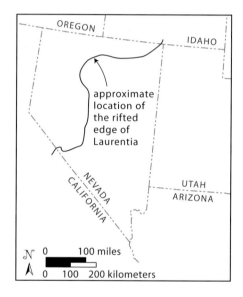

Approximate edge of the rifted margin of Laurentia in late Proterozoic time.

PALEOZOIC ERA
542 to 252 million years ago

After rifting was complete, the continental crust of Laurentia was joined to the oceanic crust to the west within a single lithospheric plate. Thus, there were no plates interacting along the western margin of Laurentia to produce violent earthquakes or intense volcanic activity. This type of geological setting is described by geologists as a passive continental margin. Rivers flowing from Laurentia deposited sediments into the nascent seaway over the rifted margin of the continent. In time these sediments built up an immense elongated wedge that thickened to the west, toward the deeper parts of the new ocean basin. Sediment collected beneath the shallow water of the continental shelf while the newly rifted lithosphere cooled and sank. The seafloor subsided continuously,

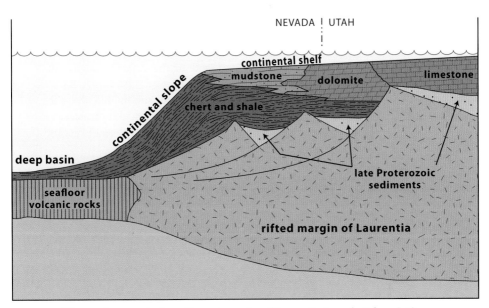

NEVADA | UTAH

continental shelf

mudstone   dolomite   limestone

continental slope

chert and shale

deep basin

seafloor
volcanic rocks

late Proterozoic
sediments

rifted margin of Laurentia

The passive margin along the western edge of Laurentia in early Paleozoic time.

allowing more than 20,000 feet of sediment to accumulate in relatively shallow water. In addition to the sand and silt derived from land, carbonate minerals precipitated from the seawater built up thick layers of limestone and dolomite. For more than 400 million years, eastern and central Nevada were submerged under shallow tropical seas, explaining the prevalence of early Paleozoic limestone and dolomite in such eastern mountain ranges as the Monitor, Egan, Schell Creek, and Arrow Canyon Ranges. Thick sequences of limestone, dolomite, shale, and sandstone accumulated on the continental shelf and collectively form what geologists refer to as the early Paleozoic shelf domain of the eastern Great Basin.

In central Nevada, the early Paleozoic continental shelf descended down a relatively steep continental slope to the deeper ocean floor. Here, under cold and murky water, fine silt, clay, and ooze accumulated at the same time that the limestone and dolomite were deposited on the continental shelf. The deep-sea deposits solidified into shale, siltstone, and chert and are associated with some oceanic volcanic rocks that made up the ancient seafloor. This collection of early Paleozoic rocks is known as the slope and basin domain and is present in central and western Nevada. As we will soon discover, some of these deep-sea deposits were later thrust by compressive forces eastward over the edge of the carbonate platform in crumpled heaps of transported rock.

Antler Orogeny

By middle Paleozoic time, a series of new plate tectonic settings began to develop along the western edge of the ancient continent, with oceanic lithosphere converging toward the rifted margin. At the same time, Laurentia began to collide with continental masses to the east during the early phases of the construction of Pangaea, a supercontinent that would eventually form at the end of the Paleozoic Era. The plate convergence that began in the mid-Paleozoic Era resulted in a lengthy interval of subduction along the western coast as various oceanic plates were forced downward near the edge of Laurentia. After 400 million years of geological serenity, the converging and subducting plates led to a series of geological upheavals that deformed earlier-formed rocks, elevated tracts of the seafloor as emergent land, and spawned intense volcanic activity on both the seafloor and land.

The plates also transported volcanic islands, carbonate reefs, and microcontinents to the edge of Laurentia, where they were continuously crushed into the western edge of the continent. Such masses of exotic rock added to a continental margin by plate convergence are known as accreted terranes, or simply terranes. These deformed and metamorphosed packages of rock are noticeably dissimilar to adjacent rock and are separated from bordering rock by prominent faults. Because the plate convergence that began in mid-Paleozoic time lasted for more than 250 million years, dozens of terranes were emplaced. Each terrane that arrived on a converging plate plowed into the older rocks already in place along the continental margin and became sutured to Laurentia as a mangled mass of deformed and metamorphosed rock bounded by faults. In addition, every accretion event was similar to the closing of a giant geological vise, squeezing the sediment on the seafloor that previously separated the approaching mass from the continental margin. As the two rock masses collided, the crumpled layers of deep-ocean sediment were driven up and over the edge of Laurentia as a thrust sheet along thrust faults. Sometimes, bodies of magma generated near the underlying subduction zone rose through the terranes to erupt on the surface, or to cool underground into great masses of granitic rock. Over time, the emplacement of numerous terranes extended the Laurentia landmass westward. Most of the rock that makes up the western portion of Nevada is a complex geological mosaic consisting of numerous terranes overlain by younger sedimentary and volcanic rock and intruded by igneous rocks.

The earliest major geological disturbance resulting from plate convergence in the Great Basin is known traditionally as the Antler Orogeny. An orogeny is a period of deformation in which rock layers are folded, faulted, metamorphosed, and sometimes penetrated by bodies of magma. Orogenies generally result in mountain building, though the topographic lifting of the surface may not occur at the same time as the deformation. The Antler Orogeny was named for Antler Peak on Battle Mountain, where the effects of this disturbance were first noticed by geologists in 1951. During the Antler Orogeny, rocks of the slope and basin domain were folded and thrust to the east over the edge of the continental shelf. One of the major thrust faults of this orogeny was the Roberts Mountains thrust. Deformed and fractured masses of deep-ocean deposits were heaved upward to form an elongated landmass, called the Antler highland, that ran through central Nevada from Idaho to southeastern California.

Though the main phase of the Antler Orogeny occurred in late Devonian to early Mississippian time (about 370 to 350 million years ago), there is good geological evidence that this disturbance continued for several tens of millions

WEST   EAST

Plate convergence began in western North America in the middle Paleozoic Era and continued throughout the Mesozoic Era. The accretion of numerous exotic terranes built the margin of the continent westward in a series of mountain-building events known as orogenies.

of years in central and eastern Nevada. The Antler Orogeny was long thought to be the consequence of a collision between the edge of the continental shelf and an island arc that approached from the west. More recent studies have suggested that several different terranes may be involved in this period of persistent and widespread mountain building, and at least one of them may have moved into place from the north along strike-slip faults. One such mass is known as the Nolan Belt, an intensely folded sequence of slate, schist, quartzite, and chert. The Nolan Belt extends discontinuously from Esmeralda County northward through central Nevada to the area around Mountain City in the Bull Run Mountains south of the Idaho border. In addition, it appears that some of the rocks lifted from the seafloor at this time had already been folded and deformed by earlier events.

As mountain building raised up the Antler highland, erosion of the deformed rocks led to the deposition of thick sequences of coarse sediments into basins to the west (known as the hinterland basin) and east (the foreland basin). In the area near the present Utah-Nevada state line, these sediments graded into the normal shallow sea deposits accumulating on the continental shelf. Ultimately, the Antler highland was lowered enough by erosion that by late Paleozoic time, the sea once again submerged its flanks. Sediments deposited on its uneven, eroded slopes are known as the Antler overlap sequence, a group of rocks composed dominantly of conglomerate, sandstone, siltstone, and limestone. Rocks of this sequence range in age from Pennsylvanian through early Triassic age.

Alamo Impact Event

In addition to the tectonic upheavals that affected the western edge of Laurentia during mid-Paleozoic time, there is very good evidence that an additional disturbance struck from the skies. In the late Devonian rocks of south-central Nevada, geologists have discovered chaotic masses of limestone blocks broken from the edge of the continental shelf and recemented into a jumbled mass in the deeper-water environment to the west. These strange megabreccias in the Guilmette Formation are associated with high concentrations of iridium, an element that is extremely rare on Earth but much more abundant in some types of meteorites. Moreover, distinctive gravelly rubble has been identified in the late Devonian sediments of south-central Nevada, suggesting that strong tsunamis swept across broad areas of the continental shelf several times. These peculiarities provide strong evidence that an asteroid or large meteorite struck the shallow seas that covered eastern Nevada about 382 million years ago. Though the precise site of this prehistoric impact is unknown, it appears to have struck the shallow Devonian seas in the vicinity of the Timpahute Range in southern Lincoln County, not far from Rachel, a small town made famous by its reputation for extraterrestrial encounters! This event is generally known as the Alamo impact event because the evidence for it is especially well-recorded in the rocks exposed near the small settlement of Alamo. No fragments of the impacting object have yet been recovered from Devonian rock layers in Nevada, but the amount and distribution of the rock shattered by this powerful event suggest that it excavated a crater about 1 mile deep and some 30 miles in diameter.

Humboldt and Sonoma Orogenies

Near the end of Paleozoic time, several more geological disturbances affected the Nevada region as multiple terranes were accreted along the western edge of North America. Some of these events were relatively small, causing only localized deformation and mountain building, such as the Humboldt Orogeny, the effects of which were first recognized in 1977 in the rocks of the Piñon Range region of north-central Nevada.

The Sonoma Orogeny of late Permian to Triassic time was the next major geologic disturbance to follow the Humboldt Orogeny. During the Sonoma

Generalized map of major accreted terranes and thrust sheets in Nevada. Rock masses west of the Antler rocks were added to the edge of North America incrementally beginning about 360 million years ago. Smaller terranes may exist but are not shown here.

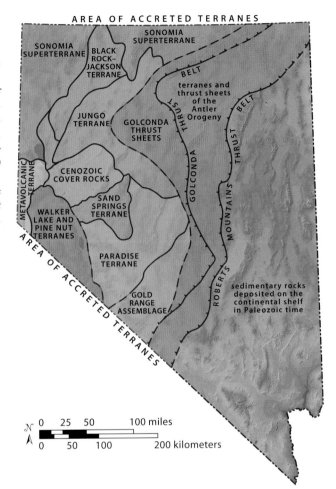

AREA OF ACCRETED TERRANES

SONOMIA SUPERTERRANE

SONOMIA SUPERTERRANE   BLACK ROCK–JACKSON TERRANE

terranes and thrust sheets of the Antler Orogeny

BELT

JUNGO TERRANE   GOLCONDA THRUST SHEETS

THRUST BELT

METAVOLCANIC TERRANE

CENOZOIC COVER ROCKS

GOLCONDA THRUST

MOUNTAINS THRUST

WALKER LAKE AND PINE NUT TERRANES

SAND SPRINGS TERRANE

PARADISE TERRANE

ROBERTS

sedimentary rocks deposited on the continental shelf in Paleozoic time

GOLD RANGE ASSEMBLAGE

AREA OF ACCRETED TERRANES

N

0   25   50   100 miles

0   50   100   200 kilometers

Orogeny, a complex assemblage of rocks that previously formed in a Paleozoic ocean basin were thrust eastward over the rocks of the Antler overlap sequence. This thrust sheet, known to some as the Golconda allochthon or terrane, is a thick sequence of deformed and mostly metamorphosed basalt, shale and siltstone, chert, and limestone. Rocks within this mass range in age from late Devonian through late Permian, a span of some 125 million years, and are named for exposures near Golconda Summit, where I-80 crosses Edna Mountain east of Winnemucca. For the most part, the rocks of the Golconda terrane originated in a deep ocean basin somewhere west and north of the continental shelf. As they were accreted to the edge of the shelf, these rocks were deformed into complex slices that were folded and transported over previously deformed rocks along a regional fault known as the Golconda thrust. The Golconda terrane is associated with another exotic mass of rock known as the Sonomia superterrane, or microcontinent, that arrived in western North America at about the same time as the Golconda thrusting. Sonomia was a large and complicated mass of rock that most geologists consider to represent an oceanic island arc. The Sonomia superterrane is composed of several different packages of rock that had different origins and histories before they became sutured together in what geologists call an amalgamated terrane. These packages include the Walker Lake, Paradise, and Pine Nut terranes, which will be described in more detail where you can see them alongside roads. The collision of the Sonomia superterrane added enough rock to the western edge of North America to extend the continent as far west as the Klamath Mountains region of northern California. The precise extent of the Sonomia superterrane is unknown because the southwestern margin of it was disrupted and moved to new locations (probably south) by later Mesozoic faulting along the edge of ancient North America.

——————— MESOZOIC ERA ———————
252 to 66 million years ago

Convergent plate interactions continued along the western margin of Laurentia throughout the Mesozoic Era and into the early part of the Cenozoic Era, and several terranes were added to the growing western edge of the continent. The Black Rock–Jackson terrane was accreted in northwest Nevada during Jurassic and Cretaceous time. This complex sequence of rocks includes volcanic material that originated during the construction of offshore volcanic islands, as well as the deep-ocean sediments (chert, siltstone, shale, and tuff) that accumulated on the surrounding seafloor. The rocks within the Black Rock–Jackson terrane range in age from late Paleozoic to mid-Triassic age. Deep-sea sediments caught between the terrane and the continent were also accreted and are known as the Jungo terrane. About the same time that the Black Rock–Jackson terrane was being sutured to Laurentia in northwest Nevada, other terranes of broadly similar oceanic rocks were accreting in the western foothills of the Sierra Nevada and Klamath Mountains in California. During each accretion event, more land emerged along the west coast of Laurentia, and by the end of Mesozoic time, all of Nevada was exposed as dry land above sea level. The contorted rocks of many different terranes had become assembled into a gigantic geological collage and lifted above sea level under the influence of the strong compressive forces that were generated by plates crashing together along the western edge of ancient North America.

The terranes that were accreted to California and Nevada during the Mesozoic Era arrived on several different oceanic plates, the largest and best known of which was the Farallon Plate, an enormous easterly moving oceanic plate that existed in the ancient Pacific Ocean basin. This oceanic plate was produced by seafloor spreading along an oceanic ridge system that also produced the Pacific Plate, which moved west from the ridge, opposite of the direction of the Farallon Plate. For hundreds of millions of years, the Farallon Plate descended to the east under the edge of ancient North America in what geologists describe as the Farallon subduction zone. Many of the terranes of western Nevada were originally masses of rock riding on the Farallon Plate that were deformed and detached from this plate as it descended in the subduction zone.

As the Farallon Plate sank deep into the subsurface, it eventually encountered higher pressures and temperatures. At depths of about 60 miles or so, water vapor escaped from the oceanic rocks of the Farallon Plate and mixed with the surrounding semisolid rock. The water vapor induced melting of the hot rock, creating large bodies of molten rock, or magma. Throughout the Mesozoic era, these bodies of magma ascended into the overlying rocks of the accreted terranes and eventually erupted on the surface, building volcanic peaks, or slowly cooled underground, creating large bodies of plutonic igneous rock like granite. Magma that rose from the Farallon subduction zone built the Sierra Nevada magmatic arc—the granite core the Sierra Nevada and an extensive chain of overlying volcanoes. The older rocks intruded by the Mesozoic igneous rocks were metamorphosed, and sometimes strongly mineralized, by the heat, pressure, and chemical activity associated with the invading bodies of magma. The Mesozoic volcanoes have mostly been eroded away, but remnants of them can be seen in many places in western Nevada.

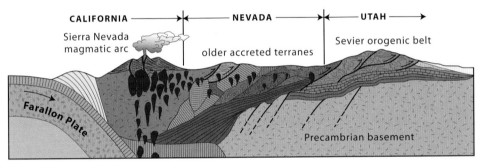

The subduction of the Farallon Plate beneath North America during the Mesozoic Era established the tectonic framework for Nevada's geological history for nearly 200 million years. The subsurface magma bodies that formed granitic plutons, the folding and faulting of older accreted rocks, and the development of the Sevier orogenic belt are all related to the Farallon subduction zone.

The rate of convergence between the east-moving Farallon Plate and the west-drifting North American Plate was particularly high in the Cretaceous Period. This interval of 144 to 66 million years ago was when the greatest volumes of magma were generated beneath western North America, and numerous terranes were accreted along the west coast. This high rate of convergence, magma generation, and terrane accretion is probably a reflection of the rapid breakup of the supercontinent Pangaea. The strong compression between the Farallon and North American Plates signified the rapid movement of the continental plate to the west as it separated from the rest of Pangaea via the opening of the Atlantic Ocean basin.

Thrust Faults and the Sevier Orogeny

One important consequence of the intensified compression along the western edge of North America was the development of many extensive thrust faults in Nevada during the later portions of the Mesozoic Era, particularly in the

Cretaceous Period. Thrust faults are gently sloping fractures that can transport sheets of rocks significant distances over underlying rocks. Because they cut downward through rock sequences, thrust faults can place older rocks on top of younger rocks, reversing the normal arrangement of layered sequences. In northwestern Nevada, the Luning-Fencemaker thrust fault began to develop about 180 to 160 million years ago in the Jurassic Period, thrusting rocks of the Jungo terrane eastward. Around 140 million years ago, in the early Cretaceous Period and continuing for millions of years, compressive forces associated with the Farallon subduction zone migrated east, resulting in the Sevier Orogeny, a period of major mountain building in the eastern Basin and Range region.

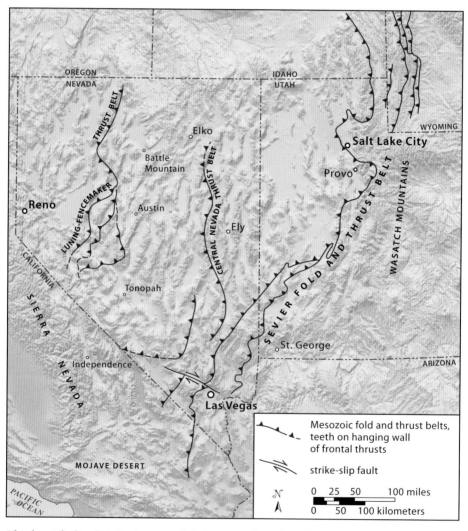

The thrust faults of the Sevier orogenic belt are mostly of late Cretaceous age, while those of the Central Nevada and Luning-Fencemaker thrust belts formed earlier in the Mesozoic Era.

Great sheets of rock were crumpled and transported eastward, where they piled up on one another to create the mountainous Sevier orogenic belt in western and central Utah. The western foothills of this mountain range descended into eastern Nevada in Cretaceous time as a rugged highland formed of strongly folded and faulted rock layers.

The Sevier orogenic belt curved southwest from central Utah into southern Nevada, where various thrust faults are prominently exposed. Among these are the Keystone thrust in the Spring Mountains, the Gass Peak thrust in the Las Vegas Range, and the Muddy Mountain thrust northeast of Las Vegas. Northward from the Las Vegas area, through central Nevada, other thrust faults that formed in the late Cretaceous Period make up the Central Nevada thrust belt, which includes several faults that transported sheets of crumpled rock to the east in the foothills of the Sevier orogenic belt. Collectively, the geological disturbances of the Sevier Orogeny lifted much of central Nevada into a high undulating plain, called the Nevadaplano by geologists.

CENOZOIC ERA
66 million years ago to present

The Nevadaplano, the undulating plain elevated by the Sevier Orogeny and consisting of a 40-mile-thick mangled assortment of older terranes, persisted into the earlier epochs of Cenozoic time, as the Farallon Plate continued to descend beneath the North American Plate. About 60 million years ago, the angle of subduction appears to have decreased significantly, allowing the Farallon Plate to slide much farther east before it encountered the conditions necessary for the generation of magma. The igneous activity that had characterized the Sierra Nevada magmatic arc and areas to the east in Nevada and Utah during much of the Mesozoic Era abruptly terminated at this time. The decrease in the angle of subduction also allowed the Farallon Plate to apply shear stresses to the base of the North American Plate as far east as the Rocky Mountain region. In response, the initial uplift of the modern Rocky Mountains began in the early Cenozoic Era in an event known as the Laramide Orogeny. Continuing uplift and deformation may have occurred in Nevada during the Laramide Orogeny, but the effects of this geological disturbance are much more prominent to the east. Thus, though there may have been some geologic activity in Nevada at the time, the Laramide Orogeny represents a brief lull in the geologic evolution of Nevada. The quiescence didn't last long, though, because by about 40 million years ago, a whole new kind of geologic rampage began in Nevada.

Supervolcanoes and Their Calderas

About 45 million years ago, during the Eocene Epoch, the angle of subduction beneath western North American began to steepen, probably caused when a thinner and more dense portion of the Farallon Plate began to sink. It pulled away from the base of the overriding continental lithosphere in a phenomenon that geologists call rollback. When this happened, magma was once again generated beneath Nevada and adjacent parts of western North America, and a

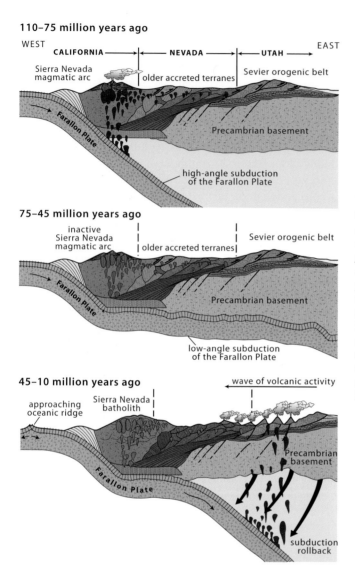

110–75 million years ago

WEST

CALIFORNIA ⟶ ⟵ NEVADA ⟶ ⟵ UTAH ⟶

EAST

Sierra Nevada
magmatic arc

older accreted terranes

Sevier orogenic belt

Farallon Plate

Precambrian basement

high-angle subduction
of the Farallon Plate

75–45 million years ago

inactive
Sierra Nevada
magmatic arc

older accreted terranes

Sevier orogenic belt

Farallon Plate

Precambrian basement

low-angle subduction
of the Farallon Plate

45–10 million years ago

wave of volcanic activity

approaching
oceanic ridge

Sierra Nevada
batholith

Precambrian
basement

Farallon Plate

subduction
rollback

The angle of subduction of the Farallon Plate beneath western North America flattened during the Laramide Orogeny, producing a lull in igneous activity in the Great Basin. The angle steepened again in the middle of the Eocene Epoch, igniting a wave of volcanic blasts in the Nevada region.

great wave of volcanic activity began to sweep through the region. The earliest volcanoes erupted in the northern part of Nevada in Eocene time, about 43 million years ago. Volcanic activity migrated into central Nevada during the Oligocene Epoch and reached the southwest part of the state in the Miocene Epoch.

The scale and violence of the volcanic blasts that buried the ancient landscape under thousands of feet of ash are hard to imagine, primarily because no volcanic eruptions ever witnessed by humans come close to rivaling these prehistoric paroxysms. The tuffs of the Great Basin record one of the fiercest volcanic rampages ever documented by geologists in the 4.6-billion-year history of our planet. Between 36 and 18 million years ago, an estimated 17,000 cubic miles of lava was ejected during no fewer than 250 violent eruptions in

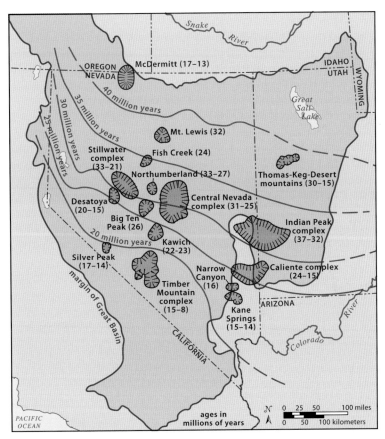

Volcanic activity and caldera formation (purple) in the Great Basin (green) began in Eocene time in northern Nevada and migrated south through Oligocene and Miocene time. The red lines represent the time of inception of the activity. The McDermitt caldera in the north does not fit the pattern because it is related to the Yellowstone hot spot.

Nevada. On the basis of the distribution of layers of tuff and ignimbrite sheets in the southern Great Basin, geologists have concluded that at least thirty of these eruptions discharged more than 200 cubic miles of ash. For comparison, during the cataclysmic 1980 eruption of Mt. St. Helens in southern Washington that killed fifty-seven people, approximately 0.7 cubic mile of ejected volcanic materials accumulated downwind. Any one of the aforementioned thirty mid-Cenozoic volcanoes would have been equivalent to six hundred simultaneous eruptions the size of Mt. St. Helens. Supervolcanoes, technically volcanoes that produce more than 240 cubic miles of lava and ash, repeatedly incinerated the landscape of the Great Basin during the middle portion of the Cenozoic Era.

The violence of the mid-Cenozoic eruptions in Nevada was largely the consequence of both the gases dissolved in the magma—water vapor, carbon dioxide, sulfur dioxide, and hydrogen sulfide—and its thick and viscous nature, making it prone to obstructing its own upward path to the surface. Most of the molten rock was moderately rich in silica (silicon and oxygen) and was erupted at temperatures around 1470 to 1650°F. These factors make lava sluggish and sticky in comparison to hotter and less silicic lava, such as that erupted from Hawaiian volcanoes. Such lava does not flow readily from its subterranean reservoir through fractures and conduits leading upward to the surface. Instead, it tends to block the underground volcanic plumbing. As magma ascends toward the surface, the gases separate as bubbles that pressurize the cavities filled by the rising fluid. The buildup of pressure within and beneath a mass of sticky lava plugging the volcanic vent can give rise to devastating explosions, capable of blasting ash and rock particles across hundreds or even thousands of square miles. The depressions excavated by such volcanic eruptions are called calderas, such as the one that was created 7,700 years ago in southern Oregon when the upper 4,000 feet of ancient Mt. Mazama was blasted away to form Crater Lake.

a. pre-eruption stratovolcano

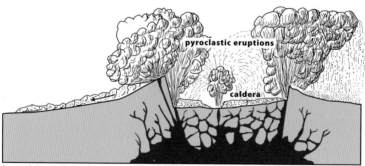

b. caldera-forming pyroclastic eruption

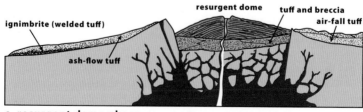

c. resurgent dome phase

Stages of caldera formation and collapse.

The caldera at Crater Lake is about 5 miles across, but those that resulted from mid-Cenozoic caldera-forming eruptions in Nevada were as large as about 35 miles, based on the remnants of them that are preserved in the mountains of south-central Nevada. No fewer than seventy large calderas formed in Nevada from late Eocene to Miocene time.

The most intense and persistent caldera-forming eruptions occurred in south-central Nevada in the vicinity of Tonopah and several nearby mountain ranges such as the Monitor, Hot Creek, Reveille, and Kawich Ranges. Many of the calderas in this area erupted more than once, and the original depressions were filled with volcanic materials erupted in later cycles of activity. Since their formation, most of the calderas have also been disrupted by normal faulting, and the downfaulted margins of many of them are concealed beneath a cover of younger rocks. The caldera-forming eruptions are primarily documented by extensive sheets of ash-flow tuff, representing ejected ash particles that blanketed the surrounding terrain and became welded into solid rock. These tuffs are of andesitic composition and commonly exhibit flow structures and banding. Some of the ash accumulated as microscopic grains of glassy material after traveling hundreds of miles through the air. These ash deposits were compacted over time to form layers of the crumbly rock geologists describe as air-fall tuff. At times during the mid-Cenozoic volcanic flare-up, great clouds of incandescent ash accumulated on the scorched surface to become welded into dense glassy ignimbrite, a term that literally means "fire cloud rock." Some lava was also erupted from the exploding calderas, but the flows were typically less voluminous than the ash and far more restricted in distribution. And not

A cliff to the north of US 93 west of Caliente exposes a thick mass of Miocene-age tuff (right) that filled a canyon eroded into layered, ash-rich sandstone and conglomerate (left).

all of the magma fueling the volcanic activity was erupted; some of it remained underground, where it cooled slowly to form subvolcanic plutons of diorite or granite. In places such as the Battle Mountain, Cherry Creek, Mt. Hope (Eureka County), and Pioche mining districts, these masses of igneous rock played important roles in the hydrothermal systems linked to mineralization.

Ancestral Cascade Arc

The violent caldera-forming eruptions continued in southwest Nevada until about 7 million years ago. However, the rocks produced by these eruptions overlap in space and time with another zone of volcanic activity in western Nevada, known as the Ancestral Cascade arc. Along the current trend of the Sierra Nevada crest and extending into western Nevada, a chain of large conical composite volcanoes was formed beginning about 16 million years ago in mid-Miocene time. These volcanoes formed when the southwest wave of volcanism associated with the rollback of the Farallon Plate encountered the thick mass of granitic rock in the Sierra Nevada batholith. This chain of volcanoes produced primarily andesitic lava flows, avalanche breccias, and lahar (volcanic mudflow) deposits with only minor ash (or tuff). The name Ancestral Cascade arc was inspired by the similarity in composition, eruptive behavior, and alignment of these ancient cones with the volcanoes of the modern Cascade Range in California, Oregon, and Washington.

The volcanoes of the Ancestral Cascade arc were still active when the Walker Lane began to form around 12 million years ago in response to the development of the San Andreas transform plate boundary to west. The Walker Lane includes numerous northwest-trending right-lateral strike-slip faults that formed when the shear stresses associated with the transform plate boundary migrated into western Nevada. Where the ends of these faults overlapped each other (zones called step-overs by geologists), rocks were stretched, basins collapsed, and subsurface rocks were liquefied into magma. The magma erupted through the fractured rock to form enormous volumes of volcanic rock on the surface. Some of the most intense late Cenozoic volcanic activity in the Ancestral Cascade arc was associated with these volcanic centers developed in the Walker Lane. Examples include the Southwest Nevada volcanic field (16 to 6.5 million years ago), the Little Walker caldera complex west of Walker Lake (11 to 9 million years ago), and the Ebbetts Pass region around Topaz Lake (6.3 to 4.8 million years ago). The surge of magma into the region of the Ancestral Cascade arc during Miocene time played an important role in the hydrothermal mineralization of many important mining centers in western Nevada, including the Comstock, Olinghouse, Goldfield, Paradise Peak, and Searchlight districts.

Bimodal Volcanism

During the most recent phase of volcanic activity over the past 10 million years or so, the character of the eruptions shifted again to a pattern of basalt lava flows alternating with thick masses and domes of rhyolite. Rocks that formed during this phase of volcanic activity are known throughout Nevada as the late Cenozoic bimodal basalt-rhyolite assemblage. The term *bimodal* describes the two compositionally distinct types of volcanic rocks that typify these young volcanic sequences: dark-gray or black basalt and typically pinkish-brown or tan rhyolite. These young volcanic rocks are particularly widespread along the northern border of the state in Washoe, Humboldt, and Elko Counties, and in the Western Nevada volcanic field. Also, in southern Nevada, rocks of the bimodal basalt-rhyolite assemblage cover extensive tracts of land in Esmeralda, southern Nye, and Lincoln Counties.

As the Cenozoic volcanoes of Nevada discharged clouds of ash and lava across the Nevadaplano, tensional forces began to tear the land into a series of fault blocks bounded by normal faults. Thus, the era of intense volcanic activity overlapped with the beginning of the crustal extension that ultimately created the corrugated terrain of modern Nevada (see the section on Basin and Range earlier in this chapter). The onset of tensional stress in the region can, in part, explain the shift in the character of volcanic activity in Miocene time. As the rigid lithosphere was stretched, thinned, and broken, the pressure exerted on the underlying soft mantle was reduced, leading to melting of the upper mantle rocks and the production of the bimodal basalt-rhyolite eruptions.

Some of the bimodal volcanic activity has continued to the very recent geological past. Nevada has many small cinder cones and associated lava flows that were formed during the Pleistocene ice ages. Some of these volcanic centers, such as those in the Lunar Crater volcanic field of northern Nye County, may have been active as recently as 15,000 years ago. Coupled with the ongoing seismic activity in the state, these young volcanic features remind us that the geological evolution of Nevada continues to the present day. The lithosphere is still being stretched to the breaking point, mountain blocks continue to rise as the valleys descend along normal faults, and there will undoubtedly be future volcanic eruptions in Nevada.

Metamorphic Core Complexes

The tensional forces that began to stretch the Basin and Range Province in early Cenozoic time have approximately doubled the width of the region over the past 40 million years. This extension has occurred along faults at the surface, as well as through the ductile flow of rock softened by the subterranean heat at depths of about 15 miles below the surface. This extreme stretching led to significant thinning of the crust in Nevada as immense masses of rock were pulled apart and transported laterally. So much weight was removed from the Basin and Range that the lower portion of Earth's crust began to rise upward as the overlying rock masses were shed laterally. Because crustal rocks are supported by more dense material below, any reduction in the thickness of the crust will result in a tendency for the land to rise. This behavior, known as isostacy, is similar to the way that a small boat rises higher in the water as weight is removed from it.

In several places in the Basin and Range Province of western North America, so much rock was shifted laterally during tectonic extension that large bulging masses of deep crustal rock rose to the surface during Miocene and Pliocene time. Because these rock masses rose from great depths, the rock in them had been metamorphosed by the enormous pressures and high temperatures that exist deep underground. The metamorphic rock is overlain by faulted and tilted blocks of younger materials, all arched upward into a dome. In the 1980s geologists named such areas metamorphic core complexes, and today they are uniquely associated with highly extended regions. In many recent studies of these structures, it has become common among geologists to drop the term *metamorphic* and simply refer to these areas are core complexes. There are more than two dozen core complexes in western North America, and the Basin and Range Province, because of its highly extended structure, contains some of the best-studied examples.

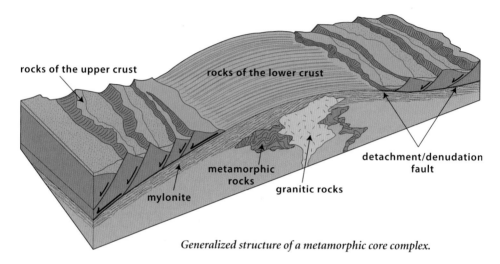

rocks of the upper crust

rocks of the lower crust

detachment/denudation fault

metamorphic rocks

granitic rocks

mylonite

Generalized structure of a metamorphic core complex.

Though each metamorphic core complex in North America has some unique geological elements, the overall architecture of these structures is fairly consistent from one to another. Rocks of the upper crust of core complexes are intensely faulted into tilted blocks that have been transported outward over the underlying slopes of an arched mound of lower crustal rock. The faults in the upper plate rocks are a combination of normal, listric, and detachment faults, all of which reflect the brittle response to the extensional forces. The domed surface beneath the faulted blocks is a major zone of lateral movement known variously as a denudation fault or a regional detachment fault. In some core complexes, the faulted blocks above this surface have been transported more than 50 miles away from the apex of the dome. Beneath the detachment, rocks of the lower crust have risen to form a large convex dome. The rocks in the core of the dome are metamorphic, generally schist, gneiss, and slate, having been exposed to deep crustal levels of heat and pressure, and/or affected by earlier tectonic events, prior to their uplift. The metamorphic rocks are commonly sheared into a streaky rock known as mylonite near the detachment surface. Lower in the dome, the metamorphic rocks are folded in bewilderingly complex patterns, the result of ductile deformation of rock under the elevated temperatures and pressures that prevail in the deeper crust. In some of the metamorphic core complexes, the lower crustal rock also includes masses of Mesozoic plutonic rock such as granite or granodiorite.

In Nevada the two major packages of rock in core complexes, the brittle and broken upper crust and the deformed and arched lower crust, both developed in response to Cenozoic stretching of the Basin and Range.

A simple way to envision the nature of metamorphic core complexes is to imagine stretching a slab of hardened plaster resting on a layer of squishy jello. As the plaster breaks into pieces that move apart from each other, the underlying jello might flow upward in the cracks, tilting the plaster plates in opposite directions. Envision the oozing jello hardened into a solid dome between the tilted and broken pieces of plaster and you have a reasonably good mental image of a metamorphic core complex.

The domed metamorphic materials in many of Nevada's core complexes are cut by bodies of generally Oligocene age and younger granitic rocks. Geologists are still uncertain about the role magma played in the development of the core complexes, but there is a good correlation between the age of these granitic rocks and the apparent time of core complex development.

Core complexes are such large geological structures that it is impossible to see any of them in their entirety from a single vantage point. In addition, normal faulting in the Great Basin continued well beyond the time of core complex development, so that they are commonly disrupted by younger faults and buried beneath the alluvium that fills the downfaulted valleys between mountain ranges. The two best-known metamorphic core complexes in Nevada are the Ruby Mountains–East Humboldt core complex near Elko and the northern Snake Range core complex just west of the Nevada-Utah border. A third core complex is situated in the vicinity of the Grant Range in eastern Nye County but is not so well exposed or as clear a case as the other two.

Elsewhere in the Basin and Range of central Nevada, low-angle Cenozoic extensional faulting has exposed mid-to-deep crustal metamorphic rocks without developing the domed profile, mylonite zones, and regional detachment faults that characterize true metamorphic core complexes. Such areas include

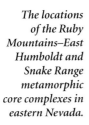

The locations of the Ruby Mountains–East Humboldt and Snake Range metamorphic core complexes in eastern Nevada.

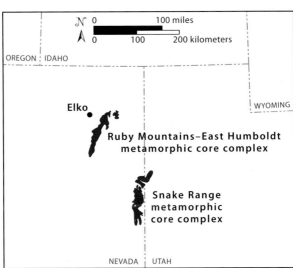

the Schell Creek, Egan, Toano-Goshute, and northern Pequop Ranges of eastern Nevada. In these areas, you will also encounter roadside exposures of metamorphic rocks that represent lower crustal materials.

ICE AGE NEVADA

The Pleistocene Epoch (2.6 million to 11,600 years ago) was a time of great climatic instability worldwide. For much of Pleistocene time, cyclic variations in solar energy reaching Earth caused the climate to swing back and forth between cold intervals, known as glacials, and warmer interludes, known as interglacials. Collectively, these climate oscillations are known as the ice ages, even though there were many times during this interval when the climate was just as warm, or perhaps even warmer, than it is today. In general, the Pleistocene glacial intervals were long (typically 50,000 to 100,000 years) and developed gradually, while the intervening warm interglacials were relatively abrupt and brief, lasting only 10,000 to 20,000 years. During the cold glacial episodes, ice caps expanded over level ground and great tongues of ice flowed down canyons in mountainous regions. Under the warmer climates of the interglacials, more ice melted than was formed each year, causing the glaciers to gradually recede and, in some of the warm periods, disappear completely. Climatologists estimate that during the last glacial peak, from 22,000 to around 18,000 years ago, the mean annual temperatures in Nevada were 8 to 15°F cooler, annual rainfall was about 8 inches more, and the annual rate of evaporation was as much as 13 inches lower than today.

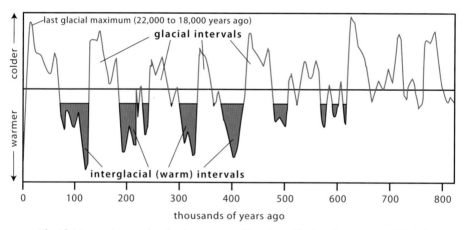

The Pleistocene ice ages involved numerous climatic oscillations between cold glacial intervals and warm interglacial periods. The horizontal line represents the long-term average temperature in Pleistocene time.

Mountain Glaciers

Nevada was a relatively dry place during the Pleistocene Epoch. The scarcity of moisture rather than the temperature limited the development of mountain glaciers, but glaciers did form in the highest of Nevada's mountains. The

Ruby Mountains, with numerous peaks exceeding 11,000 feet in elevation, were extensively glaciated several times during the Pleistocene Epoch, as were some equally high locations in the nearby East Humboldt Range. Smaller areas in the Snake, Schell Creek, White Pine, and Grant Ranges of eastern Nevada also experienced Pleistocene glaciations. In addition, relatively small Pleistocene glaciers formed in the Toiyabe, Toquima, and Monitor Ranges of central Nevada. The Spring Mountains of southern Nevada, with elevations as high 11,918 feet at Charleston Peak, may also have been glaciated during the Pleistocene Epoch, but the geological evidence is not so clear in this range as it is elsewhere in Nevada. In any event, compared to the massive glaciers that developed repeatedly in the Sierra Nevada to the west during the Pleistocene Epoch, the mountain glaciers in Nevada were relatively small and probably less persistent.

Ice Age Lakes

While only a few of the mountains of Nevada were heavily glaciated in the Pleistocene Epoch, the climatic oscillations of the time had a dramatic effect on the landscapes at lower elevations. As the climate cooled during the glacial episodes, more rain fell and less evaporated in the lowlands between the mountain ranges. Because many of the basins in Nevada are completely encircled by higher ground, the water that gathered in them formed lakes, some of impressive size. These ice age lakes are known as pluvial lakes, in reference to the source of their water; in Latin, *pluvia* means "rain." The pluvial lakes of Nevada underwent several cycles of growth and decline in rhythm with the climatic cycles of the Pleistocene. The last major development of ice age lakes in the Great Basin peaked between 20,000 and 13,000 years ago, about the same time that the glaciers in the higher elevations were at their most recent maximum stage. Thus, the ice age lakes in Nevada were not the result of glacial meltwater collecting in the lowlands; the lakes developed at the same time that the ice existed in the nearby mountains.

During the ice ages, dozens of large lakes existed in Nevada. As the lakes developed during the glacial intervals, the rising water submerged the lower slopes of the mountain ranges. Where the fluctuating lake levels were stabilized for a few centuries, the combination of wave and current erosion left prominent horizontal terraces on the lower mountain slopes, and sand and gravel deposits associated with the shorelines represent ancient beaches. The longer the period of stability, the more prominent the shoreline features became. These ancient shorelines, along with fine-grained silt and mud that accumulated on the lake bottoms, have been used to reconstruct the depth, size, and duration of the prehistoric lakes. Water emerging from springs on the lake bottoms supplied calcium, which reacted with the alkaline lake water to form mounds and masses of tufa, a hard rock composed of calcium carbonate.

The largest, deepest, and most extensive of Nevada's ice age lakes was Lake Lahontan, a huge body of water that submerged several interconnected basins in northwest Nevada. Lake Lahontan grew and declined several times during late Pleistocene time, reaching its last peak 14,000 to 13,000 years ago, when it inundated more than 8,600 square miles, comparable to modern Lake Erie in the Great Lakes region. Elsewhere in Nevada, smaller Pleistocene lakes also

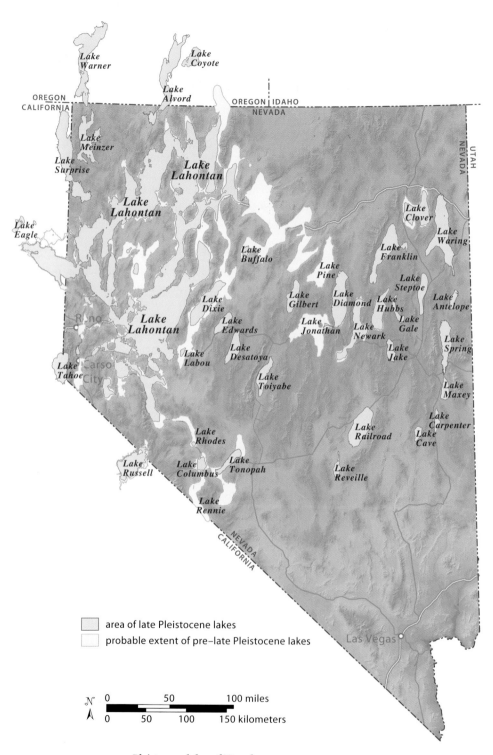

Pleistocene lakes of Nevada. —Modified from Reheis, 1999

developed adjacent to the Ruby Mountains (Lakes Franklin, Clover, and Waring) and in such arid and desolate valleys as Smith Creek Valley (Lake Desatoya), Big Smoky Valley (Lake Toiyabe), and Railroad Valley (Lake Railroad). In addition to these named lakes, perhaps hundreds of smaller and more ephemeral bodies of water dotted the landscape of Nevada during the Pleistocene Epoch.

In the 1870s famous American geologist Clarence King recognized the widespread lake sediments and prominent shoreline terraces engraved on many mountain slopes throughout northwest Nevada as evidence of an immense prehistoric body of water. He named the lake in honor of the French explorer Baron de Lahontan. Though King did not know the precise age of the lake, nor the climatic complexities that led to its development, the geological evidence of inundation of the arid lowlands was as unmistakable then as it is now.

Geologists, after analyzing the sedimentary record of Lake Lahontan and the shoreline terraces, have developed a fascinating chronology of Lake Lahontan. As is true of most of the ice age lakes in Nevada, the Lake Lahontan basin was submerged more than once during the Pleistocene ice ages, as the lake developed during cool intervals and withered during warmer and drier episodes. A lake-deposited sequence of silt, mud, sand, gravel, and volcanic ash, called the Sehoo deposits, records three cycles of lake growth from about 35,000 to 12,000 years ago. The most recent of these cycles peaked 15,000 to 13,000 years ago, when Lake Lahontan was 920 feet deep in the vicinity of modern Pyramid Lake. The high water had spilled into many basins adjacent to Pyramid Lake, forming an irregular lake consisting of many interconnected passages. In the Carson Sink area, southwest of Lovelock, Lake Lahontan was about 500 feet deep, and the ancestral Humboldt River entered the lake far upstream near the site of modern Winnemucca. Lake Lahontan also collected water from the ice age ancestors of the modern Quinn, Truckee, Carson, and Walker Rivers. Prior to the Sehoo inundation, an earlier version of Lake Lahontan existed from about 340,000 to 130,000 years ago. The sediments that document this phase of lake development are known as the Eetza deposits, which consists of older shoreline gravels and associated deeper-water silt and mud. Careful study of the Eetza sediments reveals evidence for at least three cycles of lake growth and decline. Between the lake deposits of the Sehoo and Eetza deposits, windblown sand deposits and ancient soil horizons provide evidence of a dry interval during which no bodies of deep water existed in western Nevada. Even older Pleistocene sediments provide some evidence of still earlier lake cycles 700,000 to 600,000 years ago and also between about 1.1 and 1.0 million years ago. Thus, no single age can be assigned to Lake Lahontan. Instead, the term describes a series of lakes that developed in northwest Nevada at various times during the Pleistocene ice ages in rhythm with the erratic swings of the climate in North America.

As the Pleistocene Epoch came to a close, the climate began a progressive shift toward a warmer and drier state. The level of Lake Lahontan fell steadily, and the connected waterway separated into numerous small lakes which, in turn, ultimately vanished from the landscape around 10,000 years ago, leaving only the parched lakes bottoms encrusted with silt, salt, and tufa. However, in places where modern rivers drain into enclosed basins, permanent lakes, such

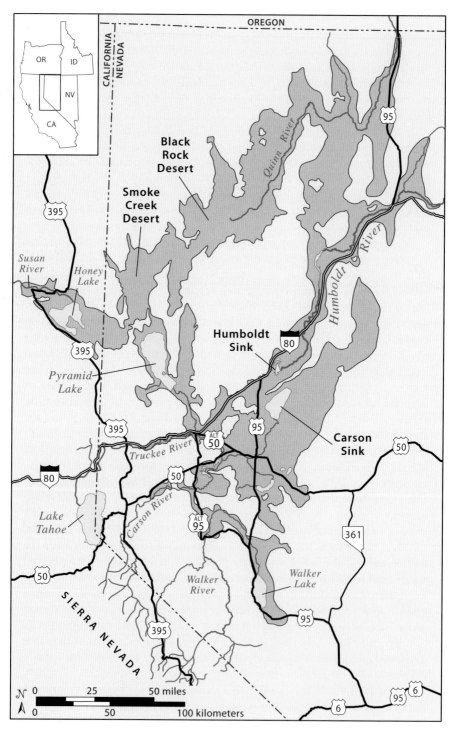

The maximum extent of Lake Lahontan in western Nevada.

Gravel pit south of US 95 on the north side of the Mopung Hills. Note the inclined layering (cross-bedding) in the Lake Lahontan gravel deposits and the underlying fine-grained silt (on the right) deposited when the lake was deeper.

as Pyramid and Walker Lakes, survive to the modern time as tiny remnants of the once majestic ice age lake. Many of the roads described in this book pass over dry and desolate valley floors that were once submerged under hundreds of feet of sparking blue water.

THE FUTURE

The Nevada landscape continues to be shaped by geological processes. The ever-threatening earthquakes are a constant reminder than Nevada's mountains and basins are still adjusting to tectonic stresses in the lithosphere. Geological evidence suggests that molten rock is only a few kilometers underground in some areas, a sober reminder that the age of volcanoes in Nevada may not be completely over. In our modern era of profound and rapid climate change, we can anticipate equally significant responses in such geologically influenced phenomena as groundwater flow, river erosion, landslides, soil development, and subsidence of lowlands. Nonetheless, exploring how the distant past has shaped what we see from Nevada's roads is still a fascinating adventure. Let's take a look what can be discovered from the rocks and landforms along the byways of the magnificent Silver State.

Las Vegas Area

Las Vegas, Spanish for "the meadows," seems an odd name for this desert basin, but old topographic maps of the Las Vegas Valley show there were many natural springs here, extending northwest as far as Indian Springs and Cactus Springs. Recharged by snowmelt and precipitation in the high Spring Mountains to the west, artesian springs created the meadows. Several of the springs still form oases in the dry valley floor, including Corn Creek Springs at the Desert National Wildlife Range and Tule Springs at Floyd Lamb State Park. At Corn Creek Springs, the main entry point for the Desert National Wildlife Range, scientists are attempting to preserve a pupfish found only in a desert springs.

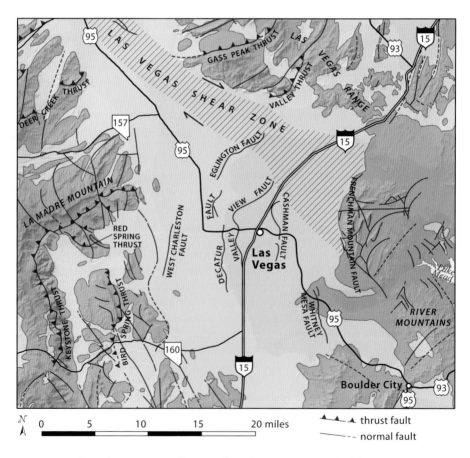

Faults in the Las Vegas Valley. Note how the mountains north of the Las Vegas Valley curve to the west near the Las Vegas shear zone.

Numerous faults cross the Las Vegas Valley, including the 95-mile-long, northwest-trending Las Vegas shear zone, part of a zone of right-lateral strike-slip faults along the California-Nevada border. Although not exposed, the shear zone was interpreted from the bending of mountain ranges on either side of the Las Vegas Valley and from geophysical measurements in the subsurface. All the western ridges of the mountain ranges between Las Vegas and Indian Springs change from a northerly to a westerly trend to the east of US 95, suggesting a right-lateral offset along the shear zone. Correlation of northeast-trending thrust faults on either side of the valley indicate that approximately 30 to 60 miles of right-slip offset has occurred along the Las Vegas shear zone, mostly between about 14 and 8 million years ago.

The Las Vegas Valley, like most other valleys in the Basin and Range Province of western North America, is bounded by faults that have dropped the valley down relative to the surrounding mountain ranges. Alluvium that fills the valley may be as much as 13,000 feet thick in the northeastern part of the valley in the vicinity of Nellis Air Force Base. Subtle changes in the flat valley floor were once attributed to subsidence of fine-grained sediments in the basin, but subsequent studies show these are fault scarps. If movement occurs on one of these active faults, the earthquake could cause substantial damage in the Las Vegas Valley.

The most expressive fault is the Cashman fault, which is responsible for a step up in topography between Eastern Avenue and Las Vegas Boulevard. Further west, the Valley View fault and the Decatur fault also step up to the west. A good example of the Decatur fault can be seen at the intersection of Charleston Boulevard and Decatur Boulevard. Near the intersection with I-215, Ann Road crosses the Eglington fault scarp. It has as much as 75 feet of vertical offset and steps down to the southeast. Surface expression of the Frenchman Mountain fault, which bounds the east side of the valley, can be seen just south of Lake Mead Boulevard in the vicinity of East Owens Avenue. Whitney Mesa, west of US 95 in the Whitney Ranch area, is cut by two fault scarps with down-to-the-east displacement. Some springs occur along the faults.

Tule Springs Fossil Beds National Monument

Tule Springs Fossil Beds National Monument, east of US 95 along Moccasin Road at the northern edge of the city, was established in 2014 to preserve a portion of the Las Vegas Wash where light-colored, fine-grained deposits host the remains of ice age mammals. Paleontologists have found thousands of fossils of mammoths, bison, American lions, camelops (a larger version of today's Bactrian camels), sloths, and ancient horses. The area is particularly significant because the sediments span a lengthy interval of Pleistocene time, between 700,000 and 10,000 years ago. Many of the excavated fossils are housed in the San Bernardino County Museum in California.

The extensive deposits, which runoff dissects into badlands, can be seen to the east of US 95 throughout the northern part of the valley and as far northwest as Indian Springs. Early geologists thought the sediments were lake deposits but couldn't account for the difference of 1,000 feet in elevation between the Indian Springs deposits and those in the Las Vegas Valley. In the 1990s, analysis of the mollusk shells found in the sediments revealed that the primary environment was one of freshwater springs. The fine-grained silts were captured by the vegetation in wetlands and meadows. Today, gravels from the surrounding alluvial fans, as well as housing developments, are covering them, and they are a playground for off-road vehicles.

Spring Mountains

The Spring Mountains extend from California northward along the west side of the Las Vegas Valley as far north as Amargosa Valley. The range, isolated from other nearby ranges, is a classic island in the desert, and some plants and animals are found only in this range. Charleston Peak, at 11,918 feet, is at a sufficiently high elevation to collect snowfall in the winter and induce summer thunderstorms, enabling the range to replenish the groundwater of the Las Vegas Valley on the east and the Pahrump Valley on the west. The present form of the mountain range is the result of faulting that began about 15 million years ago as basins dropped down during Basin and Range extension.

The range is composed of mostly Paleozoic marine sedimentary rock that collected on the continental shelf of the ancient craton. The stratigraphic pile thickens from 9,800 feet on the east side of the mountains to approximately 30,000 feet on the west side. The addition of about 10,000 feet of Proterozoic sediments, outcropping on the northwest side of the mountains at the base of the Paleozoic section, accounts for half of that increase. Another substantial increase is in the 3,500-foot-thickness of the Pennsylvanian-age Bird Spring Formation in the middle of the range. The sedimentary rocks were not directly affected by the Antler Orogeny in Devonian to Mississippian time, but there are no rocks from the upper half of the Mississippian Period. The region was likely elevated at that time. Soil, as well as karst, formed on the eroding Mississippian surface, which subsequently was buried by Triassic sediments.

The sequence of strata is relatively intact despite being disrupted by three major thrust faults—the Keystone, Lee Canyon, and Wheeler Pass thrust

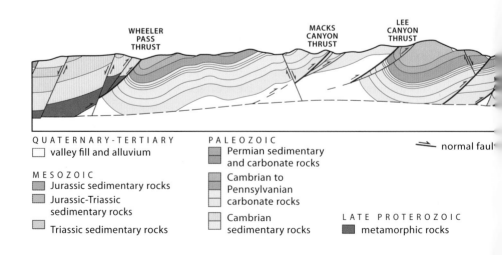

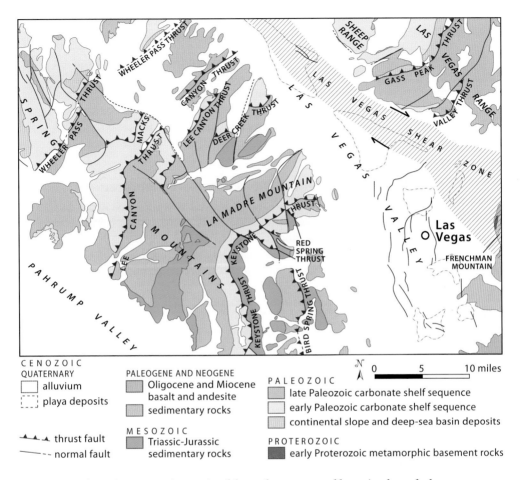

CENOZOIC		PALEOGENE AND NEOGENE	PALEOZOIC

CENOZOIC
QUATERNARY

☐ alluvium

⌐⌐⌐ playa deposits

▲▲▲▲ thrust fault

——--- normal fault

PALEOGENE AND NEOGENE

Oligocene and Miocene basalt and andesite

sedimentary rocks

MESOZOIC

Triassic-Jurassic sedimentary rocks

PALEOZOIC

late Paleozoic carbonate shelf sequence

early Paleozoic carbonate shelf sequence

continental slope and deep-sea basin deposits

PROTEROZOIC

early Proterozoic metamorphic basement rocks

0   5   10 miles

The Spring Mountains consist of thrust sheets separated by major thrust faults.

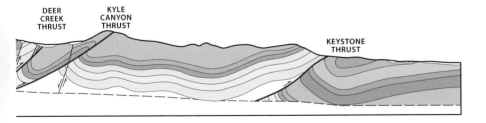

Cross section of the Spring Mountains showing thrust sheets of layered Paleozoic sedimentary rocks. —Modified from Page and others, 2005

faults—that cut diagonally across the Spring Mountains from southwest to northeast. They continue north into the Sheep and Las Vegas Ranges but are offset 30 to 60 miles by the Las Vegas shear zone. These thrust faults were active around 110 to 100 million years ago during the Sevier Orogeny when compressional forces shoved older rocks up and over the top of younger rocks. The Keystone thrust fault, one of the best exposed thrust faults in the western United States, carried Paleozoic strata eastward over the spectacular Jurassic-age sandstone exposed at Red Rock Canyon.

Red Rock Canyon National Conservation Area

The natural feature most famously associated with Las Vegas is Red Rock Canyon National Conservation Area, on the west side of the Las Vegas Valley. To reach the 2,000-foot-high sandstone cliffs, head west on Charleston Boulevard, which turns into NV 159. A one-way loop road on the north side of NV 159 provides access to the sandstone, overlooks, picnic areas, and hiking and climbing trails. The visitor center at the entrance to the loop road has several informative displays regarding the natural environment and is a good place to start your visit.

An overlook on NV 159 between milepost 8 and milepost 9, uphill from the visitor center, provides many insights into the geologic setting of Red Rock Canyon. The red and tan cliffs are Aztec Sandstone, which consolidated from a large field of sand dunes in Jurassic time. Among the distinctive features of the sandstone are the bold bands of color across the cliff faces. The movement of fluids through the sandstone after consolidation formed the color. If the coloration follows bedding planes, it is coincidental, or perhaps because the bedding plane provided either an easy flat flow path or a barrier to flow. On the skyline in the distance behind the cliffs is gray limestone of Paleozoic age, part of the Keystone thrust sheet that was shoved over the top of the Aztec Sandstone in Cretaceous time.

The north-trending line of towering sandstone cliffs ends abruptly to the north of the overlook. The La Madre fault, a normal fault that trends perpendicular to the Keystone thrust, has dropped the sandstone down about 4,000 feet, accounting for its disappearance. The Keystone thrust is displaced only 300 to 600 feet across the La Madre fault, indicating that most of the offset along the La Madre fault occurred prior to emplacement of the Keystone thrust. The La Madre fault extends 30 miles from NV 159 northwestward across the Spring Mountains. Jurassic-age rocks can be seen on the north side of the fault in the Calico Basin area.

Another geomorphic feature clearly seen from the overlook is the vast quantity of alluvial fan material that has been eroded, mostly from the limestone mountains to the north. At least four ages of alluvial fans are visible from the overlook.

You can also see red Jurassic sandstone and thrust faults on the north side of Calico Basin, an oasis in the desert created where springs emerge from the base of the sandstone. As you head west from Las Vegas on NV 159, turn north toward Calico Basin just west of the campground turnoff and before reaching

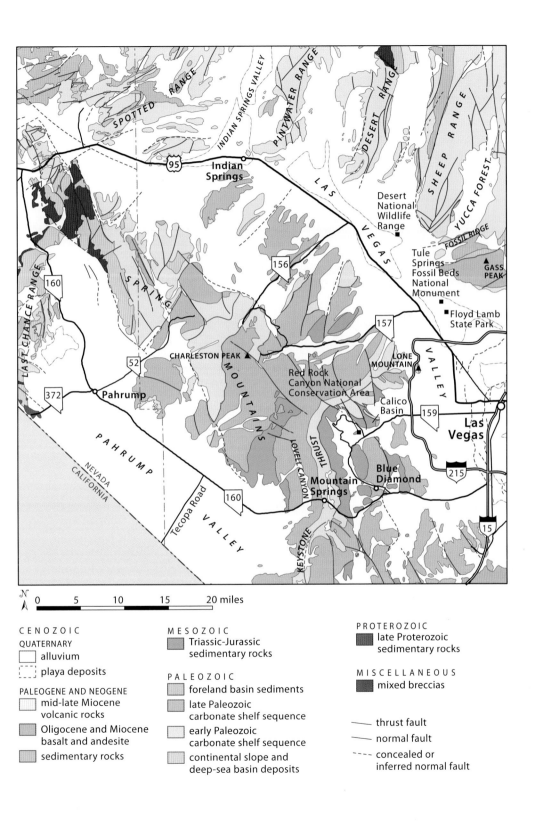

CENOZOIC

QUATERNARY

☐ alluvium

┆┄┆ playa deposits

PALEOGENE AND NEOGENE

☐ mid-late Miocene
volcanic rocks

☐ Oligocene and Miocene
basalt and andesite

☐ sedimentary rocks

MESOZOIC

☐ Triassic-Jurassic
sedimentary rocks

PALEOZOIC

☐ foreland basin sediments

☐ late Paleozoic
carbonate shelf sequence

☐ early Paleozoic
carbonate shelf sequence

☐ continental slope and
deep-sea basin deposits

PROTEROZOIC

☐ late Proterozoic
sedimentary rocks

MISCELLANEOUS

☐ mixed breccias

—— thrust fault

—— normal fault

---- concealed or
inferred normal fault

View west from Red Rock Overlook toward cliffs of Aztec Sandstone of Jurassic age. Paleozoic limestone forms the skyline in distance behind the cliffs.

Red Rock Canyon. Straight ahead down the road to Calico Basin is a mountain with the dark red and tan of the Aztec Sandstone exposed in the lower two-thirds of the slope overlain by tan-gray limestone of the Cambrian-age Bonanza King Formation in the upper third of the mountain. The horizontal line separating the two units is the Red Spring thrust fault, which predates the Keystone thrusting. With binoculars, it is possible to discern a thin, dark-brown to brownish-pink unit, the conglomerate of Brownstone Basin, between the sandstone and the overlying limestone. Streams deposited this conglomerate, usually in a matrix of reworked Aztec sand, on the weathered surface of Aztec Sandstone.

The easternmost limestone ridge at Calico Basin is not faulted over the sandstone but rather is breccia of a debris flow. About 11 million years ago, a debris flow carrying limestone rock fragments flowed down a narrow canyon in the sandstone. Over time, the sandstone eroded to the current level, and the more resistant limestone debris flow forms the capping rock. Note how the contact between the gray breccia and the underlying pinkish sandstone is irregular.

Lee Canyon

NV 156 heads up Lee Canyon 15 miles to the Las Vegas ski area. Note that the milepost numbering starts at the ski area. As the road climbs the alluvial fan surface, for about 11 miles it follows the Mack Canyon thrust fault, a splay of the Lee Canyon thrust fault. The splay is offset to the north at the La Madre fault, which the road crosses at milepost 4. The western 4 miles of the road follows the Lee Canyon thrust to the ski area.

Older alluvial fans flanked the mountains in late Tertiary to early Quaternary time. Remnants of these older fans are preserved in Lee Canyon, particularly on the south side of the road. Look for cemented gravels at milepost 3. A water well drilled a half mile west of the NV 158 intersection encountered 450 feet of gravel before reaching bedrock. Projected to the highest fan surface, this narrow valley at one time had 750 feet of fill.

The upper reaches of the road along the Lee Canyon thrust feature dramatic scenery. The limestone of the Devonian Sultan and Mississippian Monte Cristo rock units forms a succession of vertical cliffs on the west side of Mummy Mountain south of Lee Canyon Road. The upper rocks are some of the youngest in the Keystone thrust sheet. On the north side of the road are older rocks at the base of the Lee Canyon thrust sheet. The entire ski bowl, up to the high ridgeline, is developed on the Pennsylvanian Bird Spring Formation, part of the Keystone thrust sheet, but the parking lot is in Ordovician limestone of the Lee Canyon thrust sheet.

The northern point of Mummy Mountain, viewed from near milepost 3 on NV 156. The Devonian limestone of the Sultan Formation makes up the base, and the massive, cliff-forming Mississippian Monte Cristo Limestone caps the mountain.

Kyle Canyon Road to Mt. Charleston

Kyle Canyon Road (NV 157) is the gateway to relief from the summer heat. Trails that begin near Mt. Charleston wander through pine forests and up treeless ridges to 11,918-foot Charleston Peak. Milepost numbering starts at Mt. Charleston, so the numbering decreases going uphill from the intersection of NV 157 with US 95 in the Las Vegas Valley.

Just west of the intersection, the dip slope of massive beds of the Mississippian Monte Cristo Limestone dominate the skyline to the south. Strata exposed in the hill closer to the road around milepost 16 also exhibit the eastward dip and consist of the Pennsylvanian Bird Spring Formation, which overlies the Monte Cristo. The characteristically thin- to medium-bedded nature of the Bird Spring Formation aids in identifying it throughout this stretch of highway. The mine south of the road around milepost 14 is excavating gypsum from the Bird Spring Formation.

The high ridgeline to the south is La Madre Mountain, capped by the resistant Monte Cristo Limestone. A prominent whitish patch is a relatively fresh landslide scar, where a block of the limestone slipped downslope along a bedding plane in the limestone. A rubble pile of large blocks can been seen at the base of the slide.

The tilted layers of Bird Spring Formation flank both sides of the highway until milepost 12, where the road drops down into the Kyle Canyon wash, which is incised into a veneer of Pleistocene alluvial fan deposits. The bedrock that is occasionally visible beneath the gravel is limestone of the Bird Spring

Pleistocene alluvial gravel between milepost 9 and milepost 8 on NV 157.

Formation. The folds seen in these beds likely formed 100 to 90 million years ago during the Sevier Orogeny. Across from the intersection of Harris Springs Road between milepost 9 and milepost 8, you can see a prominent change in the color of the gravels in the gravel cliffs to the north of the road. The lower half of the exposure is more reddish than the top half, likely reflecting a Triassic source rock for the lower layer.

The prominent low cliffs south of the Mt. Charleston resort around milepost 4 are cemented alluvial fan gravels. In the early 2000s, the hotel attempted to create a golf course at the base of these cliffs, but the venture did not last long. The upper surface of the cliffs is the oldest alluvial surface in the area, and the deposits are at least 800,000 years in age.

The La Madre fault trends northwesterly across NV 157 just east of the intersection with Deer Creek Road (NV 158), which connects Kyle Canyon with Lee Canyon. Deer Creek Road flanks the eastern edge of the higher elevations of the Spring Mountains and generally follows the northwest trend of the La Madre fault. Impressive roadcuts expose older alluvial fan material that was deposited on an eroded surface of the older Paleozoic bedrock.

Near the upper end of Kyle Canyon Road, faults trending more or less perpendicular to the road form spectacular vertical cliffs hundreds of feet high. The road crosses a splay of the Griffith Peak normal fault at the Rainbow residential area near milepost 1. Cathedral Rock looms straight ahead and Echo Cliff is to the south, all composed of Mississippian Monte Cristo Limestone with Devonian-age limestone of the Sultan Formation at the base. The canyon cliffs are overlain by the monotonous Bird Spring Formation, all the way to the top of the ridges encircling the canyon and the top of Charleston Peak. At the westernmost end of the canyon, under Charleston Peak, the Bird Spring Formation is delightfully distorted into a series of chevron folds, a result of the thrust faulting. Look for the folds in the cliff face above the trail to Big Falls, or from Mary Jane Falls, or from the North Loop Trail to Charleston Peak.

The La Madre fault separates Devonian through Mississippian limestone of Fletcher Peak, on the left, from the more subdued topography developed in the Pennsylvanian Bird Spring Formation, on the right.

Lone Mountain is primarily Mississippian-age limestone of the Monte Cristo Limestone.

Lone Mountain

People who live near the beltway (I-215) on the northwest side of Las Vegas are close to trailheads that access rugged outcrops of Paleozoic rock layers. Lone Mountain is the solitary hill east of I-215 between the Cheyenne Avenue and Lone Mountain Road exits. The Mississippian Monte Cristo Limestone forms the bulk of the mountain, with the uppermost member of the Devonian Sultan Formation only exposed as the light-gray beds at the base. Different members of the Monte Cristo Limestone account for the change from the gray-colored upper third of the mountain to the underlying dark bands of chert-rich limestone layers. Although its stratigraphy is very similar to that of the hills to the west of the highway, geophysical studies indicate that Lone Mountain is not structurally attached to the hills to the west and is, instead, a large block that has slid to its present position.

Pahrump Road (NV 160)
See map on page 53.

NV 160, the Pahrump Road, crosses through the Spring Mountains at Mountain Springs Summit and then follows the western flank of the mountains northwest to Pahrump. For the first 7 miles west of I-15, NV 160 gradually ascends an extensive alluvial fan derived from the Red Rock Canyon area to the west. In the distance, you can see the massive cliffs of Aztec Sandstone in the Spring Mountains. A small hill at about milepost 4 consists of Kaibab Limestone of Permian age and is the northern expression of the Arden Dome, an upward doming of the bedrock in the hills to the south. Farther west, the road passes through a gap eroded through a continuous ridge of Permian rock dipping gently to the west. Underneath a limestone cap are several small mining operations focused on a horizontal bed of gypsum along the cliff face. To the west, the rock is overlain by early Triassic, thin-bedded, yellowish-tan Virgin

CONGLOMERATE AT BLUE DIAMOND

You can take a short trip on NV 159 to see a conglomerate with an interesting history. After passing through limestone cliffs of the Toroweap and Kaibab units at milepost 2, you'll come to milepost 3 at Castalia Street, which heads southwest toward Blue Diamond. Just east of the intersection is a 3- to 4-foot-high, dark-brown outcrop of conglomerate of the Timpoweap Formation on the northeast side of NV 159. This conglomerate, the basal member of the Moenkopi Formation, was deposited in stream channels on an eroded surface of Kaibab Limestone in Triassic time. The Kaibab Limestone, deposited in middle Permian time, must have been uplifted above sea level. The conglomerate is well sorted and contains many pebbles of quartzite and very few of limestone. The well-sorted, rounded pebbles must have been deposited in a well-developed and lengthy stream system, having a source area where quartzites of Cambrian rock were exposed to erosion. The sea then inundated the area for the last time, depositing the Virgin Limestone Member of the Moenkopi Formation over the top of the conglomerate. The hills directly west of Blue Diamond consist of the evenly spaced, light yellowish-gray beds of the Virgin Limestone.

Limestone, which is the last rock to have been deposited in an ocean in southern Nevada. All younger sedimentary rocks accumulated on land or in streams and lakes.

You can see a gypsum processing plant to the north near the intersection with NV 159, which loops back to Las Vegas and provides access to the village of Blue Diamond and the Red Rock Canyon National Conservation Area. A rather extensive gypsum mining area at the top of the cliffs was active until the 1990s, and the material was transported to the plant by way of a sluice pipe down the cliff face. The plant still manufactures gypsum wallboard, using rock material trucked in from east of Las Vegas. The red, less-resistant rock near the base of the cliffs is early Permian red beds, and the gray and brown limestone cliffs are the Toroweap and Kaibab rock units of middle Permian age. A fault trending northward along the base of the cliff juxtaposes the older rocks against the Triassic Virgin Limestone to the east.

Between milepost 13 and milepost 16, the small hills to the north of the road are capped by medium-gray rubble—a landslide deposit consisting almost entirely of limestone and a few large sandstone blocks. The age of the landslide is unknown. The landslide material filled channels on the preexisting bedrock surface, but because it is more resistant than the Aztec Sandstone, it now caps the hills in the Blue Diamond area north of NV 160. An outcrop of the limestone debris flow is reasonably accessible at the mountain biking trailhead at milepost 15. On the south side of the road, strata of the Permian Kaibab Limestone form hogbacks that slope toward the road at about a 25-degree angle.

The road climbs toward Mountain Springs Summit, a gap formed in the cliffs along the Cottonwood fault. Prior to the Keystone thrust faulting in Cretaceous time, the range was structurally uplifted along this fault relative to the block to the north. The Keystone thrust fault, which is traced southward to the California border, juxtaposes Cambrian rock over Mississippian limestone south of the pass and Cambrian rock over Jurassic sandstone north of the pass.

The wash on the north side of the highway has been eroded along the Cottonwood fault, and the trend of the fault can be viewed around milepost 18. Near milepost 19, Mt. Potosi Canyon Road intersects NV 160 on the south. Look up this road from the intersection to see the change in bedrock from cliffy Mississippian Monte Cristo Limestone on the left to more rounded hills of Cambrian Bonanza King Formation on the right. The change occurs because Mt. Potosi Canyon Road follows the trace of the Keystone thrust fault. Just uphill of the Mt. Potosi Canyon Road intersection, around the bend in the road, the Keystone thrust fault truncates the limestone hill on the east side of the road. It is possible to look to the north skyline and see the dark-gray Cambrian rock thrust over the red and tan sandstone of the Aztec Formation.

Mountain Springs, at the summit of the pass, was a watering spot for travelers on the Old Spanish Trail on their way to the dry Pahrump Valley. West of the pass, NV 160 traverses upward through the stratigraphic section. Overlying the Cambrian and erodible Ordovician rocks is Devonian limestone. The cliff-forming Mississippian Monte Cristo Limestone forms the higher hills to the south at the top of the pass. On the west-facing slopes the medium-bedded Bird Spring Formation of Permian to Pennsylvanian age is exposed from milepost 22 to 23. The Lovell Canyon Road, which intersects NV 160 north of milepost 24, follows the easily eroded lower Permian red beds, which can be seen as red coloration in the gullies below the Permian limestone cliffs on the west side of Lovell Canyon Road. Look for minor faults that offset bedding in the limestone cliffs. Around milepost 26 a recumbent fold in the limestone is visible north of the road.

Between the base of the pass and Pahrump, NV 160 follows the west side of the Spring Mountains. The paved road to Tecopa, California, intersects NV 160 at milepost 38. This road follows the Old Spanish Trail, and wagon tracks from a century ago can still be seen approaching Emigrant Pass, where the road crosses the Nopah Range, the first mountain range in California. Tecopa Road crosses the state line close to the intersection of two Quaternary fault systems. The Stateline fault zone, paralleling the border between California and Nevada, has been mapped over a distance of 105 miles using geophysical data. The fault zone is a series of steep-sided pull-apart basins caused by strike-slip faulting. A series of gravel-capped, rounded hills trending northwest at the state line marks a horst ridge between the basins. The strike-slip faulting may accommodate some strain on the San Andreas fault. The other Quaternary fault, the West Spring Mountains fault zone, is marked by a more northerly alignment of west-facing scarps in Quaternary alluvial fan surfaces, extending from the Tecopa Road to north of Pahrump.

SHEEP AND LAS VEGAS RANGES

The Sheep and Las Vegas Ranges north of Las Vegas are included within the Desert National Wildlife Range, a remote, nearly inaccessible area. The Las Vegas Range is directly north of Las Vegas, and photovoltaic panels on its high point, Gass Peak, can sometimes be seen reflecting light. This mountain range consists almost entirely of marine sedimentary rocks deposited on the continental shelf in late Paleozoic time. The lowermost lighter-colored rocks along its southern base are older Mississippian units, altered limestones of the Bullion Member of the Monte Cristo Limestone, and Gass Peak is Pennsylvanian- to Permian-age Bird Spring Formation. The same thrust faults that cut the Spring Mountains to the west also cut the Las Vegas Range but are offset to the southeast. The Gass Peak thrust fault, which lies along the northern base of Gass Peak, is a continuation of the Wheeler Pass thrust fault. Late Proterozoic and Cambrian rocks mapped along the base of Gass Peak mark the leading edge of the Wheeler Pass thrust sheet. The prominent dark and light banding along the southern cliff face of Fossil Ridge, a narrow ridge north of Gass Peak, is a distinctive characteristic of the Cambrian Nopah Formation.

On the northern side of Gass Peak, an east-trending valley separates the mass of the peak from Fossil Ridge. The intervening valley is a Miocene-age pull-apart basin that still contains light-colored freshwater lakebeds and ash-rich sediments deposited around 20 to 15 million years ago. The sediments are perched 1,000 feet above the modern valley floor. In places, slide blocks up to 1,500 feet across and composed of Paleozoic rock derived from the adjacent ranges are enclosed by the lakebeds.

Sedimentary rock layers in the Sheep Range, the large range north of the Las Vegas Range, are almost entirely Paleozoic limestones and dolomites that become progressive younger above the Gass Peak thrust fault. Cambrian

View looking east across the Las Vegas Valley toward the Sheep Range from Lee Canyon Road. The lower prominent dark and light banding is the Cambrian Nopah Formation, and the upper dark band with a thin white bed below it is the Ordovician Eureka Quartzite and the overlying Ely Springs Dolomite. In between is the tan-colored late Cambrian to middle Ordovician Pogonip Group. The dark rock on the ridgeline is the Devonian Devils Gate Limestone.

rocks are at the base, and the uppermost ridgetops of the southern part of the range are Devonian-age rocks. Although cut by several normal faults, the banded stratigraphy of the Sheep Range indicates the relatively intact nature of the Paleozoic sediments to the northwest of the Gass Peak thrust fault. All of the Sheep Range is in the Wheeler Pass thrust sheet, whereas the portion of the Spring Mountains directly across the valley is in the Keystone thrust sheet.

The abrupt, steep western front of the Sheep Range, best seen in profile from northern Las Vegas, has been uplifted along west-dipping normal faults. Although there has been no known earthquake activity in the past 10,000 years, fault scarps cut the Quaternary-age alluvial fans along the mountain front. The older fans near the base of the mountains are deeply incised by drainages that now carry debris past them to outer, younger fan surfaces.

Valley of Fire State Park

A large area of brightly colored rock of the Aztec Sandstone is exposed at Valley of Fire State Park, about 45 miles northeast of Las Vegas. The sandstone solidified from a huge area of shifting dunes that existed 200 to 175 million years ago, in Jurassic time, when the region lay within 10 degrees of the equator. The sea of sand was similar to the Sahara Desert today. The source of the sand was westward-flowing rivers eroding the enormous Appalachian Mountains that formed during the assembly of Pangaea. The Aztec Sandstone, which is also exposed at Red Rock Canyon west of Las Vegas, is equivalent to the Navajo Sandstone of the Colorado Plateau. Prior to Cenozoic time, the Aztec Sandstone was much closer to the outcrops of Navajo Sandstone in southwestern Utah; it has since been transported to its current position by extensional Basin and Range faulting.

The Aztec Sandstone is composed of well-rounded grains of almost pure quartz sand with no clay or silt. A prominent feature of the sandstone exposures is the crossbedding, which forms when the wind shifts directions. As the dune field got buried by successive layers of sand, the grains of sand gradually cemented together into hard sandstone. The color of the sandstone is attributed to minerals, particularly red iron oxide (hematite) and hydroxide that coated the grains during deposition and to some extent sulfides, and to the remobilization of minerals as groundwater moved through the rock during and after the sand solidified into rock.

To reach Valley of Fire State Park, take exit 75 from I-15 north of Las Vegas. The road crosses an expanse of dry desert for 7 miles before crossing a slight rise that marks the California Wash fault, an active and potentially dangerous fault (see road guide I-15 in this chapter). After crossing the fault, the road passes into Paleozoic rocks of two different Sevier thrust sheets. The erosion of the overlying thrust sheets here opened a window into the Jurassic rock below.

From the west entry station to east of the visitors' center, the road parallels the Valley of Fire Wash, which has carved the valley along the axis of an anticline. Exposed in the core of the anticline are the easily eroded mudstones, siltstones, and sandstones of the Triassic Moenkopi, Chinle, Moenave, and

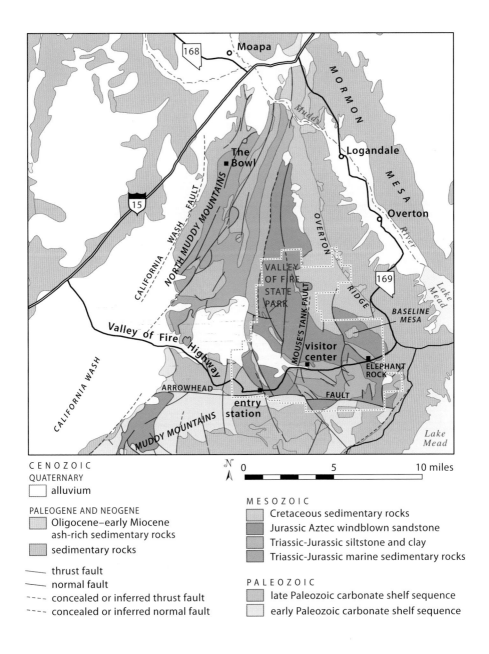

CENOZOIC
QUATERNARY

☐ alluvium

PALEOGENE AND NEOGENE

▨ Oligocene–early Miocene
   ash-rich sedimentary rocks

▨ sedimentary rocks

—— thrust fault
—— normal fault
---- concealed or inferred thrust fault
---- concealed or inferred normal fault

MESOZOIC

☐ Cretaceous sedimentary rocks
▨ Jurassic Aztec windblown sandstone
▨ Triassic-Jurassic siltstone and clay
▨ Triassic-Jurassic marine sedimentary rocks

PALEOZOIC

▨ late Paleozoic carbonate shelf sequence
☐ early Paleozoic carbonate shelf sequence

Kayenta Formations. The more resistant, younger Jurassic Aztec Sandstone is preserved on both sides of the anticline, as are the very resistant limestones to the south of the valley. Remnants of the Horse Spring Formation, deposited on the landscape in Miocene time, are also visible from the highway.

Most of the points of interest in the park are in the Aztec Sandstone to the north of the Valley of Fire Road, and some side roads provide access in that area. The sandstone mass is crisscrossed by joints and faults, along which

Red and white colors in the Aztec Sandstone.

View southeast from the area of the west entry station to Valley of Fire State Park. The orange-red Aztec Sandstone contrasts vividly with the gray Paleozoic rocks of the Muddy Mountain thrust sheet. In the middleground, the Cambrian Bonanza King rocks are nearly vertical and are overlain by the reddish-brown Miocene Rainbow Gardens Member of the Horse Spring Formation. The banded gray strata on the far left horizon are Cambrian carbonates.

erosion has created crevices, passageways, and drainages and lots of nooks and crannies. Two miles into the park is a turnoff to the north for Atlatl Rock, known for its petroglyphs, which were carved into the desert varnish on the sandstone by early peoples who lived in the area about 3,000 years ago. Another reason to climb the metal staircase to the petroglyphs lies overhead, in the sandstone slab overhanging the petroglyphs at the top of the stairs. Look closely to find approximately eight mammal-like reptile footprints on the bottom of the slab. These fossil tracks are known as *Brasilichnium* and are thought to have been made by a small mammal-like reptile. Few body fossils of the unknown creature have been preserved. Across the road from the Atlatl Rock turnoff is a turnoff to see petrified logs, remnants of ancient pines now preserved along the crest of the Valley of Fire anticline.

The visitors' center is situated at the base of the cliffs north of the road. Inside, along the windows looking south across the valley, is a discussion of the geologic history of the area. The view south is of the Muddy Mountains, composed of gray Cambrian through Pennsylvanian strata of the Muddy Mountain thrust sheet.

From the visitors' center, which is constructed on the Moenave and Kayenta Formation, of Triassic age, a side road proceeds northward, through the Aztec cliffs, to an area known as the White Domes. As the road climbs out of the valley, halfway up the hill it crosses the contact between the Moenave and Kayenta rocks, which are dipping about 25 degrees to the north, and the base of the Aztec Sandstone. The road passes through the sandstone, following a straight gully eroded along the north-trending Mouse's Tank fault.

Proceeding north past the trailhead for Mouse's Tank to the Rainbow Vista turnout, the road is in the lower part of the Aztec, a well-cemented unit with a distinctive reddish-brown color. Just north of the Rainbow Vista parking area the color changes to white, yellow, and purple, representing the middle member of the Aztec Sandstone. The offset of this coloration change is the basis for deducing that about 500 feet of left-lateral slip has occurred on the Mouse's Tank fault. You'll notice the rock turns whitish first on the left (west) side of the road. To the northeast of the view area, limited exposures of the Cretaceous-age Willow Tank Formation are identifiable by their gray banding.

Near the end of the White Domes Road, just before swinging southward to the parking lot, the massive red sandstone cliffs to the east of the road are a remnant of the Summit thrust sheet, with Aztec Sandstone thrust over the Aztec along the road, and over the Cretaceous Willow Tank Formation along the eastern side of the block. The White Domes area is formed in the middle sandstone unit, which is less cemented and weathers to domes.

Heading east from the visitors' center on the main road, the sandstone cliffs to the north of the road in the vicinity of the Cabins recede sharply to the northeast, reflecting offset along a fault, and the road continues through Triassic Moenkopi, overlain by the Chinle, and then the Moenave and Kayenta, up to the base of the Aztec Sandstone at Elephant Rock. The entry station on the east side of Elephant Rock is in the Moenave and Kayenta, which is in fault contact with the sandstone to the west.

Aztec Sandstone eroding to white domes.

If you enter the park from the east, the prominent flat-topped mesa to the northwest of the road is Baseline Mesa, formed of Pliocene Muddy Creek deposits and protected by a well-developed layer of caliche. If you look west upon passing Elephant Rock, some nicely developed terrace surfaces slope northward from the Muddy Mountains escarpment to the south in the Fire Alcove area.

FRENCHMAN MOUNTAIN VIA LAKE MEAD BOULEVARD

Frenchman Mountain, the prominent two-peak mountain on the east side of the Las Vegas Valley, can be seen from virtually everywhere in the valley. Its western face displays a spectacular stratigraphic section of Paleozoic rocks that is very similar to that seen in the Grand Canyon, but with a total

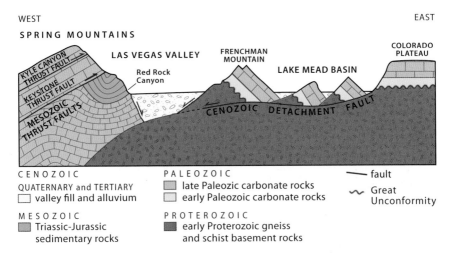

WEST

EAST

SPRING MOUNTAINS

LAS VEGAS VALLEY   FRENCHMAN MOUNTAIN   COLORADO PLATEAU

Red Rock Canyon

LAKE MEAD BASIN

KYLE CANYON THRUST FAULT

KEYSTONE THRUST FAULT

MESOZOIC THRUST FAULTS

CENOZOIC DETACHMENT FAULT

CENOZOIC	PALEOZOIC	—— fault
QUATERNARY and TERTIARY	▢ late Paleozic carbonate rocks	
▢ valley fill and alluvium	▢ early Paleozoic carbonate rocks	⌇ Great Unconformity
MESOZOIC	PROTEROZOIC	
▢ Triassic-Jurassic sedimentary rocks	▢ early Proterozoic gneiss and schist basement rocks	

Frenchman Mountain has shifted to the west, probably from a combination of strike-slip and extensional faulting. —Modified from Rowland, http://geoscience.unlv.edu

thickness almost twice that of the central Grand Canyon, due in large part to the thicker Cambrian section. The mountain is a fault block that is tilted 50 to 60 degrees to the east. Lake Mead Boulevard cuts east-west across the block, allowing essentially a traverse of the Grand Canyon strata, including the Proterozoic rocks at the bottom.

The low hills on the western side of the mountain are Proterozoic in age, and the Cambrian rocks compose more than half of the visible strata, up to the base of the conspicuous dark band across the face of the mountain, which is limestone of the Devonian-age Sultan Formation (equivalent to the Temple Butte Limestone in the Grand Canyon). Dolomite of the Mississippian Monte Cristo Limestone (similar to the Redwall Limestone of the Grand Canyon) continues above the dark band to the top of the northern peak, with a bit of the Pennsylvanian Callville Formation (equivalent, in part, to the Supai Group in the Grand Canyon) capping the southern, higher peak with the radio towers.

Geologists think the whole Frenchman Mountain block has been "rafted" to its present location, probably by a combination of strike-slip and extensional faulting in the Lake Mead basin. A distinctive sedimentary breccia on the east side of the mountain could only have come from a source rock to the east of Lake Mead.

We'll begin our guide at the intersection of Lake Mead Boulevard and Hollywood Boulevard. At a wide pullout on the south side of the road 1 mile east of Hollywood Boulevard, the Great Unconformity Geologic Interpretive Trail leads across the wash to the contact between the Proterozoic-age rocks, consisting of granites and garnet-biotite schist, and the coarse, crossbedded Tapeats Sandstone of Cambrian age. The contact represents 1.1 billion years of missing Earth history and is referred to as the Great Unconformity. It is

Aerial view of the western face of Frenchman Mountain.

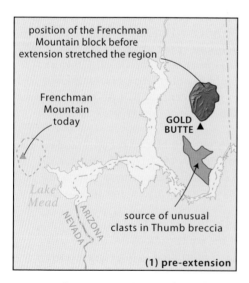

position of the Frenchman
Mountain block before
extension stretched the region

Frenchman
Mountain
today

Lake
Mead

GOLD
BUTTE ▲

source of unusual
clasts in Thumb breccia

NEVADA | ARIZONA

(1) pre-extension

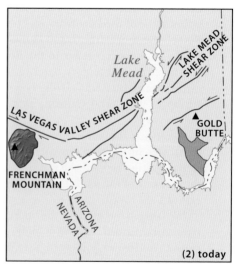

Lake
Mead

LAKE MEAD
SHEAR ZONE

LAS VEGAS VALLEY SHEAR ZONE

GOLD
BUTTE ▲

FRENCHMAN
MOUNTAIN ▲

NEVADA | ARIZONA

(2) today

Frenchman Mountain moved west by movement on the Lake Mead shear zone, as well as detachment faulting. —Modified from Rowland and others, 1990

the same Great Unconformity that can be seen in the bottom of the Grand Canyon, at the top of the Vishnu Schist. With the exception of the Laughlin area (see the NV 163 road guide) and Owens Avenue (see below), this is one of the few places in southern Nevada where you can easily see Proterozoic-age rock. Beyond the outcrop beside the wash, the trail winds up the hill where more of the contact and rocks of both ages can be seen.

Lake Mead Boulevard exits the Las Vegas Valley along a east-trending fault trace that juxtaposes Permian-age limestone ridges of Sunrise Mountain, to the north of the road, against Cambrian rocks of Frenchman Mountain, to the south of the road. The Cambrian Tapeats Sandstone, with its clean quartz sand, was deposited as a beach on the shore of the continent. By the end of early Cambrian time, the exposed landmass was inundated by an advancing and rising sea, and the shoreline gradually moved eastward. As you drive eastward along Lake Mead Boulevard and up through the stratigraphic sequence, you'll see olive-green shale in a small valley south from the highway, to the east of the Great Unconformity exposure. This Cambrian unit, equivalent to the Bright Angel Shale in the Grand Canyon, contains abundant olenellid trilobite fossils that lived 516 to 513 million years ago in fine-grained muddy sediments deposited offshore. Eventually, the shoreline moved so far east that no more sediment reached the area of eastern Nevada, and calcium carbonate was precipitated directly from the ocean water. These Cambrian limestones are exposed above the shale and upward to the base of the dark band of limestone of the Devonian Sultan Formation, midway up the face of Frenchman Mountain.

PRECAMBRIAN ROCK AT OWENS AVENUE

Along Owens Avenue south of Lake Mead Boulevard is a good place to view Proterozoic gneiss and also Quaternary earthquake scarps along the base of Frenchman Mountain. From the intersection of Lake Mead and Hollywood Boulevards, proceed south on Hollywood for 0.75 mile and turn east (left) onto East Owens Avenue. In the first roadcut going up the hill, fanglomerate of late Tertiary to Pleistocene age is downfaulted against Proterozoic gneiss and schist that are about 1.7 billion years old. Note that this fault does not offset the ground surface at the top of the roadcut, which is capped with a calcic soil estimated to be 250,000 to 130,000 years old. There has been no displacement along this section of this fault in that time frame.

However, when driving up East Owens Avenue to this outcrop, look to the south to see that this same fan surface continues toward the valley, then ends abruptly along a west-facing scarp that parallels the face of Frenchman Mountain. The scarp is about 35 feet high, elevated during several earthquake events. Using the length of the fault, which is estimated to be 15 to 20 miles long, as an indicator of the potential magnitude of an earthquake occurring on the fault, a single event may create a scarp 3 to 6 feet high. This correlates to an earthquake magnitude of 6.5 to 7.0. Thus, the Frenchman Mountain fault is one of the known seismic threats to Las Vegas.

The eastern ridgeline of Frenchman Mountain, near milepost 10, capped with Permian Kaibab Limestone, with the Permian Toroweap Formation underlying the slopes below the cliffs.

Just east of the top of the pass, a dirt road to the south, west of milepost 9, accesses the towers on top of Frenchman Mountain and climbs steeply along the contact between Mississippian Monte Cristo Limestone on the west and Pennsylvanian limestone of the Callville Formation to the east. The Callville, about 1,000 feet thick here on Frenchman Mountain, is the time equivalent to the Bird Spring Formation in the Las Vegas Range north of the Las Vegas Valley.

The Callville ridge parallels the road for a short distance, and the next valley to the east is formed in the Permian Hermit Formation and is bordered on the east by the high ridges of the Permian Kaibab Limestone. Note that the ridges appear to repeat themselves, due to apparent right-lateral offset along a fault cutting through the ridge. Paleontologists excavated the fill in Gypsum Cave, a hole at the base of the Kaibab Limestone cliffs, and found the bones of a ground sloth that lived in Pleistocene time. A paved road leads north past the cave to a gypsum mine.

Between the end of the Kaibab ridge and the roadway, the orange-red outcrops are Jurassic Aztec Sandstone, capped by a dark conglomerate of Miocene age. Here, as well as elsewhere in the Lake Mead area, the conglomerate above the Jurassic sandstone is the basal unit of the Horse Spring Formation. The contact between the conglomerate and the Aztec Sandstone is an unconformity representing a considerable gap in time. Whatever sequence of younger rocks was deposited on top of the 200-million-year-old sandstone was eroded away before the conglomerate was deposited around 17 million years ago.

A dirt four-wheel drive road from the west provides access for high-clearance vehicles to the Rainbow Garden area, so named because of colorful exposures. The oldest member of the Horse Spring Formation, the Rainbow Gardens Member, takes its name from this area, reflecting its banded tan, white, and red-colored rocks. Directly across Lake Mead Boulevard from the

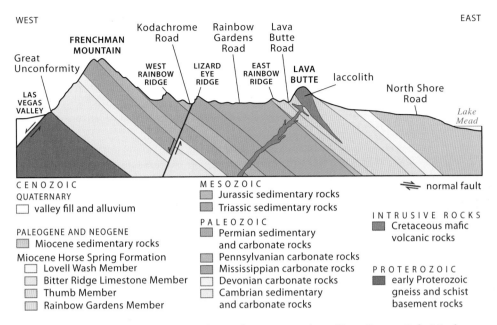

Cross section from Las Vegas through Frenchman Mountain and Lava Butte to Lake Mead.
—Modified from Castor and others, 2000

Rainbow Gardens turnoff, a small hill is capped with the Thumb breccia, the rock unit that has been key to interpreting the recent movement of the Frenchman Mountain block. The breccia, part of the Thumb Member of the Horse Spring Formation, is composed of fragments of rock that could only have been derived from bedrock sources on the east side of Lake Mead.

The prominent black hill to the south of the highway is Lava Butte, which is not a volcano, nor does it have lava flows. It is small, flat-floored igneous intrusion known as a laccolith. The magma penetrated upward through the Horse Spring Formation about 13 million years ago, forcing its way laterally along layers of the formation. Composed of dacite, which is much more resistant to erosion than the surrounding Horse Spring rocks, the intrusion now stands above the siltstones and mudstones at its base. Its dark color is due to desert varnish, or rock varnish, which is a surficial coating of iron and manganese minerals. On a fresh surface, the Lava Butte dacite is light gray to lavender.

HOOVER DAM

Hoover Dam, constructed across the Black Canyon of the Colorado River in the early 1930s, impounds Lake Mead, the largest reservoir in the United States. US 93 used to cross over the dam, but it now spans the Black Canyon a half mile downstream on a bridge completed in 2012. The old US 93 provides public access to the dam and to the walkway on the new bridge from the Nevada side.

The dam access road winds along the base of dacite cliffs, oxidized to reddish brown, along a fault that separates the dacite from the Boulder City pluton to the south of the road. After a turn to the left, a new vista opens up, with more subdued topography of light-brown and gray rocks related to the Tuff of Hoover Dam. The dacite flows are also exposed at the Lakeview Overlook accessed to the left from this road. The craggy cliffs between the overlook and the dam are the Tuff of Hoover Dam and other units of the Black Canyon volcanic assemblage.

As the road winds down through the tuff units to the dam, darker rock of a dike is exposed at the last hairpin turn to the left, underneath the towers for the bridge (this is easier to see coming up the hill). Parking is available on the Nevada side of the dam, in the parking structure, or at pullouts on the Arizona side of the dam. The massive, 13.9-million-year-old Tuff of Hoover Dam, a poorly to moderately welded ash-flow tuff with abundant rock fragments, is exposed throughout the area. Some of the most accessible exposures are along the walkway from the dam to the parking garage, and from the stairways in the parking garage. The tuff is 600 feet thick at the dam and thins quickly in all directions, leading to the conclusion that the source of the tuff is in the immediate vicinity of the dam.

A breccia unit fills a channel eroded in the pinkish Tuff of Hoover Dam above the spillway on the Arizona side of Hoover Dam. The close-up shows welded clasts in the tuff.

Dark mafic dikes of olivine basalt and basaltic andesite cut through the lighter tuff on both sides of the canyon. The dikes are, in turn, offset along near-vertical normal faults. The dark dome-shaped hill between the dam and the new highway on the Arizona side is Sugarloaf Mountain, composed of a pink to pinkish-gray dacite flow derived from a source about 1 mile southeast of the dam. This dacite unit intrudes the Tuff of Hoover Dam and has an age of 13.1 million years.

Northshore Road
Las Vegas Bay—Overton
54 miles

Lake Mead, impounded behind Hoover Dam, is a major recreation area for Las Vegas residents and visitors. The Northshore Road generally parallels the northwest margin of Lake Mead, connecting the Las Vegas area with the eastern entrance to the Valley of Fire State Park and the farming towns of Overton and Logandale on the Muddy River. The route, a well-paved road with pullouts and informational signs, is a geologist's playground, with new vistas and stories around every bend.

The Lake Mead region seems to have been squeezed between the main Basin and Range to the north, the highly extended Colorado River corridor to the south, and the Colorado Plateau to the east. The Lake Mead shear zone, a group of northeast-trending, left-lateral strike-slip faults, displaces rock units several miles along trend. Blocks between the faults, some consisting of basin fill deposits as young as 20 million years, are folded to nearly vertical.

The road passes through the deposits of several basins that formed here in Miocene time, probably from movement in the Lake Mead shear zone and from Basin and Range extension. The older basin deposits, constituting the Horse Spring Formation, formed between about 24 and 13 million years ago. The younger fill, the Muddy Creek Formation, accumulated between 10 and 5 million years ago. The Horse Spring Formation contains conglomerate at its base, sandstone and freshwater limestone in the middle and upper units, and it has been folded and faulted by tectonic forces. In contrast, the Muddy Creek Formation is relatively undeformed and consists primarily of lake-deposited sandstone and mudstone, with beds of gypsum, and conglomerate from alluvial sources around the edges of the basins.

There are plenty of young volcanic rocks along the Northshore Road, too. The youngest outpouring in the Lake Mead area is 5.9-million-year-old basalt that caps the flat-topped Fortification Hill, an easily identified geomorphic feature on the Arizona side of the lake. The black surface consists of more than fifty individual lava flows.

The high mountain south of Fortification Hill is Wilson Ridge, made of a quartz monzonite pluton dated at 13.4 million years that intruded the surrounding Precambrian rock. Dikes and small plugs of the same quartz monzonite intrude the northern half of Saddle Island, an elongate ridge parallel to

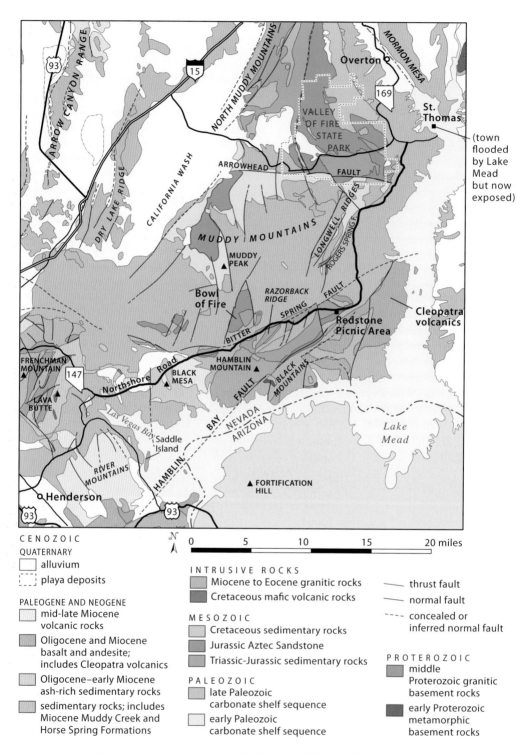

CENOZOIC

QUATERNARY
- [ ] alluvium
- [dashed box] playa deposits

PALEOGENE AND NEOGENE
- mid-late Miocene volcanic rocks
- Oligocene and Miocene basalt and andesite; includes Cleopatra volcanics
- Oligocene–early Miocene ash-rich sedimentary rocks
- sedimentary rocks; includes Miocene Muddy Creek and Horse Spring Formations

INTRUSIVE ROCKS
- Miocene to Eocene granitic rocks
- Cretaceous mafic volcanic rocks

MESOZOIC
- Cretaceous sedimentary rocks
- Jurassic Aztec Sandstone
- Triassic-Jurassic sedimentary rocks

PALEOZOIC
- late Paleozoic carbonate shelf sequence
- early Paleozoic carbonate shelf sequence

— thrust fault
— normal fault
---- concealed or inferred normal fault

PROTEROZOIC
- middle Proterozoic granitic basement rocks
- early Proterozoic metamorphic basement rocks

0   5   10   15   20 miles

Geology along Northshore Road in Lake Mead National Recreation Area.

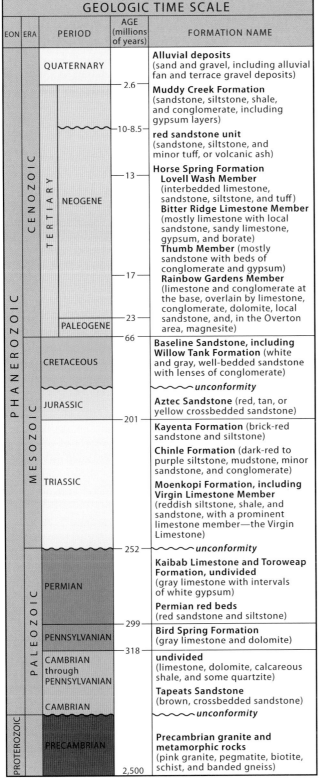

GEOLOGIC TIME SCALE

EON	ERA	PERIOD	AGE (millions of years)	FORMATION NAME
PHANEROZOIC	CENOZOIC	QUATERNARY		**Alluvial deposits** (sand and gravel, including alluvial fan and terrace gravel deposits)
			2.6	
		TERTIARY — NEOGENE		**Muddy Creek Formation** (sandstone, siltstone, shale, and conglomerate, including gypsum layers)
			10-8.5	**red sandstone unit** (sandstone, siltstone, and minor tuff, or volcanic ash)
			13	**Horse Spring Formation** **Lovell Wash Member** (interbedded limestone, sandstone, siltstone, and tuff) **Bitter Ridge Limestone Member** (mostly limestone with local sandstone, sandy limestone, gypsum, and borate) **Thumb Member** (mostly sandstone with beds of conglomerate and gypsum) **Rainbow Gardens Member** (limestone and conglomerate at the base, overlain by limestone, conglomerate, dolomite, local sandstone, and, in the Overton area, magnesite)
			17
			23
		PALEOGENE		
	MESOZOIC	CRETACEOUS	66	**Baseline Sandstone, including Willow Tank Formation** (white and gray, well-bedded sandstone with lenses of conglomerate)
				unconformity
		JURASSIC		**Aztec Sandstone** (red, tan, or yellow crossbedded sandstone)
			201	**Kayenta Formation** (brick-red sandstone and siltstone)
		TRIASSIC		**Chinle Formation** (dark-red to purple siltstone, mudstone, minor sandstone, and conglomerate)
				Moenkopi Formation, including Virgin Limestone Member (reddish siltstone, shale, and sandstone, with a prominent limestone member—the Virgin Limestone)
			252	*unconformity*
	PALEOZOIC	PERMIAN		**Kaibab Limestone and Toroweap Formation, undivided** (gray limestone with intervals of white gypsum)
				Permian red beds (red sandstone and siltstone)
			299	
		PENNSYLVANIAN		**Bird Spring Formation** (gray limestone and dolomite)
			318	
		CAMBRIAN through PENNSYLVANIAN		**undivided** (limestone, dolomite, calcareous shale, and some quartzite)
		CAMBRIAN		**Tapeats Sandstone** (brown, crossbedded sandstone)
				unconformity
PROTEROZOIC		PRECAMBRIAN		**Precambrian granite and metamorphic rocks** (pink granite, pegmatite, biotite, schist, and banded gneiss)
			2,500	

Muddy Creek Formation

Thumb Member

Aztec Sandstone

Virgin Limestone

Kaibab Limestone (top)
Permian red beds (bottom)

Stratigraphic sequence of sedimentary rocks around Lake Mead National Recreation Area, including Valley of Fire State Park.

Lakeshore Road on the west shore of Lake Mead. (It is only an island during high stands of Lake Mead.) A major detachment fault passes through the saddle on the island and has transported rocks containing the quartz monzonite from the Wilson Ridge area. The north half of the island is reddish, with rugged outcrops, whereas the south half is dark-colored, with a greenish hue, and has a smoother appearance.

The Las Vegas Valley Water District built access structures on Saddle Island to withdraw and treat water from the lake to supply the water needs of the Las Vegas Valley, which derives 90 percent of its drinking water from Lake Mead. The original intake is the white structure on the southeastern side of the island; it draws water at an elevation of 1,050 feet in the lake. The second straw was constructed in the vicinity of the first intake, as a backup in case of failure of the first intake. Low water levels have led to the construction of a third intake at 860 feet in the event that the lake level drops below the levels of the first two intakes.

Northshore Road heads north from Lake Mead Parkway (NV 564) and at milepost 1 crosses Las Vegas Wash, which carries the treated wastewater of metropolitan Las Vegas and Henderson, after it first flows through the Las Vegas wetlands. Las Vegas Wash is diverted under Lake Las Vegas, a man-made lake to the west of Northshore Road. The ledge-forming conglomerate exposed in the banks of Las Vegas Wash filled a channel deposit cut within the older Muddy Creek Formation in late Pliocene to Quaternary time. Remnants of this young alluvium cap low ridges east of the wash, overlying pale reddish-brown Muddy Creek deposits. The latter are exposed in a channel cut adjacent to the road around milepost 2. Dark volcanic boulders are scattered over the surface of the reddish Muddy Creek sediments. The highway cuts through a hill with a veneer of volcanic rock just east of its intersection with Lake Mead Boulevard, between milepost 3 and milepost 4. The volcanics here are related to those of Callville Mesa farther to the east, in the area of milepost 12. Lava Butte, a 13-million-year-old

View of Saddle Island looking northeast from Lakeshore Road. A detachment fault in the saddle separates the younger, reddish rock of the upper plate (left side) from the older, darker Precambrian rock of the lower plate (right side).

laccolith intruded into the light-colored sediments of the Horse Spring Formation, is prominently visible to the west (see the discussion in the Frenchman Mountain section).

East of milepost 4, Northshore Road crosses a series of relatively flat washes draining to Lake Mead. These are dry 99 percent of the time but can quickly fill with swiftly moving water during a flash flood. Periodically, the flow is sufficient to rip up the roadway, and it does not take much current to wash a vehicle downstream. Do not cross a wash in flood! When dry, the washes provide nice exposures in their vertical banks. On the northwest side of Gypsum Wash, just east of the Upper Gypsum Road junction, sandstone and siltstone of the Muddy Creek Formation are tilted, dipping to the south, and are overlain by horizontal beds of hardened Quaternary alluvium that may be 1 to 2 million years old.

In the wash near milepost 6, a haystack-shaped pillar on the south side of the road is an erosional remnant of the Muddy Creek deposits with a bed of gypsum at its base. On the west side of the wash, a turnoff labeled "Photo Opportunity" provides a view from which you can see the white gypsum bed continuing down the wash, separating the upper and lower strata of the Muddy Creek Formation.

Between milepost 8 and milepost 9, the red sandstone unit crops out to the north of the highway and extends across it. This formation, which lies between the Muddy Creek Formation and the Horse Spring Formation, contains layers of Callville volcanics, and a date of 11.7 million years has been derived from an ash layer near the base of the red sandstone unit. Good exposures of the red sandstone unit are available around milepost 16.

Near milepost 9, a small hill on the south side of the road is bright red at the base with a dark cap. The entire hill is the Thumb Member of the Horse Spring Formation. The dark cap, which looks volcanic, is actually the Thumb breccia, a geologically important unit. The Proterozoic gneissic and granitic boulders included in the breccia provide evidence that Frenchman Mountain was transported to the west (see the discussion in the Frenchman Mountain section). As the highway swings to the north between milepost 9 and milepost 10, it passes between two small hills, the dark caps of which are also Thumb breccia.

An unobstructed view of Black Mesa emerges after passing the two hills. The colorful exposures in the wash along the base of the mesa are the Horse Spring Formation, which is folded and tilted in this area. The lighter units contain volcanic ash. Quite noticeable are the red sedimentary rocks of the red sandstone unit exposed high up on the slopes of Black Mesa, and the capping volcanic layer is not very thick. Some landslide slumping is visible along the western margin of the mesa.

The Callville Bay Road, which heads south at milepost 11, rewards the traveler with colorful displays of the Horse Spring units, interspersed with Callville volcanics, with additional roadcuts displaying the red sandstone unit, as well as the cemented sands and gravels of the Muddy Creek Formation. At Callville Bay, the rugged skyline to the northeast is the andesitic volcanic mass of Hamblin Mountain. The left-lateral, strike-slip Hamblin Bay fault cuts the south side of the mountain, offsetting these rocks from the Cleopatra volcanics farther east. The Hamblin and Cleopatra volcanics erupted from a large stratovolcano 13.5 to 11.5 million years ago.

At milepost 12, the view transitions from the relative geologic tranquility of valley deposits and volcanics of the Miocene-age basins into the realm of the Las Vegas shear zone and faulted blocks of Paleozoic, Mesozoic, and Cenozoic formations for the next 30 miles. At West End Wash, the highway crosses into the bright orange-red Aztec Sandstone of Jurassic age, part of a football-shaped structural block caught between strike-slip faults of the Las Vegas shear zone. The parking lot on the north, just east of milepost 13, is a good place for an overview of this structure.

The Northshore Road between milepost 16 and milepost 20 follows the Bitter Spring fault, a left-lateral strike-slip fault with a postulated 28 miles of offset. The fault controls the northwestern margin of the Paleozoic block south of the highway. At milepost 19, the pullout to the left includes an informational sign pointing out the Bowl of Fire, an orange-red outcrop area in the Aztec Sandstone to the north, and also Muddy Peak, higher on the skyline. The Muddy Mountains are a remnant of the Sevier-age thrust faulting, which occurred between 140 and 110 million years ago, and Muddy Peak is composed of the Cambrian Bonanza King Formation.

View from the parking lot east of milepost 13 of the Aztec Sandstone in the foreground with the southward-tilted Chinle and Moenkopi Formations in the distance, culminating with the yellow-gray Virgin Limestone Member of the Moenkopi Formation, forming the steeply south-dipping carapace of the ridge. The older Permian limestone of the Kaibab and Toroweap rock units forms the dark mass at the core of the ridge.

As you go uphill past milepost 20 toward the rest area at the crest, you can see red beds on the north side of the road, part of the Thumb Member of the Horse Spring Formation; close to the top, they occur on both sides of the highway and are faulted against the Permian and overlying Triassic rocks along the Bitter Spring fault. From the parking lot and rest area a quarter-mile trail leads to a topographic high point from which you can see the Bowl of Fire and Muddy Mountains.

Eastward from the overlook at milepost 20 is the wide open space of the Bitter Spring Valley, eroded into the nonresistant beds of the Thumb Member. The somewhat younger, thin-bedded limestones of the Bitter Ridge Member

ANNIVERSARY NARROWS AT LOVELL WASH

The turnoff to the north at milepost 16 onto a dirt road provides good views of the deformation in the Horse Spring Formation and a chance to do a bit of rockhounding. The turnoff is in the red sandstone unit, deposited around 11 million years ago. In less than one-tenth mile, stay to the left to exit the wash. The road follows a synclinal fold in the younger Lovell Wash Member of the Horse Spring Formation, and the tilted resistant rocks to the south, west, and north are the older Bitter Ridge Limestone Member, both deposited about 14 to 13 million years ago in lake environments. The Bitter Ridge Limestone contains stromatolites, which are fossilized mats of algae. Lovell Wash is the location for the type section for the Lovell Wash Member.

To the north, in an end-on view, is a depositional unconformity between the chocolate-brown basal conglomerate of the Horse Spring Formation and the red Aztec Sandstone underneath, now tilted to the west about 45 degrees. To the south, the northward-dipping Bitter Ridge Limestone is faulted against the dark Permian limestones. To the southeast, reddish-brown sandstone and conglomerate beds of the Horse Spring Thumb Member dip steeply to the east. Colemanite, altered borax, was mined from the Horse Spring Formation at the Anniversary Mine in the early 1920s.

View to the south from Anniversary Narrows of northward-dipping Bitter Ridge Limestone faulted against dark Permian limestones.

form a prominent, light-brown vertical cliff face on the northern side of the valley, just west of dark-gray limestones of the Paleozoic Longwell Ridges. The Permian limestone beds on the south side of the road east of the overlook are overlain by the recognizable yellow-gray, medium-bedded Virgin Limestone Member of the Moenkopi Formation of Triassic age. The road curves around the northern end of a serrated ridgeline, aptly named Razorback Ridge, composed of the dark, resistant conglomerate of the Rainbow Gardens Member. Here it unconformably overlies the Moenkopi Formation, and both are dipping 30 to 40 degrees to the east.

At milepost 25, a parking area with an emergency call box has Virgin Limestone exposed on the north side of the lot, dipping steeply to the north, and Permian limestones form the cliffs on the south side of the road. From this

Razorback Ridge, south of Northshore Road at about milepost 21, is resistant conglomerate of the Rainbow Gardens Member at the base of the Horse Spring Formation.

View northwest from the milepost 20 overlook at the red Bowl of Fire and the Muddy Mountains in distance. Sandstones of the Thumb Member of the Horse Spring Formation are in foreground.

viewpoint, you can see the colorful outcroppings of the Aztec Sandstone at the Redstone Picnic Area down the road to the east.

As you approach the Redstone Picnic Area at milepost 27, you can see at least two levels of high alluvial terraces covering the sandstone outcrops to the south of the road. The terraces, isolated relics of an earlier topography, formed when the valley bottom was at the terrace level. Short hiking trails at the Redstone Picnic Area lead out to knobs of Aztec Sandstone, some exhibiting petroglyphs created by folks dwelling in the area hundreds of years ago.

At milepost 30, a dirt road to Boathouse Cove intersects the Northshore Road. Here, too, is the intersection of the Hamblin Bay and Bitter Spring faults, two major left-slip faults of the Lake Mead fault system. The warp of the ridge to the northwest may be due to drag on the fault system. The Boathouse Cove Road accesses the innards of the Cleopatra volcanic complex of Miocene age.

North of the Boathouse Cove Road, the Northshore Road is constructed on Tertiary or Quaternary sedimentary rock and alluvium. The broad, very flat, alluvial surfaces slope down toward the Overton Arm of Lake Mead, the flooded valley of the Virgin River. Note the thin, resistant cap of caliche developed on these surfaces. To the west is the broad expanse of the Bitter Spring Valley, and colorful white, orange-tan, and beige fine-grained sediments of the Thumb Member of the Horse Spring Formation. At the bridge over Echo Wash, the tilted Horse Spring strata are unconformably overlain by younger, horizontal sands and gravel.

East Longwell Ridge, to the west of the road, is composed of limestones of the Mississippian Monte Cristo Limestone and Pennsylvanian Bird Spring Formation. The Rogers Spring fault bounds the abrupt eastern face of the ridge. Rogers Spring, at milepost 40, and Blue Point Spring, to the northeast at milepost 41, mark the location of the Rogers Spring fault, which provides a conduit for groundwater flow. Rogers Spring is one of the largest in southern Nevada and flows at a rate of 400 gallons per minute, staying at a temperature of 80 degrees throughout the year. Look for turtles and enjoy the sound of flowing

Two high alluvial terraces cover the red Aztec Sandstone at Redstone Picnic Area near milepost 27. In the distance are dipping Cambrian limestone layers.

water, but don't put your head underwater, because a nasty amoeba populates the spring and can cause death.

The limestone mountains are abruptly terminated to the north along the east-west-trending Arrowhead fault, a normal fault that intersects the northeasterly trending Rogers Spring fault in the vicinity of Blue Point Spring. North of the spring, views westward from the highway are of outcroppings of the orange, downdropped Jurassic Aztec Sandstone juxtaposed against the high, gray limestone Paleozoic cliffs to the south.

Between Blue Point Spring and the boundary of the Lake Mead Recreation Area near milepost 48, the highway winds in and out of either Muddy Creek Formation or alluvium of Pleistocene age. Tan-colored, fine-grained sediments, with occasional whitish beds of gypsum, characterize the Muddy Creek strata, as does the tendency to erode into badlands. In places, you can see thin, black flows of volcanic rock to the east of the highway.

A distinctive landmark, a very flat-topped mesa known as Baseline Mesa, looms to the northwest of the intersection of NV 169 and the Valley of Fire Road. The protective cap consists of an alluvium surface developed on the finer-grained deposits of the underlying Muddy Creek Formation. A long period of landscape stability, perhaps as much as 4 to 5 million years, is represented by the thick layer of caliche formed on the alluvium.

North of milepost 7 on NV 169, light claystones of the 100-million-year-old Willow Tank Formation are exposed in the vicinity of the intersection with Sand Mine Road from the east. These rocks and the overlying Baseline Sandstone, also of Cretaceous age, were deposited in foreland basins developed during Sevier-age thrusting events to the west. Between Sand Mine Road and Overton Ridge, the high point on this section of road, the white sandstone member of the Baseline Sandstone is being mined to produce quartz sand for use in foundry applications and glass production.

Overton Ridge is composed of conglomerate of the Rainbow Gardens Member of the Horse Spring Formation, about 24 to 19 million years in age, dipping about 45 degrees to the northeast. The conglomerate is about 325 feet thick and contains interbeds of sandstone. In the roadcut at the top of the grade, you can see conglomerate-filled channels cut into the underlying, tilted, fine-grained strata. The route of the road through the ridge takes advantage of a small, north-trending fault that has slightly offset the ridgeline on the east side of the road to the north, relative to the ridge exposures to the left.

Overton is situated where the Muddy River flows into Lake Mead, at least when Lake Mead is high. Low bluffs of the tan-colored Muddy Creek sediments border the valley from about milepost 9 to milepost 22. Badland topography develops from the erosion of the fine-grained parts of the formation. The cemented nature of the gravel layer capping this surface forms mesas, including the very extensive flat surface of Mormon Mesa, east of Overton. For a closer look at the Muddy Creek strata, drive a short distance up the gravel road near milepost 11 (about 2 miles south of the Lost City Museum and at the base of the grade that climbs south out of the valley). This gravel road to the sand mine is used by mine traffic, so proceed with caution.

Conglomerate of the Rainbow Gardens Member of the Horse Spring Formation forms the dark, resistant top of Overton Ridge.

The southern end of Mormon Mesa as viewed from St. Thomas, a farming and trading town that was vacated by the rising waters of Lake Mead in 1938 but has recently been exposed by lowering of the lake level. A layer of resistant caliche caps the easily eroded Muddy Creek Formation.

Another point of interest in the Overton area is the Lost City Museum, which displays artifacts of the early peoples that occupied the Overton area as much as 10,000 years ago, as well as the culture of Native Americans that lived in the area when white settlers arrived. The Lost City was a 30-mile-long series of Anasazi adobe ruins along the Muddy River, now inundated by the Overton Arm of Lake Mead. Archeologists scrambled to record these sites and retrieve artifacts in the 1930s before the sites were drowned. One exhibit at the museum describes salt mines used by the Anasazi along the Virgin River. Other salt exposures, now inundated by the lake, occurred along the Overton Arm between Echo Bay and Overton Beach. The salt is inferred to be part of the Muddy Creek Formation but may be associated with an older unit.

Interstate 15
Primm—Las Vegas
34 miles
See map on page 91

Between Primm and Las Vegas, I-15 follows low-lying areas between Precambrian rocks overlain by Cenozoic volcanics on the east and Paleozoic carbonate strata on the west. The Precambrian rocks occur along the northwestern flank of the Kingman Arch, perhaps uplifted during the Laramide Orogeny 70 million years ago. The overlying Paleozoic and Mesozoic strata were removed by erosion from the highland. East of Primm, the Lucy Gray Mountains are composed primarily of gray gneissic Precambrian granite intruded by a 1.4-billion-year-old porphyritic granite. The McCullough Spring conglomerate was deposited in channels eroded in the Precambrian rock between 40 and 18.5 million years ago, when the extensively deposited Peach Springs Tuff, erupted from Arizona, covered the channels and provided an age date. The conglomerate contains pebbles of Precambrian rock and Paleozoic carbonates but no Mesozoic rocks, suggesting that the Paleozoic rocks had not been completely eroded yet, but Mesozoic rocks were long gone by the time the conglomerate was deposited.

On the west side of I-15 at Primm, a ridge of Paleozoic rock comes down to the highway, and exposures of siltstones, shales, and limestones can be seen in the northern parking lot of the Whiskey Pete's Casino. Just to the north of this ridge is the higher, pyramid-shaped summit of Devil Peak, a Miocene rhyolitic plug that intrudes through the Paleozoic carbonate rocks. About 6 miles to the north of Devil Peak, another eruptive center forms Table Mountain. Flat-lying ash-flow tuffs create a level surface on the otherwise serrated skyline. Numerous dikes and sills of granitic porphyry of early Jurassic age (190 to 180 million years old) also intrude the Paleozoic sediments.

The southern part of the Spring Mountains is riddled with more than seventy mines, all part of the Goodsprings mining district, one of the nation's major producers of zinc in the early part of the twentieth century. The Mormons were the first to mine galena, a lead mineral, from the Potosi Mine in the northern part of the district in 1856, but the zinc content in the lead caused it to be unusable for bullets, and the mine closed. Gold and silver were also produced in the area, but it wasn't until 1906 that an engineer from New Mexico finally recognized the zinc ore that had been discarded in mine dumps. Production of lead and zinc peaked during World War I, and a strategic metal stockpile was located at Jean during World War II.

The light-colored, layered mountain southeast of Jean is Sheep Mountain. Here, the Precambrian basement to the south gives way to overlying, north-dipping early Cambrian to Mississippian sediments. The low hills on the south side of Sheep Mountain are dolomitic Cambrian rocks; limestone of the Devonian Sultan Formation composes the interval up to the cliffy portion. Above the prison facility at the base of the hill and northward, the remainder of the mountain is Mississippian Monte Cristo Limestone.

The Paleozoic rocks on the east side of the highway extend only a short distance north of Jean. The entire McCullough Range north of Jean is volcanic rock, erupted from many different vents. On the skyline directly east of Jean, and visible after passing north of Sheep Mountain, the low indentation on the skyline is the location of a Miocene caldera that erupted about 14 million years ago. East and south of the caldera, domes and cones define the remains of older volcanoes that erupted flows and breccias ranging in composition from dacite to basalt between 18.5 and 15.2 million years ago. Closer to the road, in the vicinity of a blue emergency sign, the lower, gently northward-sloping ridge with ramps of light-colored sand on its western slopes is composed of andesite flows erupted between 14.1 and 13.1 million years ago. The higher hill at the north end of the sloping ridge, toward the road, consists of massive flows and domes of dacite, with a small, shallowly emplaced dacite body on its north side. Erupted 13.1 million years ago, these are some of the Sloan volcanics, the youngest volcanic rocks in the northern McCullough Range. The Sloan volcanics form much of the topography east of the interstate all the way to the Sloan exit. They erupted from four volcanoes that surround Hidden Valley, an aptly named depression east of the McCullough Range but not visible from the interstate. A hole drilled in the valley penetrated 700 feet of alluvium without reaching bedrock.

To the west of the highway between Jean and Sloan are Paleozoic sedimentary rocks, cut by normal faults as well as a few thrust faults from the Sevier Orogeny. The Bird Spring Range, the higher hills to the west of Jean, is composed of Mississippian Monte Cristo Limestone, and the lower brown hills directly to the northeast are rocks of the Cambrian Bonanza King Formation. On the eastern side of the Bird Spring Range is the oldest Sevier-age thrust fault, the Bird Spring thrust, which shoved Cambrian rock over Permian through Triassic strata.

The low hills directly southeast and northeast of Sloan Road (exit 25) are composed of Paleozoic carbonate rocks. The low hills to the west at the Sloan exit are nearly flat-lying Devonian to Permian sedimentary rocks. Nearly pure deposits of dolomite are mined from the Monte Cristo Limestone in the quarry visible west of the Sloan area.

East of the Sloan exit, the McCullough Range forms the higher skyline to the east. This part of the range is the westward-dipping flank of a Miocene volcano, composed of basalt and andesite flows interlayered with volcaniclastic units. The location of the vent for the volcano is not known but is suspected to be near Railroad Pass west of Boulder City on US 93/US 95. Petroglyph Canyon, an important rock art site in southern Nevada, is in the McCullough Range, protected within the Sloan Canyon National Conservation Area. Early peoples created the petroglyphs by etching desert varnish off the volcanic rock. Numerous trails, accessed from the south side of Henderson, wind through the area.

Interstate 15
Las Vegas—Arizona Border
72 miles

We'll begin this guide at exit 52, for the Las Vegas Beltway. The Old Spanish Trail roughly parallels I-15 here, and occasionally you can see the cement obelisks that mark the trail. As I-15 climbs gradually from the Las Vegas Valley, the tan, slightly cemented, fine-grained deposits of the Muddy Creek Formation are exposed in roadcuts and bluffs to the east of the highway. These sediments were deposited 10 to 5 million years ago in a basin that has since been disrupted by the Las Vegas shear zone. Although the Muddy Creek deposits collected in basins created by tectonic deformation, the deposits themselves are, in general, not deformed. The gray bedrock ridges on either side of I-15 in this area are limestones of Mississippian to Permian age.

The flat, white surface to the north of the junction of I-15 with US 93 is a playa; playas form when freshwater in a shallow lake evaporates, leaving behind precipitated salts. Mississippian to Permian limestones of the southern end of the Arrow Canyon Range lie to the west of the playa. The well-defined regular strata of these limestones are exposed in the face of a ridge to the east of the highway. The highway passes through this limestone ridge about 7 miles north of the US 93 junction. The ridge continues northward from the highway as a series of low, dissected rocky hills protruding from the alluvium. Cambrian through Mississippian limestones of the Arrow Canyon Range to the west are thrust over the Mississippian to Permian limestones that form the small ridge east of the playa.

North of the ridge, the vista opens to a broad expanse of primarily Quaternary alluvial deposits. California Wash drains this featureless terrain, which conceals an eastward-tilting basin filled with sediments 1.5 to 2 miles thick. The faulted mountains on the east side of the basin, the North Muddy Mountains, are Permian to Cretaceous rocks deposited on land, including the red Aztec Sandstone featured in Valley of Fire State Park. (See the separate section for a discussion of the geology of this park.) At exit 75, for Valley of Fire State Park, a 4-foot-tall cement obelisk marks the Old Spanish Trail along the entry ramp heading west. The white deposits west and east of exit 75 are spring deposits of Pliocene to Quaternary age.

Between exits 75 and 84, you can see the west-facing scarp of the California Wash fault in the early morning light. The scarp is only about 10 to 20 feet high

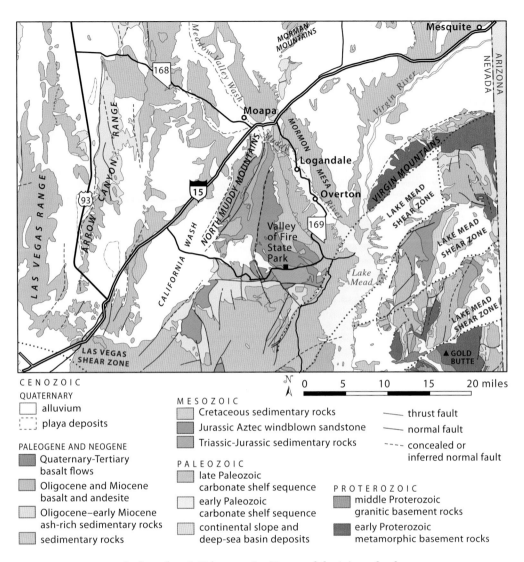

Geology along I-15 between Las Vegas and the Arizona border.

but is visible because the low sun angle casts a distinct linear shadow across the alluvial fans at the base of the ridge to the east. The road to the Valley of Fire State Park crosses this scarp, and I-15 crosses the northern continuation of the California Wash fault in the vicinity of the Muddy River (exits 90 and 91). Geologists study the earthquake history of faults by excavating trenches across fault scarps and examining the disruption of the deposits. Such studies conducted on this fault indicate that the scarps record up to five earthquakes, the most recent about 2,000 years ago. Based on the 20-mile length of the fault and the amount of displacement observed for previous events, this tectonically

The regular bedding in the Dry Lake Range east of I-15 north of the US 93 junction, is characteristic of Mississippian to Permian limestones in southern Nevada.

active fault is capable of generating a magnitude 6.9 earthquake in the future. This seismic hazard was considered in the engineering design of the new bridge at Hoover Dam.

To the north of the Moapa and Logandale/Overton exits (exits 88 to 93), prominent tan cliffs of the Miocene to Pliocene Muddy Creek Formation can be seen in the near distance. The Muddy Creek sediments collected between 10 and 5 million years ago in isolated depositional basins that may have been intermittently connected with an adjacent basin. This deposition ceased with development of an integrated lower Colorado River system that carried the sediment to the Gulf of California. Now, erosion by the tributaries of the Colorado River is exposing the Muddy Creek deposits. After crossing the Muddy River, which you won't see if you blink, I-15 climbs onto Mormon Mesa, which is formed on the Muddy Creek Formation. The mesa surface is protected by a cemented calcic soil known as caliche. The cementing agent is calcium carbonate, which is introduced into the soil by windblown material deposited on the surface. The limestone outcrops throughout the area provide abundant source material for the calcium carbonate, which is transported from the ground surface and down through the soil profile by rainwater. Because of the arid environment, the transporting water evaporates, depositing the calcium carbonate in the soil profile, where it accumulates. You can see the well-cemented nature of the capping caliche, which is on the order of 10 feet thick, in gully exposures eroded into the margins of the mesa. The thick calcic soil records climatic conditions over the last 4 to 5 million years.

Although it is not visible from the car, east of Mormon Mesa the interstate crosses the Virgin River depression, a structural basin in which sediments have been accumulating for millions of years. A drillhole on Mormon Mesa penetrated Cretaceous and Jurassic clastic rocks at a depth of 6,700 feet and Proterozoic crystalline rocks at 19,150 feet. The eastern subbasin between Mesquite and the Virgin Mountains has possibly 26,200 feet of late Cenozoic fill, making it the deepest known basin in the Basin and Range.

THE BOWL

Between exits 80 and 88 of I-15, the ridge to the south of the highway hides the Bowl, where erosion has exposed overturned rock layers in a fold. Reddish beds of the Moenkopi Formation of Triassic age are exposed at the bottom of the bowl, whereas Permian strata form the cliffs at the top. To reach the Bowl with a four-wheel-drive vehicle, take exit 88 and follow the dirt road southeast to the westernmost of the two communication towers at the top of the ridge.

View to the north of the Bowl.

Roadcuts along the lengthy descent of I-15 from Mormon Mesa down to the stream terraces of the Virgin River expose cross sections of channel deposits in several hundred feet of fine-grained sediments of the Muddy Creek Formation. South of the Virgin River, steep, dissected Pliocene alluvial fans emanate from the Virgin Mountains, but farther northeast, only Quaternary alluvial fans border the range front. The Virgin Mountains are cored with metamorphic and plutonic rocks of Precambrian age. A normal fault cuts across the Quaternary fan surfaces, parallel to the range front, and in the early morning light, you can see its west-facing fault scarps. To the southeast, in the area of the Tertiary alluvial fans, a slice of the Precambrian bedrock has been displaced 26 miles along a left-lateral fault that is a continuation of the range-front fault and part of the Lake Mead fault system.

At Mesquite, the highway skirts the northern side of the Virgin River, which hugs the base of the Tertiary deposits to the north of the road. East of Mesquite, the highway climbs back up onto the surface of Muddy Creek Formation and overlying alluvial fan gravels. Arroyos cutting perpendicular to I-15 expose the steepening of beds toward the basin to the south.

US 95
California Border—Las Vegas
58 miles

US 95 crosses from California into Nevada on the broad, creosote-covered alluvial fans of the Piute Valley, which is bordered by the Piute Range on the west and the Newberry Mountains on the east. Piute Wash, which occasionally carries water to the Colorado River at Needles, follows the north-trending structural grain of the Colorado River extensional corridor, a region of extreme extension. For most of its length, this section of US 95 is in valleys along the western margin of the corridor, with the Colorado River 10 to 15 miles to the east.

Between the California state line and the intersection with NV 163, a darkly weathering Proterozoic granite with large feldspar crystals is exposed in easily accessible outcrops along the highway. The Proterozoic rocks continue north of the NV 163 intersection as dark-colored ridges paralleling and east of the highway for another couple of miles. The light-colored outcrops of the Newberry Mountains on the skyline farther to the north and east are the granitic rocks of the Spirit Mountain batholith, which intruded the dark Proterozoic granite about 17 million years ago. (See the NV 163 road guide for more on Spirit Mountain batholith.) The abundance of Proterozoic rocks in this southernmost tip of Nevada is indicative of the uplift along the Kingman Arch. The overlying Paleozoic and Mesozoic rocks were eroded here.

To the west of the highway, the plateau-like Piute Range is composed of gently westward-tilted Miocene volcanic rocks extruded about 14 to 13 million years ago. The range is primarily within California and outside of the northern Colorado River extensional corridor and therefore has not undergone extensional faulting. At the northern end, the range to the west, with a jagged skyline, is the Castle Mountains, also primarily in California and consisting of Miocene volcanic rocks.

Light-colored Miocene granite of the Spirit Mountain batholith contrasts sharply against the dark, 1.7 billion-year-old rock it intruded.

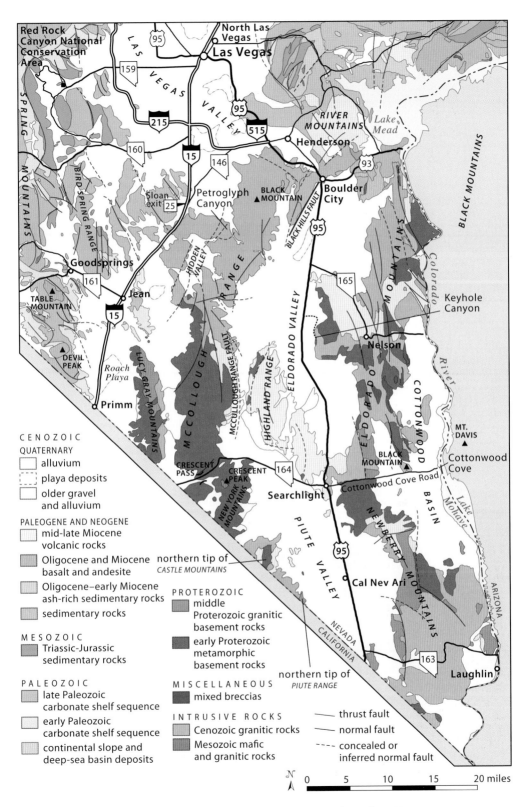

Geology along US 95 between the California border and Las Vegas.

As the highway ascends up the long grade from Piute Valley to Searchlight, it passes a hill with black scree close to the west side of the road. The Miocene volcanic breccia here contains exceptionally large angular fragments of rock. The next hill to the north on the west side of the highway is Proterozoic gneiss intruded by a volcanic rock with large crystals. Closer to Searchlight, the outcrops on the west are a combination of Miocene volcanic flows and intrusive rock. The hills to the east of US 95 directly north and south of Searchlight are exposures of the upper part of the Searchlight pluton, a quartz monzonite body emplaced about 16.4 million years ago into slightly older volcanic flows.

Searchlight

Mineral deposits in the Searchlight area were discovered in 1897, and gold, silver, lead, and copper were mined between 1902 and 1953. The Searchlight district was the second most productive mining district in Clark County. The minerals are in a zone of alteration around the top of the pluton and in the overlying older Miocene volcanic rock to the west of US 95. The overlying

CRESCENT PASS ON NV 164

NV 164, the Nipton Road, crosses Crescent Pass (15 miles west of Searchlight) between the McCullough Range to the north and the New York Mountains to the south. The barren, reddish peak on the skyline to the south of the road is Crescent Peak. High-quality turquoise was first mined here by Native Americans. Gold was found in the 1860s, and silver was found in 1904. Uranium and thorium were discovered in the 1950s, although further prospecting has not resulted in any large mines. The geology is very complex, with Proterozoic rocks intruded and altered by younger Proterozoic intrusions, as well as Cretaceous intrusions. Roadcuts one-quarter mile west of Crescent Pass expose dark biotite granitic rock of Proterozoic age containing 1- to 2-inch-long potassium feldspar crystals.

Large feldspar crystals in Proterozoic granite at Crescent Pass.

Southwest-dipping, tilted fault blocks north of NV 164 are light-colored, nonwelded ash-flow tuff of the Highland Range volcanics overlain by basaltic flows.

NV 164 TO COTTONWOOD BASIN

NV 164 heads east 14 miles to the Colorado River. Most of the hills to the north of NV 164 and east of US 95 are granitic rock of the Searchlight pluton. East of the Searchlight hills, you get an expansive view to the east. Black Mountain is the large, dark hill straight ahead composed of andesitic rock erupted from the Mt. Davis volcanic center in Arizona between 15.2 and 12.8 million years ago. Similar massive dark hills can be seen on the Arizona side of the river, including Mt. Davis. On the west side of Black Mountain, the road crosses the Dupont Mountain fault, a low-angle, eastward dipping normal fault that separates the granitic rocks west of the fault from the Mt. Davis volcanic rocks on the eastern, downdropped side.

Around milepost 6, Pleistocene and Holocene alluvial fans slope down to the Colorado River toward the Cottonwood Basin. A large lake filled the basin in Pliocene time, prior to the development of the Colorado River, to about the elevation of the fee station of the Lake Mead National Recreation Area, at milepost 7. The spectacular view across the river into Arizona highlights colorful Miocene volcanic deposits erupted during tectonic extension.

The prominent surface to the north of the boat marina, about 250 feet above river level, is the Chemehuevi terrace. Middle to late Pleistocene fan gravels at its base underlie its cap of Colorado River deposits that are no younger than 40,000 years and perhaps as old as 250,000 years.

The Chemehuevi terrace above Cottonwood Cove.

volcanics of the Highland Range, mostly north and west of Searchlight, are 18.5 to 15.2 million years old and erupted from the magma chamber that became the Searchlight pluton. Extensional faulting has moved the volcanics to the east relative to the pluton. The orange hills to the west of US 95 north of town are rhyolite that has been hydrothermally altered to kaolinite, alunite, and quartz.

From NV 164 west of Searchlight, you can look north to see fault-tilted blocks of the Highland Range. Northeast-dipping normal faults of the Colorado River extensional corridor tilted these blocks of volcanic rocks about 30 degrees to the southwest. The poorly exposed McCullough Range fault, to the west of the Highland Range, marks the western boundary of this extension.

Eldorado Valley

US 95 follows the Eldorado Valley north to Boulder City. Around milepost 35 the traveler is greeted by a signpost indicating the city limits of Boulder City, although the town can barely be seen at this point. The solar farms visible a few miles farther north on the west side of the road are inside the city limits, and Boulder City leases the land to the power-generating companies. The solar farms are conveniently located adjacent to the high-voltage power transmission lines carrying power generated at Hoover Dam to Los Angeles.

East of the highway between milepost 35 and milepost 38, the reddish-tan granite of the Keystone pluton forms the lone high ridge between the road and the main spine of the Eldorado Mountains farther east, formed of darker Proterozoic gneiss. To reach an archeological site with petroglyphs at Keyhole Canyon along the west-facing side of the granite ridge, take a nonmaintained dirt road to the east between milepost 37 and milepost 38, about 6 miles south of the NV 165 intersection. Drive southeast to the powerline road, then turn to the right. Walk into the canyon to see the petroglyphs, as well as a cylindrical dry waterfall carved in the light-gray granite.

The western skyline is formed by the McCullough Range, with McCullough Pass marking the lower topography directly west of the solar panels. Volcanics at the pass erupted from the McCullough Pass caldera, active about 14 million years ago. Rock exposures north of the pass are west-dipping flows of a volcano that pre-dates the caldera. The lower, light-colored part of the cliff faces consists of andesitic flows and volcanic breccias that were subsequently altered to their current light color. The vent area from which these older flows were erupted in middle Miocene time, 18 to 15 million years ago, has not been located but may have been in the Railroad Pass area at the north end of the range, and was subsequently masked by intrusion of the Railroad Pass pluton, dated at 15 million years. The ridgeline of the McCullough Range is capped by dark-colored andesitic flows erupted 14 million years ago on the flanks of the volcano; some vent areas have been identified on the west-facing slopes of the ridge. The quarrying operation to the southwest of the merging of US 95 with US 93 is in quartz monzonite of the pluton, which forms a sharp ridgeline. The McCullough Range is cut by hundreds of dikes, the abundance of which decrease with distance from the pluton.

North of the NV 165 intersection and on the west side of the dry lakebed, a linear shadow created by the scarp of the Black Hills fault occurs along the

TECHATTICUP MINE AT NELSON

NV 165 heads southeast 11 miles to the old mining town of Nelson in the Eldorado Mountains. After climbing a creosote-covered alluvial fan for 8 miles to the southeast, the road intersects outcroppings of Miocene volcanic rocks. The prominent pink-orange-tan unit to the east is the Tuff of Bridge Spring, a 15.2-million-year-old ash-flow tuff that was deposited throughout the region and has been a useful age marker. The source of the unit may have been a volcano farther north in the Eldorado Mountains.

The prominent pink-orange-tan unit to the east, seen along NV 165, is the Tuff of Bridge Spring, a 15.2-million-year-old volcanic ash-flow tuff.

After reaching the summit, the road steeply descends into Nelson between volcanic ridges that terminate abruptly against a large crystalline mass—the late Cretaceous Nelson pluton—that intruded into Proterozoic gneiss. Mining began in 1857, and perhaps earlier, making the Nelson area one of the oldest mining districts in Nevada. Mineralization was concentrated at the margin of the pluton along quartz and calcite veins containing pyrite, galena, and minor chalcopyrite and sphalerite. Little mining activity has occurred since 1952. A small portion of the underground workings of the largest-producing mine, the Techatticup Mine, has been reopened for tours.

base of the McCullough Range. Down-to-the-east displacement on the normal fault disrupts alluvial fans of Quaternary age, including two ruptures in the past 10,000 years. This active fault is potentially capable of generating a large earthquake.

River Mountains and Boulder City

Boulder City, a town originally established for the building of Hoover Dam, sits at the base of the River Mountains, a complicated pile of Miocene volcanics. Within the pile is a 13-million-year-old stratovolcano, a type of mountain that grows by the accumulation of lava flows on its flanks. In the River Mountains, these rocks consist of numerous dark flows of andesite, each 3 to 15 feet thick, dipping to the west of the western slope of the stratovolcano. A light-colored quartz monzonite stock, the conduit of magma for the stratovolcano, is also exposed, and several dikes of monzonite radiate from the stock into the border of altered and mineralized volcanic rock. Also present is the Red Mountain volcanic section, consisting of highly altered and oxidized reddish lavas of intermediate composition and intrusive rock, possibly related to the Boulder City pluton.

The southern portion of the Hamblin Bay fault, a left-lateral strike-slip fault of the Lake Mead fault system, forms the abrupt southern margin of the River Mountains. The hills to the south of Boulder City are grayish-tan rubbly outcrops of the 13.9-million-year-old Boulder City pluton, whereas the rugged volcanics of the River Mountains to the north are various shades of red, beige, tan, and dark gray. The Hamblin Bay fault is mapped along a southwest trend through Hemenway Wash, which runs to Lake Mead north of Boulder City.

Wilson Ridge, southeast of Lake Mead in Arizona, is a 13.1-million-year-old pluton that is chemically equivalent to the River Mountains quartz monzonite stock. One theory is that the River Mountains stratovolcano originally was positioned above the Wilson Ridge granitic body until the volcanic system was beheaded from the main magmatic core along a detachment fault and transported 12 miles to the west. The timing of the displacement has to postdate the 13-million-year age of the rocks and pre-date formation of Fortification Hill, the prominent westward-sloping, basalt-covered mesa between Wilson Ridge and Lake Mead, which was emplaced 4 to 5 million years ago.

You can get a good view of the River Mountains at the River Mountain Trailhead near the St. Jude's Ranch for Children off US 93 in Boulder City. The Red Mountain volcanic section to the west is faulted against the dark-gray to black andesite flows of the River Mountain stratovolcano to the right. You can also get good views of the stratovolcano from Lakeshore Road.

The combined US 93 and US 95 proceeds through Railroad Pass, with the Railroad Pass pluton on the south and volcanic rocks to the north. North of the pass, the highway travels on the east side of a volcanic hill, which hosts several communications towers, at the northern tip of the McCullough Range. Several nearly horizontal layers visible in the hill are dacite flows erupted from a 13-million-year-old volcanic dome.

NV 163
US 95—Laughlin
19 miles

From US 95 in Piute Valley, NV 163 climbs a gravel-covered erosional surface to the broad crest of the Newberry Mountains. With the exception of small hills of Proterozoic rocks near US 95, most of the route is in the 17- to 15-million-year-old Spirit Mountain batholith. The prominent, light-colored high peak to the northeast is Spirit Mountain, sacred ground to the Native Americans of the southern Colorado River. The entire granitic body of the Spirit Mountain batholith has been tilted 40 to 50 degrees to the west, so eastward travel on

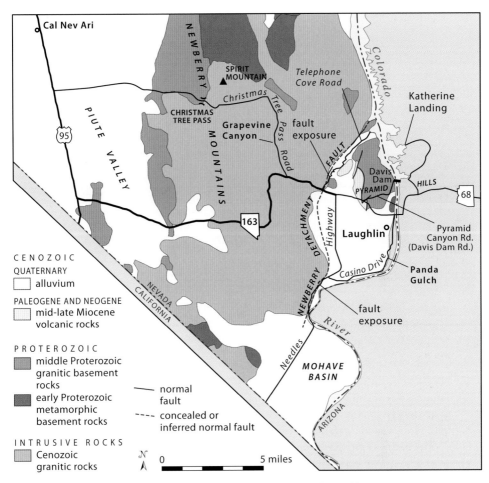

Geology along NV 163 between US 95 and Laughlin.

PETROGLYPHS AND DIKES AT GRAPEVINE CANYON

To visit Grapevine Canyon, take the gravel road heading north at milepost 13 on NV 163, at a turnoff for Christmas Tree Pass. While traveling to Grapevine Canyon, look for dark-colored dikes to the west of and parallel to the road. Two miles up this dirt road a turnoff to the west leads to a parking area and trailhead for Grapevine Canyon. A quarter-mile hike up a dry creek bed from the parking lot leads to the mouth of a small canyon where the boulders and granitic walls are covered with petroglyphs that may be up to 1,500 years old. The surrounding countryside is granitic rock of the Spirit Mountain batholith, and along the short trail to the petroglyphs are exposures of east-dipping mafic and felsic dikes cutting the granitic rock. The Newberry Mountains dike swarm trends perpendicular to the trail, and a 4- to 6-foot-thick mafic dike forms a sentinel at the start of the trail at the west end of the parking lot.

Mafic east-dipping dikes of the Newberry dike swarm that intruded into granitic rock of the Spirit Mountain batholith.

NV 163 crosses the pluton from top to bottom, in terms of its original orientation. The mineralogy changes gradationally west to east, from a high-silica, light-colored granite at the top of the batholith to granite to quartz monzonite, with more abundant dark minerals, at its base.

The highway crosses several north-trending dikes of the Newberry Mountains dike swarm between milepost 8 and milepost 13. More than one hundred dikes crosscut the batholith over a distance of about 9 miles. Their compositions vary from felsic (composed of light-colored minerals) to mafic (composed of dark-colored minerals). Initially emplaced vertically, they also have been tilted westward and now dip 30 to 40 degrees to the east. With an age of 15.6 million years, they mark the final phase of magmatism that formed the batholith. The dikes are linked to the initiation of rifting associated with east-west extensional tectonics in the Colorado River corridor.

Newberry Detachment Fault

Near milepost 13, NV 163 starts its descent into the Mohave Basin, which opened during the east-west extension that also formed enormous detachment faults. Sediments eroded from the adjoining highland have accumulated in the basin and provide a record of the extension. The Mohave Basin existed here before the Colorado River was established and drained the region.

At milepost 15, NV 163 crosses the Newberry detachment fault, a gently east-dipping surface, with the Spirit Mountain batholith to the west of the fault and Proterozoic rock overlain by Miocene sedimentary and volcanic rocks east of the fault. The Black Mountains, the Miocene volcanic layers forming the dramatic skyline on the Arizona side of the river, erupted from volcanoes directly above the magma chambers that became the Spirit Mountain batholith on the Nevada side of the river. The volcanics are not directly above the batholith now because they were transported to their current position along the Newberry detachment fault between 16 and 13 million years ago. Conglomerates

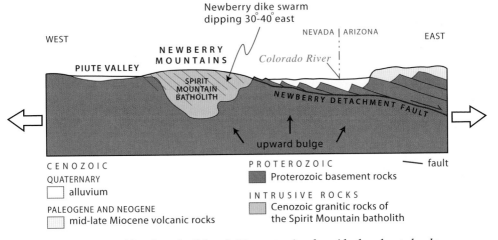

Extreme stretching along the Colorado River extensional corridor has elevated rocks upward as overlying rocks slip to the side along the Newberry detachment fault.

Looking north along the east-dipping fault plane of the Newberry detachment fault on the Needles Highway south of Laughlin. The reddish-brown rock on the hanging wall is Proterozoic Davis Dam granite. The greenish-gray granitic rock is the Mirage pluton.

accumulating in the Mohave Basin during that time frame contain only volcanic rocks. Overlying younger conglomerates, dated at 15 to 11 million years old, predominantly contain Spirit Mountain granitic debris, indicating that the batholith had been exhumed by that time.

You can see a dramatic exposure of the Newberry detachment fault along the Needles Highway south of Laughlin. From NV 163, turn south onto the Needles Highway at milepost 16 and proceed 4.5 miles past the intersection with Casino Drive. Just northwest of the entrance to Big Bend of the Colorado State Recreation Area, a reddish-brown hill on the west side of the highway is a very weathered and iron-stained remnant of the Proterozoic Davis Dam granite. It lies above the Newberry detachment fault plane, which dips shallowly to the east. Below the fault is sheared, light-green to gray granitic rock of the 15-million-year-old Mirage pluton, part of the Spirit Mountain batholith to the north. By parking near the entrance to the recreation area, it is possible to walk to this exposure of the Newberry detachment fault.

Terraces of the Colorado River

NV 163 crosses the vast alluvial fan that slopes down to the Colorado River from the Newberry Mountains. The Colorado River incised this valley in the last 5 to 4 million years. Most of the geologic history of the pre-Pleistocene Colorado River has been removed by erosion, but we do know that a number of hills around the Mohave Basin top out at an elevation of about 1,250 feet. Hills higher than that elevation are lacking, suggesting that the river formed an extensive erosion surface in the bedrock at that level at one time.

As the highway nears the river, flat-surfaced Quaternary-age river terraces become prominent. A river terrace is a generally level or gently inclined surface formed by the deposition of alluvial material by the river. A now-elevated terrace reflects the former water level of the stream and the subsequent incision of the river to a new base level. The road skirts the south side of the light-colored Davis terrace of mid to late Pleistocene age, the highest terrace here, at an elevation of about 800 feet, approximately 300 feet above the current river

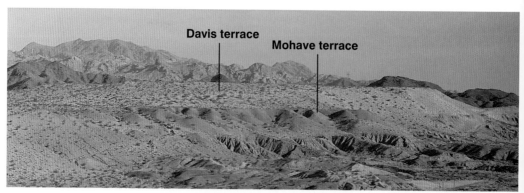

Two Pleistocene river terraces, the higher Davis and the lower Mohave, north of Laughlin. The dark hills directly behind the Davis terrace surface are made of the Proterozoic Davis Dam granite.

level. These deposits are correlated with the Chemehuevi Formation farther north along the river and are interpreted to be no younger than 40,000 years, and perhaps as old as 250,000 years.

Approximately 200 feet above the modern river level, or 100 feet below the elevation of the Davis terrace, is another surface, known as the Mohave terrace. NV 163 cuts through deposits of this terrace near its intersection with Laughlin Civic Drive; they are also exposed to the west of Thomas Edison Drive south of its intersection with NV 163.

The lowest surface, the Emerald terrace, has been almost obliterated by erosion and extensive mining for sand and gravel in the Laughlin area. This terrace was the active floodplain of the modern Colorado River until flooding was controlled by the construction of Hoover and Davis Dams upstream. Because this surface in no longer receiving deposits by the river, it is considered an inactive floodplain, and many riverfront hotels and casinos have been built on it.

The Enigmatic Bouse Formation

The Bouse Formation is a mysterious marly limestone, with varying amounts of mud, sand, and minor gravel, that is found only in the corridor of the Colorado River from south of Yuma, Arizona, to Cottonwood Valley, north of Laughlin. Limestone most often forms in oceans, so geologists originally thought it was deposited in a marine embayment that extended north from the Gulf of California 5.3 to 2.6 million years ago. They also thought that the ancestral Colorado River worked its way inland by headward erosion from the embayment. According to this theory, the uplift of the Colorado Plateau and the cutting of the Grand Canyon occurred after the establishment of the through-going river.

The thin-bedded marly limestone of the Bouse Formation in Panda Gulch, on the west side of the Colorado River south of Laughlin.

Studies from 2000 to 2005 hypothesize a completely different history. Strontium isotope ratios derived from the Bouse Formation are more similar to those ratios for the Colorado River than for those of a marine-derived deposit, indicating the Bouse Formation was not deposited in an ocean. In addition, the maximum elevations of the Bouse Formation do not increase gradually from Yuma northward but increase abruptly at points along the river. Also, some exposures are as much as 1,800 feet above sea level, and there is no evidence to support that much uplift by normal faulting. Scientists have begun to realize that the Colorado River might have developed from upstream to downstream, filling basins with deep, short-lived lakes before overtopping a bedrock divide to cascade into the next basin. It repeated this process until the river reached its current outlet in the Gulf of California. In this scenario, the limestones and marls of the Bouse Formation formed in the freshwater basin-filling lakes. In the vicinity of Laughlin, the Proterozoic Davis Dam granitic rock of the Pyramid Hills sustained a lake in the Cottonwood Basin to the north. A bedrock divide in the Topock Gorge area in Arizona (south of I-40), created a lake in the Mohave Basin.

Davis Dam Granite

Davis Dam, completed in 1951, was constructed where the Pyramid Hills, consisting of resistant Proterozoic granitic and gneissic rock, form a constriction across the Colorado River channel. The Pyramid Hills separate the Mohave Basin to the south from Cottonwood Basin to the north. The darkly weathered, reddish-brown Proterozoic rock, known locally as the Davis Dam granite, is 1.4 billion years old. Large potassium feldspar crystals, up to 2.5 inches long, give it a distinctive appearance. The potassium feldspar crystals are commonly rimmed with the mineral plagioclase, a texture known as rapakivi.

Large feldspar crystals of the Proterozoic Davis Dam granite. A quarter is shown for scale.

To reach Davis Dam, take Pyramid Canyon Road north from NV 163 at milepost 17. Pyramid Canyon Road also provides foot access to the Riverwalk Exploration Trail. You can see remnant exposures of fine-grained basin fill deposits of the Davis terrace along the road and at the equestrian trailhead. The rapakivi texture in the Davis Dam granite is easily viewed at the Pyramid Canyon Day Use Area at the end of the road, where the picnic and playground area is landscaped with boulders and rocks of the granite.

An erosional remnant of the layered silts and sands of the Pleistocene-age Davis terrace (right) overlaps the Proterozoic-age Davis Dam granite (left) along the Lakeview Trail at Katherine Landing, a marina within the Lake Mead National Recreational Area north of Davis Dam in Arizona.

Northern and Central Nevada

Interstate 80
California Border—Reno—Winnemucca
179 miles

I-80 enters Nevada following the rugged canyon of the Truckee River, which flows through Reno to Pyramid Lake in northwest Nevada. Prior to human regulation of the Truckee River, its discharge ranged wildly from large floods to a mere trickle. During the Pleistocene ice ages, when the climate was wetter, the Truckee carried great quantities of water into Lake Lahontan to the east. The flow was probably as erratic then as it is now, and occasional enormous floods, possibly triggered by the failure of glacial ice dams, filled the Truckee Canyon with a turbulent torrent of muddy water. These violent floods helped carve the canyon and washed large boulders as far as 30 miles downstream. The rocks exposed in the walls of the canyon are mostly late Miocene volcanic rocks issued from the Ancestral Cascade volcanoes, resting on a basement of late Cretaceous granitic rocks exposed as light gray-brown rocks along the roadsides.

At Verdi, the narrow canyon widens, and the Truckee River follows a more meandering path. In the area of exit 4, for the Boomtown-Garson Road, you can see Peavine Peak to the north, composed mostly of metavolcanic rocks of Triassic and Jurassic ages, cut by dikes and masses of younger Miocene volcanic rocks. Hydrothermal alteration associated with the younger volcanic activity resulted in some gold, copper, and iron mineralization of Peavine Peak, though none of it was extensive enough to support large-scale mining operations. To the south, the northern slope of the Carson Range consists of Cenozoic sedimentary deposits and volcanic rocks that conceal the granitic basement.

The Carson Range and Peavine Peak have been uplifted geologically recently along active faults. For about two months in the spring of 2008, a swarm of more than two thousand relatively small earthquakes began to rattle homes in the vicinity of Mogul, east of Verdi along I-80. The largest was a magnitude 4.7 event on April 25. Although a complex network of faults crisscross this area, the Mogul earthquake swarm may have been caused by the subterranean movement of magma.

East of the Verdi area, exposures of late Miocene and Pliocene sandstone, siltstone, conglomerate, diatomite, and ash can be seen to the south across the valley of the Truckee River, and also in several I-80 roadcuts. These sediments were deposited in rivers and lakes in a lush lowland, the Verdi Basin, which existed between 11 and 2.6 million years ago, a time when the volcanoes of the Ancestral Cascades were actively erupting. Sediments in the Verdi Basin exceed 5,000 feet in thickness and are known as the Hunter Creek Sandstone, named for a creek near Reno where the sediments are well exposed along the canyon walls. The Hunter Creek sediments have produced some interesting fossils, including mastodons and the four-tusked gomphotheres, both prehistoric elephants. Gomphotheres had two flat lower tusks shaped like paddles that might have been used to acquire aquatic vegetation along lakeshores. The remains of two species of native North American horses (belonging to the genera *Dinohippus* and *Equus*) have also been recovered, along with foot bones of a prehistoric llama-like camel of the genus *Hemiauchenia*.

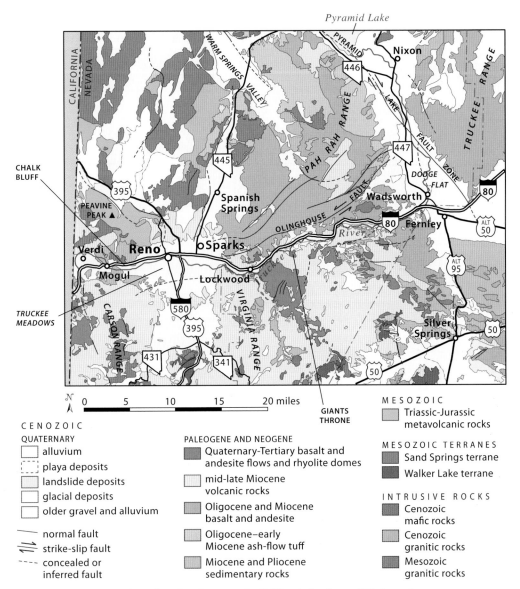

Geology along I-80 between the California border and Wadsworth.

Near the small settlement of Mogul, you can see the scars of ancient land-slides on the hills to the south of the Truckee River. The hummocky ground sloping toward the river consists of material transported downslope from the landslide scars. The Truckee River bends to the north around the heap of landslide deposits. As the Truckee River erodes the toe of the landslide mass, especially when the river is flooding, the materials upslope continue to move downhill, making this hummocky land unstable and therefore unsuitable for building.

Weathered outcrops of granodiorite north of I-80 near Mogul. The horizontal line near the base of the slope is the historic Highland Ditch, one of several built in the 1860s to carry water from the Truckee River to cultivated lands to the east.

The broad, flat terrace in the middle distance is a former floodplain of the Truckee River. The modern river flows through the tree-lined valley in the foreground, well below its prehistoric floodplain.

To the northeast of I-80 near Mogul, the knobby, brownish rock exposures are outcrops of 90-million-year-old granodiorite of Cretaceous age, part of the enormous Sierra Nevada batholith. The granodiorite, which is normally buried under younger sediments and volcanic rocks, was raised along faults near Mogul and became exposed when erosion stripped away the overlying materials. Weathering along joints, or fractures, in the light-gray granodiorite has separated it into brown knobs.

East of the Mogul area, a view south across the valley reveals several flat-topped terraces, each covered by a thin layer of gravel and sand deposited by the Truckee River. Such terraces, remnants of the river's former floodplain, are indications of recent pulses of uplift. Geologists have mapped as many as eight different terrace levels along the Truckee River in this region, each representing a period of rapid uplift of the Carson Range. Only a few are recognizable from I-80.

At the western edge of Reno, I-80 passes through a small hill known as Chalk Bluff. The roadcuts near the off-ramp to South McCarran Boulevard (exit 10) reveal white diatomite and light-gray sandstones of the Hunter Creek Sandstone, cut by many small faults. The diatomite, fine sediment rich in the siliceous skeletons of diatoms, or microscopic algae, accumulated on the floor of one of the lakes in the Verdi Basin.

Reno is located in a 12-mile-wide valley known as the Truckee Meadows in reference to a large tract of marshy ground that existed on the east side of the valley until it was transformed by urban development. Faulting and subsidence formed this low basin over the past 3 million years or so. More prominent downfaulting

Diatomite and fine gray sandstone in the Hunter Creek Sandstone exposed in a roadcut through Chalk Bluff along I-80. Note the several small faults displacing the rock layers in this location.

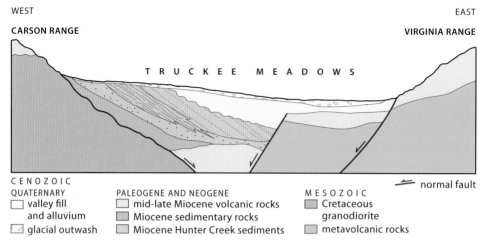

WEST   EAST

CARSON RANGE   **VIRGINIA RANGE**

T R U C K E E   M E A D O W S

CENOZOIC   ⤙ normal fault
QUATERNARY   PALEOGENE AND NEOGENE   MESOZOIC
☐ valley fill   ☐ mid-late Miocene volcanic rocks ☐ Cretaceous
  and alluvium   ☐ Miocene sedimentary rocks   granodiorite
☐ glacial outwash   ☐ Miocene Hunter Creek sediments   ☐ metavolcanic rocks

Prominent normal faulting tilts the Truckee Meadows down toward the Virginia Range on the east.

on the east side tilts the floor of the Truckee Meadows gently toward the Virginia Range. Thus, water naturally drains to the east side, which explains the location of the formerly marshy ground, as well as why north-flowing Steamboat Creek runs against the base of the Virginia Range rather than flowing through the center of the plain.

The Truckee River deposited alluvium on the floor of the Truckee Meadows over the past several million years. Within the 1,500-foot-thick alluvium are boulder and gravel deposits that provide evidence of catastrophic flooding during the Pleistocene ice ages. The granite boulders originated from bedrock in the Lake Tahoe area. Water released in these enormous floods collected on the east side of valley.

The marshy surface and the modern flood risk in the eastern Truckee Meadows have created many challenges for the people living in or traveling through this part of the valley. Gold Rush immigrants traveling the California Trail had to turn south along the foothills of the Virginia Range to avoid the marshy ground before returning to the Truckee River. When the Southern Pacific Railroad established a switching and maintenance yard at Sparks in 1903, the level of the ground was raised 18 inches to create dry land for the facilities. Damaging floods occurred here in 1955, 1986, and 1997. In 1997 a warm January storm melted large amounts of snow in the Sierra Nevada and triggered a flood that increased the flow in the Truckee River to 18,000 cubic feet per second, more than twenty-five times its normal flow. Damage was widespread, and an old gravel quarry north of I-80 was partly inundated by the floodwaters. The quarry is now the Sparks Marina, an artificial recreational lake.

Sparks to Wadsworth

Between Sparks and Wadsworth, I-80 travels alongside the Truckee River through a scenic northeast-trending canyon that follows the Olinghouse fault zone, a left-lateral strike-slip fault that originated in late Miocene through Pliocene time. As the Virginia Range to the south and Pah Rah Range to the north began to rise, the Truckee River was able to cut down into the crushed and sheared rock along the fault zone. Many earthquakes occur along the Olinghouse fault zone, indicating that uplift continues today.

As I-80 enters the western end of the canyon east of exit 21, dark-colored metavolcanic rocks are exposed along the north side of I-80. The higher canyon slopes are made up of Miocene-age andesite flows and lahar deposits. Near milepost 21, andesitic volcanic rocks are quarried and crushed from a site just north of I-80. Near exit 22, for Lockwood, the south side of the canyon is capped by the 1.1-million-year-old, dark-brown McClellan Peak basalt, which erupted from a cinder cone located about 9 miles to the southeast. The lava flowed into the ancient Truckee River canyon, and small dark outcrops, remnants of this flow, are visible in several places. The basalt flow probably impounded the Truckee River here, but there is no evidence of semipermanent inundation upstream, indicating that the lava dam was eroded rapidly when the impounded water overtopped it.

Just northeast of the Lockwood area, you can see shoreline terraces eroded by waves of Pleistocene Lake Lahontan on the lower canyon walls, as well as lake sediments near the road. The terraces and sediments record the position of a narrow arm of Lake Lahontan that flooded into the canyon from the east. The most prominent of the shoreline terraces was probably created about 13,000 years ago. The lake sediments consist mostly of fine sand and silt washed into the ancient lake by the ancestral Truckee River.

At Mustang Road (exit 23), a small hill south of I-80 is composed of the McClellan Peak basalt, while the upper canyon walls expose Miocene andesite and pyroclastic flows. South of the hill, Lake Lahontan deposits exposed along the Truckee River record several early lake stages from about 350,000 to 140,000 years ago. River terraces are capped by glacial outwash sediments dotted with large granite boulders, washed from the Squaw Valley area in California by great ice age floods.

East of the Mustang area, roadcuts north and south of I-80 reveal tuff and andesite rubble erupted 12 to 8 million years ago from the Ancestral Cascade volcanoes. East of exit 28, about where the canyon opens up, a scenic overlook offers a good view to the south of Giants Throne, a large dome-like intrusive mass of andesite and dacite. This magma likely pooled beneath a volcano and cooled there without being erupted.

South of I-80 about one-half mile west of exit 36, you can see the Derby Dam, built in the early 1900s to divert Truckee River water south to be stored in Lahontan Reservoir. The natural flow of the Truckee River is into Pyramid Lake to the north, the level of which began to drop almost immediately after diversions began in 1906. The dam also interfered with the spawning runs of the Pyramid Lake cutthroat trout, a species now endangered in this part of the Great Basin. In recent years, these impacts have been mitigated somewhat by legal limits on the amount of water diverted, along with the construction of fish ladders at Derby Dam.

Near exit 38 (Orchard), the ridge to the south of I-80 displays a prominent white band of volcanic tuff dipping gently to the west between darker brown andesite flows and breccias of the Pyramid sequence (below) and the Kate Peak Formation (above). These Miocene volcanic rocks are associated with sediments, including diatomite, that accumulated in lakes and river floodplains nestled in the lowlands between the volcanic peaks. Great blooms of diatoms would have been possible in the presence of so much dissolved silica from volcanic rocks and ash. As the diatoms completed their life cycle, their siliceous microskeletons accumulated at the lake bottoms. High up and toward the east, on the north-facing slope near the Orchard exit, you can see a steep cone of tailings from surface mining of a white diatomite layer. Diatomite is used primarily as a filtration agent because the microscopic diatom skeletons, usually circular or triangular plates, are perforated with tiny pores and open pockets.

Between exits 40 and 43, orange, pink, and lavender exposures of late Oligocene ash-flow tuffs come into view on both sides of the road in an area aptly called Painted Rocks. These tuffs formed between about 28 and 21 million years ago, when violent blasts from the volcanoes of the Ancestral Cascades sent clouds of hot ash surging across the landscape of northern Nevada. Later hydrothermal alteration produced soft clay minerals and reddish oxide minerals.

View south from I-80 near Orchard of the thick succession of Miocene volcanic rocks in the northern Virginia Range. The white layer in the middle slope is tuff composed of consolidated ash, while the dark crags above are andesite flows.

Colorful Miocene volcanic rocks are exposed in this roadcut north of I-80 in the Painted Rocks area. In the close-up view, the pinkish-gray matrix is consolidated volcanic ash and the white fragments are altered pumice.

Fernley to Lovelock

Near Wadsworth, the Olinghouse fault zone, which has controlled the alignment of the Truckee River east from Sparks, intersects the northwest-trending strike-slip faults of the Walker Lane. The river makes a nearly right-angle bend here and continues toward Pyramid Lake, following the Pyramid Lake fault zone, a component of the Walker Lane. The Wadsworth-Fernley area marks the western margin of the infamous Forty-Mile Desert, a parched stretch of barren and waterless land between the sink of the Humboldt River and the cool water and shade of the Truckee River. Gold Rush immigrants experienced severe hardships in traversing the Forty-Mile Desert in the 1800s.

Northeast of the exits for West and East Fernley, I-80 passes over Pleistocene lake sediments that provide the source for sand that is piled into dunes. For about 10 miles east of Fernley, the road passes along the edge of the Fernley Sink, a low basin separating the Truckee Range to the north from the Hot Springs Mountains to the south. Both ranges are composed predominantly of dark-colored andesite and basalt erupted 7 to 5 million years ago from local vents. Several prominent terraces of Lake Lahontan, along with heaps of lake sediments, can be seen on the lower slopes of the Truckee Range north of the road.

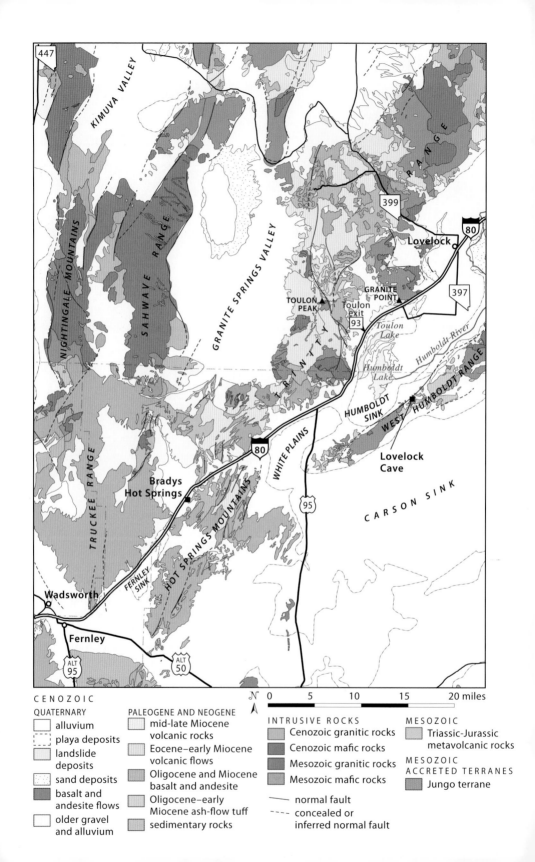

QUATERNARY

- [ ] alluvium
- [ ] playa deposits
- [ ] landslide deposits
- [ ] sand deposits
- [ ] basalt and andesite flows
- [ ] older gravel and alluvium

PALEOGENE AND NEOGENE

- [ ] mid-late Miocene volcanic rocks
- [ ] Eocene–early Miocene volcanic flows
- [ ] Oligocene and Miocene basalt and andesite
- [ ] Oligocene–early Miocene ash-flow tuff
- [ ] sedimentary rocks

INTRUSIVE ROCKS

- [ ] Cenozoic granitic rocks
- [ ] Cenozoic mafic rocks
- [ ] Mesozoic granitic rocks
- [ ] Mesozoic mafic rocks

— normal fault
---- concealed or inferred normal fault

MESOZOIC

- [ ] Triassic-Jurassic metavolcanic rocks

MESOZOIC ACCRETED TERRANES

- [ ] Jungo terrane

N

0   5   10   15   20 miles

Lake Lahontan sediments and shoreline terraces along the slopes of the Truckee Range north of I-80, west of Fernley.

South of the road near exit 65, several active hot springs, known as Bradys Hot Springs, are the targets of extensive geothermal development. These hot springs were both a blessing and a curse to the California immigrants traveling through the Forty-Mile Desert. The hot water could be consumed after it was cooled, but it was hot enough to injure or kill thirst-crazed animals that plunged into it. In the late 1950s and 1960s, the first geothermal wells were drilled and encountered subsurface water as hot as 400°F. The pipes on the surface south of I-80 are used to transport water and steam from the generating plant to injection wells, where the fluids are returned to the subsurface to be reheated.

The hot springs emerge mostly along a northeast-striking fault that extends from Fernley to Lovelock, approximately parallel to but south of I-80 along the northern margin of the Hot Springs Mountains. The superposition of strike-slip faults of the Walker Lane with normal faults related to the extension of the Basin and Range Province causes faults to extend more deeply, creating pathways for groundwater to flow deep beneath the surface. When the descending groundwater reaches hot rocks, it heats up and rises back to the surface, where it emerges along fault systems as hot springs.

A few miles northwest of Bradys Hot Springs, low white outcrops appearing north of I-80 expose diatomite deposited in an ancient lake basin during Pliocene time. The conspicuous plant to the south of the road processes and packages the diatomite mined from pits just to the north.

West of the junction with US 95, the broad flat playa, known as the White Plains, is part of the Carson Sink, where the Carson River, flowing from the Sierra Nevada to the west, terminates. Water covers the surface of the White Plains only after local downpours or when unusually high discharge from the

Brown knobs of tufa, silhouetted against the White Plains of the Carson Sink, mark the former location of springs on the floor of Pleistocene Lake Lahontan.

Carson River floods the basin. The white surface consists of fine silt encrusted with salts precipitated as the floodwaters evaporate. As I-80 skirts the northern edge of the White Plains, you can see light-brown, knoblike mounds of tufa on either side of the road. Tufa is a spongy form of calcite deposited when springs discharge calcium-bearing water on the floor an alkaline lake. The tufa mounds formed during the Pleistocene ice ages, when the entire Carson Sink was submerged to a depth of several hundred feet by the water of Lake Lahontan.

About 2 miles northeast of its junction with US 95, I-80 passes into the Humboldt Sink, a playa where the Humboldt River terminates after flowing more than 300 miles from northeastern Nevada. The divide between the Carson and Humboldt Sinks is a very subtle ridge in the vicinity of milepost 85, virtually impossible to see from the road. After carrying water hundreds of miles from opposite directions, these two great rivers vanish into sinks separated by just a few miles!

The Humboldt River has served as an important travel route across the harsh desert throughout human history. Many Native American tribes, including the Northern Paiute that currently occupy the region, utilized the Humboldt River corridor for centuries prior to the arrival of European trappers and explorers in the 1800s. John C. Frémont explored the river in 1848 and gave the stream its modern name in honor of German naturalist Alexander von Humboldt. Soon after Frémont's exploration, the river became part of the California Trail.

I-80 skirts the northeast margin of the Humboldt Sink for about 20 miles. To the north of the road lies the Trinity Range, while to the south across the sink is the West Humboldt Range. Both mountain ranges are fairly complex, consisting of a basement sequence of Triassic ocean basin sedimentary rocks that were deformed and metamorphosed by the accretion of oceanic terranes later in the Mesozoic Era. The intrusion of granitic magma during Jurassic and Cretaceous time and widespread caldera-forming volcanic activity and extensional faulting in Cenozoic time led to significant mineralization. Near milepost 88, old tungsten workings of the St. Anthony Mine can be seen to the northwest of the highway. Discovered in the early 1900s, the tungsten deposits occurred in the zone of contact metamorphism between a body of Cretaceous plutonic rock and the surrounding deep-sea sediments of Triassic age. At exit 93 at Toulon, the remains of an old mill that processed the tungsten ore stand just south of the road. From the Toulon exit, Toulon Peak is easily visible to the northwest, composed of Miocene rhyolite flows and tuffs associated with the Ragged Top caldera complex.

Lovelock Cave in the West Humboldt Range is an important archeological site that produced many artifacts in the early 1900s when bat guano was removed from the cave for use as a fertilizer. The artifacts include duck decoys made of woven tule reeds and feathers, slings used in hunting birds and mammals, fishing implements, and food-processing stone tools. The aboriginal people who inhabited the site were foraging along the edge of a large lake that occupied a portion of the Humboldt Sink more than 2,000 years ago.

A few miles northwest from the Toulon exit, I-80 passes just south of Granite Point, a brownish knob composed of Cretaceous granitic rock that has intruded Triassic metasedimentary rocks. Several dikes extend from the granitic pluton into the surrounding dark-colored slaty rocks. The rock near the dikes has been bleached to white and has, in some places, been mineralized with tungsten and molybdenum ores.

Lovelock to Winnemucca

Mining roads on the slopes of the West Humboldt Range southeast of Lovelock were developed to access gypsum deposits that formed where water evaporated from enclosed marine basins in Jurassic time. At exit 112, the Coal Canyon Road (NV 396) extends southwest from I-80 to cross the West Humboldt Range en route to several old mining camps. Coal Canyon passes through Cretaceous granitic rocks intruded into Triassic and Jurassic limestone, shale, and quartzite. The conspicuous cut north of the Coal Canyon Road is part of the Willard mining district, which produced gold and silver between 1989 and 1992. Look to the west of I-80 a few miles north of the Coal Canyon exit to glimpse the gorge of the Humboldt River. The sediments exposed in the walls are mostly lakebeds that accumulated in Lake Lahontan in Pleistocene time.

Between exit 119 (Oreana) and exit 145 (Imlay), I-80 parallels the fault-bound, steep face of the north-trending Humboldt Range. At the northern end of the range are Triassic and Jurassic deep-sea sediments of the Jungo terrane, deposited between an ancient volcanic arc to the west (the Black Rock–Jackson terrane) and the Triassic continental shelf to the east. The deep-sea sediments were thrust eastward along the Luning-Fencemaker thrust fault that slashes northeast across the northern end of the Humboldt Range. During thrusting the Triassic rock layers were intensely folded.

East of I-80 between exit 119 and exit 129, the rugged light-brown cliffs in the midslope of the Humboldt Range are exposures of the Rocky Canyon stock, a body of Cretaceous granodiorite. The heat and chemically active fluids associated with the invading magma set the stage for the formation of ore minerals in

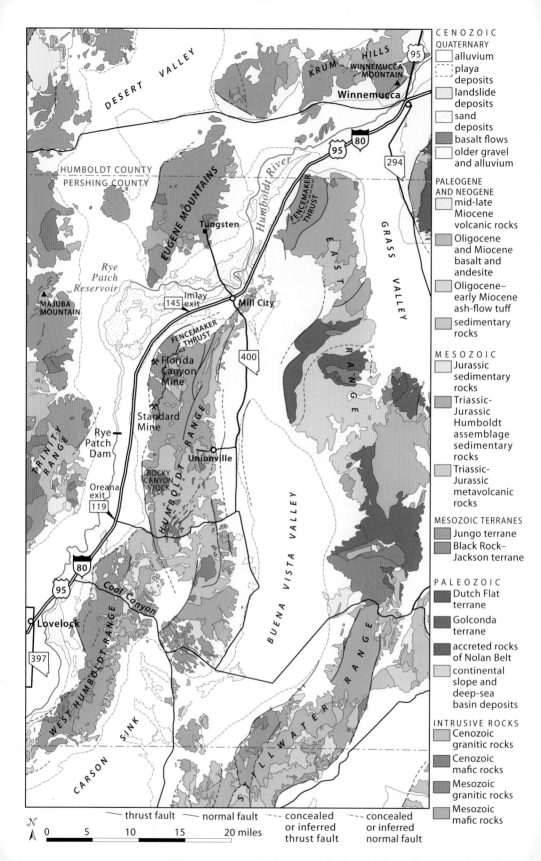

CENOZOIC
QUATERNARY
- alluvium
- playa deposits
- landslide deposits
- sand deposits
- basalt flows
- older gravel and alluvium

PALEOGENE AND NEOGENE
- mid-late Miocene volcanic rocks
- Oligocene and Miocene basalt and andesite
- Oligocene–early Miocene ash-flow tuff
- sedimentary rocks

MESOZOIC
- Jurassic sedimentary rocks
- Triassic-Jurassic Humboldt assemblage sedimentary rocks
- Triassic-Jurassic metavolcanic rocks

MESOZOIC TERRANES
- Jungo terrane
- Black Rock–Jackson terrane

PALEOZOIC
- Dutch Flat terrane
- Golconda terrane
- accreted rocks of Nolan Belt
- continental slope and deep-sea basin deposits

INTRUSIVE ROCKS
- Cenozoic granitic rocks
- Cenozoic mafic rocks
- Mesozoic granitic rocks
- Mesozoic mafic rocks

— thrust fault   — normal fault   ---- concealed or inferred thrust fault   ---- concealed or inferred normal fault

N

0   5   10   15   20 miles

the surrounding rock, mostly Triassic limestone, siltstone, and tuff. Silver- and gold-bearing veins in Triassic volcanic rocks of the Rochester mining district, about 10 miles east of the road, are about the same age as the granodiorite body.

At milepost 129, a side road leads west to Rye Patch Dam, built in 1936 to provide irrigation water around Lovelock. The 80-foot-high dam flooded an impressive canyon cut by the Humboldt River through Lake Lahontan lake-beds. You can see white and light-gray silt and clay in the upper walls of the flooded canyon west of I-80 when Rye Patch Reservoir is low enough.

In the vicinity of milepost 130, the tailings and a portion of the excavated pit of the Standard Mine are visible on the lower slopes of the Humboldt Range. Gold, discovered here in 1932, was disseminated as fine particles and micro-scopic flecks in silicified breccia that formed along faults. The tailings from the World War II activity contain small amounts of recoverable gold.

Folds such as these in the sandy limestone of Triassic age in the Humboldt Range are common throughout the Luning-Fencemaker thrust belt in central Nevada. The photo view is about 20 inches across.

Rugged granodiorite outcrops of the Rocky Canyon stock on the north slope of the Humboldt Range.

Tailings of the Florida Canyon Mine.

Between milepost 135 and milepost 136, evaporative cooling towers are visible east of the highway, the remains of a small geothermal power facility completed in 1993 but never brought on line. Though there are no hot springs at the surface in this area, drilling in the 1980s and 1990s revealed subsurface water temperatures as high as 400°F at depths up to 2,000 feet.

In the vicinity of milepost 136, you can see the massive tailings and leach pad of the Florida Canyon Mine immediately southeast of the highway. The gold mine, located in a canyon southeast of the tailings, produces ore from Triassic siltstone and mudstone. Hot mineralizing fluids deposited the microscopic gold along a network of interconnected fractures and faults that developed during the uplift of the range over the past 5 million years. The gold is mostly recovered using a heap leaching process that involves passing a sodium cyanide solution through large piles of the crushed ore. Geothermal fluids from the nearby fault zone are utilized to heat the cyanide solution to improve its effectiveness in dissolving the gold.

Just west of I-80 in the vicinity of the Florida Canyon Mine facilities, you can occasionally see low mounds of tufa and siliceous sinter deposited by hot springs that are no longer active. Farther off to the northwest, the prominent craggy mountain is Majuba Mountain, a complex mass of Miocene rhyolite lava domes, plugs, and dikes and volcanic breccia emplaced into older Triassic and Jurassic slate, marble, and quartzite. As the magma was forcefully injected along fractures in the older rock, hydrothermal alteration produced some spectacular mineralization of copper, tin, silver and molybdenum ore. The site is also famous for producing beautiful specimens of chalcopyrite, arsenopyrite, pyrite, cuprite, chalcocite, azurite, malachite, bornite, and many other minerals.

Mill City (exit 149), built in the late 1800s just north of the highway along the banks of the Humboldt River, received its name for the stamp mills that treated silver ore from several nearby mines. The Eugene Mountains, composed

mostly of deformed deep-sea Triassic sedimentary rocks of the Jungo terrane, are visible northwest of I-80, along with mining scars surrounding the old camp of Tungsten. The tungsten deposits were particularly rich in places where Triassic limestone layers were altered by the heat and reactive fluids associated with small Cretaceous plutons. Tungsten was the largest tungsten mine in Nevada at the time of its closing in 1957.

East of I-80 stand the rugged peaks of the East Range, which consist mainly of Paleozoic and Mesozoic sedimentary rocks covered by thick sequences of Cenozoic rhyolite and basalt. Limestone of the Triassic continental shelf is well exposed to the west of the Luning-Fencemaker thrust system, which passes through the northern part of the East Range.

About where I-80 crosses the Humboldt County line, you can see Winnemucca Mountain and the Krum Hills to the northeast. Gold and silver deposits were discovered around Winnemucca Mountain in 1893. Most of the gold occurred in quartz veins associated with Cenozoic volcanic rocks. Small amounts of lead and copper were also produced from these mines.

Interstate 80
Winnemucca—Battle Mountain—Elko
124 miles

Winnemucca, the county seat of Humboldt Country, sits astride the Humboldt River. The city was originally named French Ford for a French trader who settled near a crossing point along the California Trail in 1860. The name was later changed in honor of Chief Winnemucca, the leader of a local band of Paiute.

South of Winnemucca, the Sonoma Range inspired the name Sonomia for a large block of land, sometimes referred to as microcontinent or a superterrane, that many geologists think collided with the western edge of North America in late Permian and early Triassic time. As the terrane docked with the continental margin, deep-sea sediments that had accumulated on the intervening ocean floor were compressed and driven eastward over the edge of the continental shelf. Thrust sheets of these deformed deep-sea sediments now rest east of the Sonoma Range and are known as the Golconda terrane.

At exit 187, I-80 makes an approximately right-angle bend around Button Point, named for Frank Button, who started ranching in this area in 1873. Visible south of the road at Button Point are craggy outcrops of mostly Miocene lava flows and welded tuffs that were erupted from volcanoes centered to the south and east.

To the northeast from the Button Point area, you can see the southern end of the Osgood Mountains, which consist primarily of Miocene andesitic volcanic rocks resting on a complex mass of deformed Paleozoic sedimentary rocks. Cretaceous granodiorite metamorphosed the older rocks, producing some significant tungsten, gold, and molybdenum deposits. Mineralized rock of the Getchell and Twin Creeks Mines has supported mining operations for more than a century.

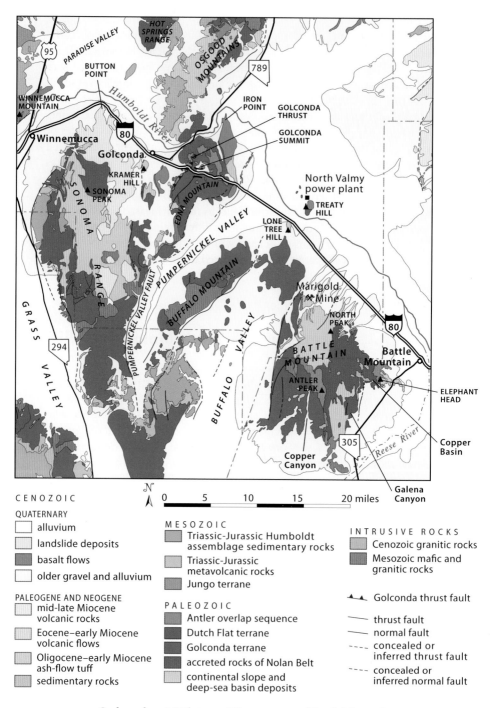

CENOZOIC

QUATERNARY
- alluvium
- landslide deposits
- basalt flows
- older gravel and alluvium

PALEOGENE AND NEOGENE
- mid-late Miocene volcanic rocks
- Eocene–early Miocene volcanic flows
- Oligocene–early Miocene ash-flow tuff
- sedimentary rocks

MESOZOIC
- Triassic-Jurassic Humboldt assemblage sedimentary rocks
- Triassic-Jurassic metavolcanic rocks
- Jungo terrane

PALEOZOIC
- Antler overlap sequence
- Dutch Flat terrane
- Golconda terrane
- accreted rocks of Nolan Belt
- continental slope and deep-sea basin deposits

INTRUSIVE ROCKS
- Cenozoic granitic rocks
- Mesozoic mafic and granitic rocks

- Golconda thrust fault
- thrust fault
- normal fault
- concealed or inferred thrust fault
- concealed or inferred normal fault

Geology along I-80 between Winnemucca and Battle Mountain.

Dark-colored knobs and crags in the northeast Sonoma Range consist of Miocene volcanic rocks.

At exit 194, for the small town of Golconda, I-80 passes north of Kramer Hill, a prominent knob consisting of light-gray, well-cemented sandstone of Cambrian age that weathers to a light brown. The sandstone is intruded by Cretaceous granitic dikes and quartz veins, some of which contained gold deposits that were discovered in 1866. North of Golconda, several active springs discharge water as hot as 165°F, and on cold winter days, you can see clouds of rising steam. The hot water is heavily mineralized, carrying copper, arsenic, lithium, and manganese, among many other soluble components.

Hot springs similar to those north of Golconda appear to have played a major role in the formation of tungsten and manganese deposits along the northeast-trending fault zone bounding the eastern flanks of the Osgood Mountains to the northeast. The source of the metals was probably the Cambrian shale, limestone, and slate that underlies the alluvium along the mountain front. Hot water rising along the fault zone during the Pleistocene Epoch carried the metals to the surface, where they became concentrated in travertine, a banded form of precipitated calcite.

Edna Mountain, crossed by I-80 at Golconda Summit, has been extremely important in unraveling the complex tectonic history of north-central Nevada. Geologists in the 1950s mapped a major thrust fault here along which mostly Pennsylvanian and Permian deep-sea sediments were transported eastward over shallow marine rocks of the same age that accumulated near the continental shelf. I-80 crosses the thrust fault, named the Golconda thrust, west of Golconda Summit. The brownish blocky rocks exposed in the largest roadcut west of the pass and west of the fault are Pennsylvanian and Permian sedimentary rocks of the continental shelf. East of the large roadcut and on the east side of the fault, which is not visible, are the generally poorly exposed rocks of the Golconda thrust sheet, or terrane, which consist of chert, shale, and siltstone that were deposited in a deep ocean basin. This heterogeneous assemblage of rocks in the Golconda thrust has traditionally been known as the Havallah sequence in northern Nevada.

East of Golconda Summit, rocks of the Golconda thrust sheet are not well exposed, but you'll see outcrops of the Pennsylvanian and Permian limestone and sandstone below the Golconda thrust fault on both sides of the road. The fault is nearly flat-lying and deformed, so it is not easy to know if you are above or below it. In the vicinity of exit 203, colorful lavender rocks exposed in the low roadcuts are composed of altered shale and chert of Ordovician age called the Valmy Formation. These rocks are structurally below the Golconda thrust fault and were originally dark gray to black ooze and mud that accumulated in the deep sea west of the continental shelf. The shale contains barium, copper, nickel, silver, vanadium, and zinc that probably formed on the ancient seafloor from hot brines issuing from deep-ocean hydrothermal vents. Oxidation of sulfide minerals containing these metals has produced the reddish shades in the roadcuts. Farther to the north, the scars and roads of the Silver Coin mining area can be seen on the slopes of the ridge known as Iron Point. Pliocene to Quaternary-age basalt caps the ridge and has prevented the underlying, ore-rich rock from eroding away.

As I-80 passes exit 205, Pumpernickel Valley extends south of the road, with the Pumpernickel Valley fault running along its west side. The Pumpernickel Valley was the area in which the Pumpernickel Formation, a sequence of Pennsylvanian shale, chert, and greenstone, was first described by geologists. These rocks are part of the Havallah sequence, deep-ocean sediments and volcanic rocks of the Golconda thrust sheet. About 12 miles south of I-80, a series of hot springs rises to the surface along the Pumpernickel Valley fault, from which water flows at a temperature of 190°F. Drilling for geothermal exploration in

Colorful exposures of altered shale and chert of the Ordovician Valmy Formation in a roadcut on the north side of I-80 near the Iron Point exit (exit 203).

this area in the 1970s discovered subsurface water as hot as 275°F, with the potential for even higher temperatures at greater depths.

Where I-80 transects Pumpernickel Valley, you can see the coal-fired North Valmy power plant to the north. The coal comes primarily from Utah and Wyoming. Between the power plant and the road, a small mound known as Treaty Hill is composed of Ordovician chert and shale overlain by Permian sedimentary rocks, capped in places by dark-colored Miocene and Pliocene basalt flows. Local lore suggests that Treaty Hill was the place where long-standing territorial disputes between the Paiute (to the west) and Shoshone (to the east) were settled. Just south of the road 1 mile west of exit 212 is Lone Tree Hill, scarred on its west side by mining activities since the 1989 discovery of gold mineralization there. South of Valmy, the lower slopes of Battle Mountain are pockmarked with small cuts and pits reflecting mineral exploration and production that occurred here mostly in the 1970s. The most obvious open pit seen to the south of I-80 marks a portion of the Marigold Mine, from which more than 1 million ounces of gold has been produced since ores were discovered in the 1930s.

Battle Mountain and the Battle Mountain Mining District

Confrontations between emigrants bound for California and local Native Americans in the 1850s and 1860s is thought to be the source of the name Battle Mountain. North Peak, the highest of several prominences in Battle Mountain, can been seen from I-80. Unlike many other Nevada mountains, Battle Mountain is not a linear range but more or less circular, with ephemeral creeks draining outward in a radial pattern. The earliest mining at Battle Mountain began after silver ores were found in Galena Canyon in 1863. Copper and silver deposits were discovered the following year in the vicinity of Copper Canyon, and the Battle Mountain mining district was formally organized in 1866. Gold ore was discovered in 1909, and barite and gem-quality turquoise have also been produced from the mines.

The bedrock of Battle Mountain is a mangled mass of Paleozoic sedimentary rocks intruded by small bodies of mostly Oligocene and Eocene granitic rocks and overlain by volcanic rocks. Within the highly deformed and altered Paleozoic rocks, geologists have identified several sheets of rock transported along low-angle thrust faults, piling up on each other somewhat like the shingles on a roof. The lowest thrust sheet, actually an amalgamation of smaller thrust sheets, was transported east during the Antler Orogeny, beginning in the late Devonian Period. These rocks were forced up into a highland during the early phases of the Antler Orogeny, and erosion planed down some of the thrusted rocks before the area was again submerged, producing a pervasive irregular surface, known as an unconformity. Thick accumulations of sandstone, conglomerate, limestone, and shale, called the Antler overlap sequence, were deposited on the erosion surface in Pennsylvanian and Permian time. The sequence and orogeny are named for Antler Peak, in the center of Battle Mountain. Near the end of the Permian Period, about 250 million years ago, new compressive forces led to the eastward thrusting of deep-ocean rocks, the Golconda thrust sheet, over the older sheets already in place. In early to middle Mesozoic time, additional terranes, such as the Dutch Flat terrane, docked from the west.

From about 90 to 38 million years ago, magma migrated from below into the stack of thrust sheets. The heat and fluids associated with this magma played important roles in the origin of the several porphyry copper and molybdenum-copper ore bodies, particularly in Copper Basin, on the east side of the mountain. In the Eocene and Oligocene Epochs, as extensional faulting began to rip the crust, magma was injected along the normal faults, forming northerly trending dikes that cut through the older rocks. Such a massive surge of molten rock into the deformed and altered Paleozoic thrust sheets led to even more mineralization. Elephant Head, the prominent rocky knob on the east side of Battle Mountain, is composed of welded ash-flow tuff dated at 34 million years.

Battle Mountain to Carlin

The Reese River, which empties into the Humboldt River at the town of Battle Mountain, has produced several damaging floods when cloudbursts or snowmelt filled its otherwise dry bed to overflowing. East from Battle Mountain, I-80 traverses an alluvial plain constructed from sediments deposited by the Humboldt and Reese Rivers. Southwest of the highway stands the Shoshone Range, with Mt. Lewis, it highest peak, visible in the distance. The northern portion of the Shoshone Range is similar to Battle Mountain, so it is not surprising that gold, molybdenum, and copper have been mined from several historically important mining areas.

About 8 miles east of the Battle Mountain exit, I-80 bends around Argenta Rim at the northern end of the Shoshone Range. The sharp boundary between the ridge and the floodplain, as well as the similarly abrupt eastern escarpment of the Sheep Creek Range to the north, is from active normal faulting. Argenta Rim is capped by 16- to 5-million-year-old lava flows, similar to those capping Shoshone Mesa, at south end of the Sheep Creek Range. These rocks are part of the Northern Nevada Rift, a great linear zone of voluminous Miocene volcanic activity stretching more than 300 miles from McDermitt, on the Nevada-Oregon border, southeast to a point south of Eureka. Along this trend, enormous volumes of lava surged onto the irregular surface of eroded Paleozoic rocks between 16 and 14 million years ago. Magma also oozed into parallel fault planes in the subsurface, creating numerous dike swarms beneath the lava flows. The volcanic activity occurred about the same time as tensional forces began to stretch the crust of northern Nevada in a northeast-southwest direction, opening a linear, fault-bounded rift basin in which several thousand feet of volcanic rock, along with associated sediments, accumulated. The opening of the Northern Nevada Rift coincided with the inception of volcanic activity associated with the Yellowstone hot spot along the Nevada-Oregon border near McDermitt.

The dark lava flows capping the Argenta Rim and Shoshone Mesa overlie thrust slices composed of deep-sea sedimentary rocks of Ordovician through Devonian age. These rocks are mostly dark-colored shales, chert, fine-grained sandstones, and greenstones that represent deep-ocean ooze, muds, gels, and submarine volcanic materials. Within the Slavern Chert of Devonian age are thick layers of barite, a barium sulfate mineral. Although silver ores were

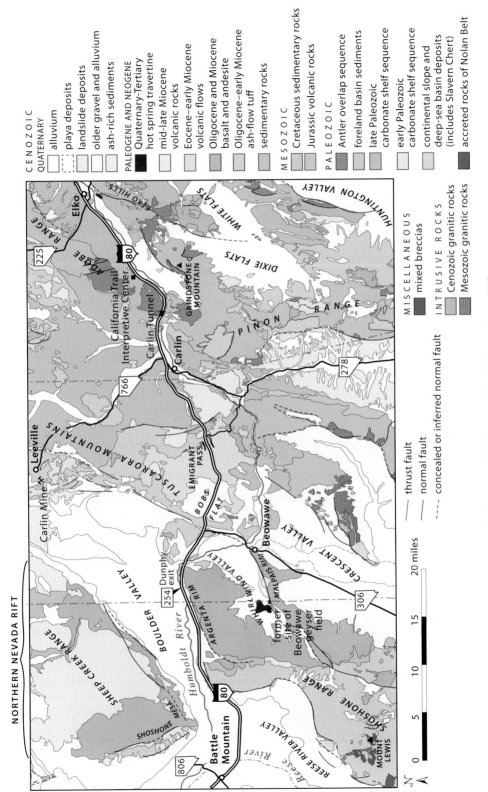

CENOZOIC

QUATERNARY
- alluvium
- playa deposits
- landslide deposits
- older gravel and alluvium
- ash-rich sediments

PALEOGENE AND NEOGENE
- Quaternary-Tertiary hot spring travertine
- mid-late Miocene volcanic rocks
- Eocene–early Miocene volcanic flows
- Oligocene and Miocene basalt and andesite
- Oligocene–early Miocene ash-flow tuff
- sedimentary rocks

MESOZOIC
- Cretaceous sedimentary rocks
- Jurassic volcanic rocks

PALEOZOIC
- Antler overlap sequence
- foreland basin sediments
- late Paleozoic carbonate shelf sequence
- early Paleozoic carbonate shelf sequence
- continental slope and deep-sea basin deposits (includes Slavern Chert)
- accreted rocks of Nolan Belt

MISCELLANEOUS
- mixed breccias

INTRUSIVE ROCKS
- Cenozoic granitic rocks
- Mesozoic granitic rocks

— thrust fault
— normal fault
--- concealed or inferred normal fault

Geology along I-80 between Battle Mountain and Elko.

Dark basaltic lava flows of Miocene age cap Shoshone Mesa at the south end of the Sheep Creek Range. The lower slope is composed of shale, chert, and siltstone of Ordovician through Devonian age. The prominent scars below the lava cap are from mining barite deposits in Devonian chert.

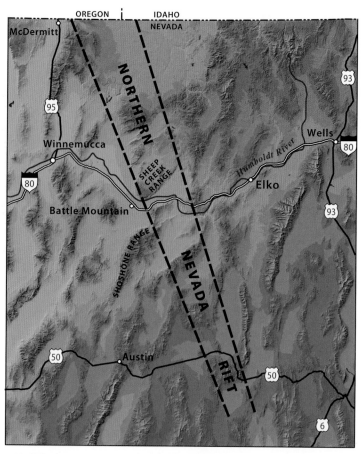

Extensional forces formed the Northern Nevada Rift about 16 to 14 million years ago.

discovered here in the 1860s, most of the pits and workings on the flanks of the Argenta Rim between Argenta (exit 244) and Dunphy (exit 254) are active or historic barite mines. Barite is extremely valuable because it is about twice as dense as most common minerals. It can be ground into a powder which, when mixed with water and other chemicals, creates a heavy, dense mud used in drilling. Nevada is the leading producer of this valuable mineral in the United States, with about half of it coming from mines in and near the Shoshone Range region. The barite occurs as irregular but sometimes thick layers interbedded with chert and shale.

About 3 miles east of Dunphy, where the Humboldt River makes a nearly right-angle bend, the TS Power Plant can be seen north of the road in Boulder

BEOWAWE GEYSER FIELD

A few miles east of the Humboldt River crossing, I-80 passes the Beowawe Rest Area, from which you can see Whirlwind Valley to the southwest. The white streak on the southern side of Whirlwind Valley is a half-mile-long terrace composed of mineral deposits built by hot springs and geysers along the Malpais fault zone. The terrace deposits, known as sinter, consist of primarily of opal, a hydrated form of silica deposited when steam and hot water condense, cool, and evaporate. Prior to geothermal exploration beginning in 1959 that altered the flow of groundwater in Whirlwind Valley, as many as twenty-seven active geysers erupted plumes of steam and water to heights of nearly 30 feet.

View south from I-80 near the Beowawe Rest Area. The white ledge at the base of the slope just left of center is a sinter terrace built by hot spring and geyser activity along the normal fault bounding Whirlwind Valley.

The geothermal exploration in the vicinity of the Beowawe geyser field encountered subsurface temperatures as high as 420°F, one of the highest subsurface water temperatures in any of Nevada's numerous geothermal areas. The source of heat is probably hot rock of the upper mantle, which is closer to the surface in the Beowawe area than elsewhere in the Basin and Range Province. Geophysical studies suggest that the crust in this area is less than about 20 kilometers thick, about half the thickness of the crust in the Sierra Nevada to the west.

Valley. The plant burns about 70,000 tons of Wyoming coal per month, producing power for several gold mines in the region. When the air is clear, you can see the dumps from the famous Carlin Mine, 25 miles to the northeast on the western flanks of the Tuscarora Mountains. The Carlin Mine is the namesake of the Carlin-type disseminated gold deposit, discussed elsewhere in this volume.

About a half mile east of the Beowawe Rest Area, the highway passes a prominent roadcut on the north side. The rocks adjacent to the westbound lanes are complexly sheared siltstone, chert, and sandstone of the mostly Ordovician-age Vinini Formation, thrust from the west during the Antler Orogeny or later tectonic events. East of exit 261 to Beowawe, I-80 traverses Bobs Flat, and you can see Miocene basalt flows along the west end of Whirlwind Valley to the southwest. Between Bobs Flat and Emigrant Pass, I-80 travels through hills and cliffs of andesite and dacite lava flows, domes, and dikes of the Emigrant Pass volcanic field, all tilted to the east by faulting. These rocks represent some of the nearly 8 cubic miles of lava erupted during a volcanic rampage between 38 and 36 million years ago in Eocene time. Geophysical evidence suggests the remaining magma cooled into large masses, or plutons, of granitic rock, buried about 2 miles deep below Emigrant Pass. The heat and fluids associated with this surge of magma led to the gold mineralization in the Carlin trend and other areas in northern Nevada.

About 3 miles west of Emigrant Pass, I-80 passes through a cut that exposes dark-colored Eocene andesite overlain by bone-white ash deposits of Miocene age. The irregular boundary was formed when the ash descended onto the surface, filling up channels and depressions previously eroded into the older andesite. At Emigrant Pass are pale tan and white roadcuts of the Vinini

Roadcut north of I-80 about 3 miles west of Emigrant Pass exposes white volcanic ash of Miocene age filling a channel in dark andesite of Eocene age.

Flow-banded perlite outcrops north of I-80 about 4 miles east of Emigrant Pass.

Formation. To the east of the pass, the highway travels back into a sequence of Miocene to Pliocene volcanic and sedimentary rocks.

On the eastern flanks of the Tuscarora Mountains, ridges and hills are commonly capped by brown rhyolite lava flows of the Palisade Canyon rhyolite, named for a spectacular gorge carved by the Humboldt River about 4 miles south of the interstate. The Palisade Canyon rhyolite was erupted about 15 million years ago from a volcanic center situated about 1 mile northeast of exit 271, for Palisade. About 4 miles east of Emigrant Pass, the roadcuts north of the westbound lanes of I-80 expose a portion of the Palisades Canyon rhyolite dominated by flow-banded perlite, a hydrated volcanic glass. The lava cooled quickly enough to develop a glassy texture and then absorbed some water molecules. Unlike water-free obsidian, perlite has a gray, translucent appearance due to water trapped in the glassy solid. Perlite is a useful commodity because when heated to 1,000°F or more, the water molecules cause perlite to expand into a popcorn-like material that is used as a light-weight filler for concrete and plaster.

As I-80 continues down the Tuscarora slope east of milepost 273 toward Carlin, it passes roadside exposures of brilliant white tuff and ash-rich sediments that make up a portion of the Carlin Formation of late Miocene age (16 to 14 million years old). The Carlin Formation, considered by some geologists a part of the thicker Humboldt Formation, also includes sandstone, limestone, and conglomerate. These stream and lake deposits accumulated in a volcanically active basin produced by normal faulting. This basin developed a little farther to the west and later in time than the older Elko Basin of Eocene age. More than 500 feet of sediments associated with the Carlin Basin have been traced from the Adobe Range near Elko to the northern Tuscarora Mountains, a distance of more than 20 miles. The source of the ash that accumulated in the

Carlin Basin was probably the Northern Nevada Rift or more distant volcanic centers along the Oregon and Idaho borders, or both. From about 5 miles west of Carlin to West Carlin (exit 279), the low roadcuts along I-80 are additional exposures of late Miocene or Pliocene sandstone and tuff.

Carlin to Elko

At exit 279 (West Carlin), I-80 passes into the main portion of the Carlin trend, one of Nevada's most productive belts of gold mineralization. Disseminated gold deposits were first discovered along this trend in 1961, and since then more than forty individual ore bodies have been identified. Most of the industrial facilities you can see from I-80 in Carlin are related, in one way or another, to the mining, processing, and maintenance of gold mines.

The hills rising south of Carlin are the northern end of the Piñon Range. The lower slopes are composed of Miocene sediments and ash layers, while the upper slopes and ledges are marine sedimentary rocks deposited in a foreland basin in Mississippian and Pennsylvanian time. Just east of milepost 283, about 3 miles east of Carlin, the reddish layers exposed north of the road are outcrops of Mississippian siltstone and limestone.

Five miles east of Carlin, I-80 passes through the Carlin Tunnel excavated through a ridge in the northern Piñon Range to bypass a loop in the original road that followed the Humboldt River. This tunnel is famous to geologists because of the spectacular angular unconformity that can be seen for a split second to the north near the west entrance to the tunnel. A much better and safer view of this feature is available by taking exit 282 for East Carlin and following

A roadcut on the south side of I-80 near milepost 273 exposes layered white tuff and ash-rich sediments of the Carlin Formation of Miocene age.

the frontage road on the south side of I-80 east toward the tunnel. This frontage road passes under the freeway and the tunnel entrance and continues along the original route of I-80 directly past the slope exposing the unconformity.

At the Carlin unconformity, nearly vertical beds of red to purplish conglomerate and sandstone of the 320-million-year-old Tonka Formation of late Mississippian age are overlain by gently east-dipping layers of gray-tan limestone and sandstone of the Strathearn Formation of late Pennsylvanian to early Permian age, about 280 million years old, part of the Antler overlap sequence. The surface at which the two sets of discordant rock layers meet is the angular unconformity. The coarse sand and gravel of the Tonka Formation, sediment shed from the Antler highland to the west, was deposited on a coastal plain and in a shallow sea of the foreland basin. After lithification turned the sand and gravel into rock, the Tonka layers were tilted, folded, and uplifted in middle Pennsylvanian time. Over time, erosion beveled the surface, truncating the nearly vertical layers. Then, in late Pennsylvanian time, the area was again submerged, and the layers of limestone of the Strathearn Formation accumulated on top of the erosion surface. Faulting in Cenozoic time uplifted the rock and tilted it gently down to the east. The time between the deposition of the Tonka sediments and the overlying Strathearn layers is approximately 50 million years, an enormous gap in the geologic record at this locality.

East of the Carlin Tunnel, the prominent yellow-gray cliffs south and north of I-80 are mostly Mississippian and Pennsylvanian limestone and sandstone. The layers are tilted down to the east as a consequence of the rotation of the Piñon Range block along normal faults.

The Carlin angular unconformity as seen from the old road through Carlin Canyon in the Piñon Range.

Hoodoos of Eocene river deposits standing along the north side of I-80 east of Carlin Canyon.

Grindstone Mountain south of I-80 near milepost 290, a few miles west of Elko. The highest gray ledges are Pennsylvanian limestone and siltstones. Note that the hill in the foreground has the same ledges. The hill is separated from the main part of Grindstone Mountain by a fault that has displaced the smaller hill downward. The smooth slopes below the ledges are composed mostly of Mississippian sandstone, siltstone, and limestone.

In the vicinity of milepost 288, you can see picturesque castles, or hoodoos, carved in conglomerate and sandstone just north of the highway. A river deposited these sediments in Eocene time, when a basin began to form during the earliest phases of extensional faulting. To the south, across the Humboldt River, the gray ledges on the upper slopes of Grindstone Mountain are outcrops of thick limestone beds of middle to late Pennsylvanian age.

For several miles east of milepost 288, sedimentary rocks of Mississippian, Pennsylvanian, and early Permian age are exposed in the roadcuts and hills on both sides of I-80. These rocks were all deposited in the foreland basin east of the Antler highland. A very distinctive conglomerate, the Diamond Peak Formation, is composed of pebbles, cobbles, and boulders of red and black chert, gray-green quartzite, and fragments of brownish-gray limestone. These rock fragments were eroded from the deep-ocean sediments that were thrust eastward to build the highlands. Late Paleozoic rivers flowing east from the Antler highland carried pieces of rock to the coastal plain and shallow seafloor, where they settled out as gravel deposits. This colorful conglomerate can be examined at many places along the road where its characteristic outcrops of knobs or ledges occur.

The California Trail Interpretive Center, on the north side of I-80 near exit 292 for Hunter, is located near a critical junction in the trail. To the southeast from the vicinity of the center, you can see the mouth of the prominent canyon of the South Fork Humboldt River. Immigrants following the Hastings Cutoff, primarily from 1845 to 1850, traveled down this canyon as an alternative to the main trail, but the cutoff proved to be a more difficult and time-consuming

Close-up view of conglomerate in the Diamond Peak Formation, exposed along the north side of I-80 east of the Carlin tunnels. Note the variable colors of the chert pebbles. A quarter is shown for scale.

path. The unfortunate immigrants who followed the Hastings cutoff included the famous Donner Party, in 1846.

North and east of the California Trail Interpretive Center, the light-colored bluffs and hills north of I-80 are composed of the Humboldt Formation, predominantly sandstones and conglomerates representing stream-deposited gravel and sand that accumulated in several interconnected basins from 16 million years ago to about 5 million years ago. Fine-grained siltstones and mudstones accumulated in several large lakes. The maximum thickness of this sequence in the Elko region is more than 5,000 feet. Fossils found in the Humboldt Formation include primitive horses, elephants, camels, sheeplike animals known as oreodonts, large wolflike carnivores, and felines similar to modern mountain lions.

Interstate 80
Elko—Utah Border
109 miles

Elko is situated along the banks of the Humboldt River near hot springs that were a popular resting spot along the California Trail. The Elko Hills, visible from I-80 to the southeast across the Humboldt River, consist primarily of Mississippian- to Permian-age limestone, conglomerate, and sandstone, with some internal thrust faults disrupting the layers. These Paleozoic rocks are overlain on the flanks by Eocene lake and stream deposits of the Elko Formation, approximately 40 million years old. All of these rocks have been gently folded upward into a broad northeast-trending anticline formed sometime after about 35 million years ago. At Elko Mountain, on the northern end of the Elko Hills, outcrops of Eocene rhyolite are thought to have formed at the same time that sediments of the Elko Formation were accumulating in nearby lakes and river valleys.

The Adobe Range, visible as hills and peaks on the skyline to the north of I-80, is composed mostly of Mississippian and Pennsylvanian sedimentary rocks folded into a broad syncline, not unlike the overall structure of the Elko

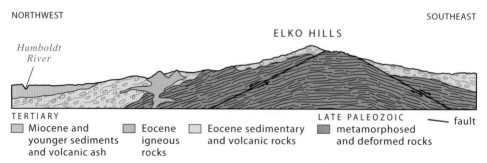

The Elko Hills are an upward-folded dome of Paleozoic rocks overlain by the Elko Formation of Eocene time.

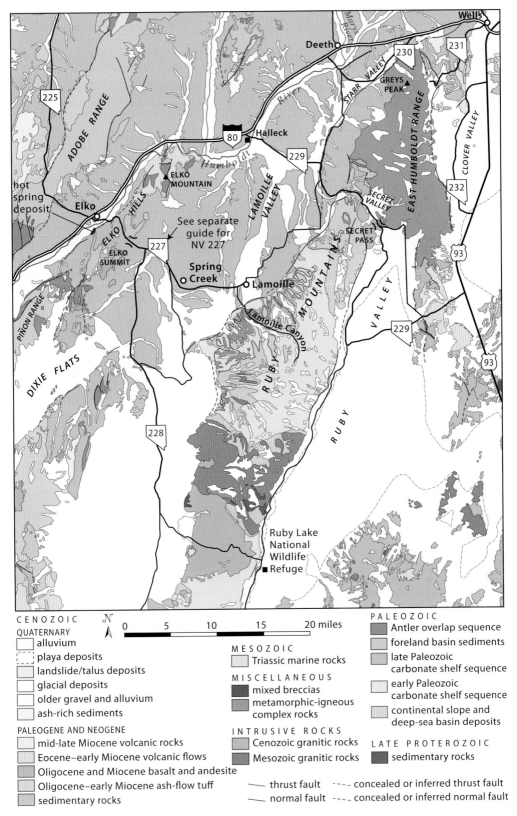

CENOZOIC

QUATERNARY
- [ ] alluvium
- [ ] playa deposits
- [ ] landslide/talus deposits
- [ ] glacial deposits
- [ ] older gravel and alluvium
- [ ] ash-rich sediments

PALEOGENE AND NEOGENE
- [ ] mid-late Miocene volcanic rocks
- [ ] Eocene–early Miocene volcanic flows
- [ ] Oligocene and Miocene basalt and andesite
- [ ] Oligocene–early Miocene ash-flow tuff
- [ ] sedimentary rocks

N

0   5   10   15   20 miles

MESOZOIC
- [ ] Triassic marine rocks

MISCELLANEOUS
- [ ] mixed breccias
- [ ] metamorphic-igneous complex rocks

INTRUSIVE ROCKS
- [ ] Cenozoic granitic rocks
- [ ] Mesozoic granitic rocks

PALEOZOIC
- [ ] Antler overlap sequence
- [ ] foreland basin sediments
- [ ] late Paleozoic carbonate shelf sequence
- [ ] early Paleozoic carbonate shelf sequence
- [ ] continental slope and deep-sea basin deposits

LATE PROTEROZOIC
- [ ] sedimentary rocks

— thrust fault   ---- concealed or inferred thrust fault

— normal fault   ---- concealed or inferred normal fault

Geology along I-80 between Elko and Wells.

SECRET PASS THROUGH A METAMORPHIC CORE COMPLEX

At exit 321, you can take NV 229 to Secret Pass, where the canyon walls expose rocks of the East Humboldt–Ruby Mountains metamorphic core complex. The exit is near the location of Fort Halleck, established in 1867 to protect immigrants traveling along the California Trail. About 8 miles southeast from I-80, NV 229 swings south and follows the Secret Creek drainage. In this area, you can see exposures of the soft sedimentary rocks of the Miocene Humboldt Formation north of the highway and in low roadcuts. These sediments accumulated in a low basin west of the East Humboldt Range and Ruby Mountains in middle Miocene time, from 16 to 10 million years ago. This basin formed in response to the onset of an intense wave of extension that accelerated the development of the core complex.

View southeast from the Fort Halleck state historic marker on NV 229. The low area on the skyline is Secret Pass, which separates the East Humboldt Range to the north (left) from the Ruby Mountains to the south (right).

About 15 miles southeast from I-80, NV 229 enters the gorge of Secret Creek, where roadside exposures are shattered and deformed Paleozoic rocks, including sandstone, siltstone, and black shale. These rocks, the upper plate of the metamorphic core complex, were transported west along low-angle faults as the core complex developed. As the road continues eastward, it cuts downward through the sheared zone marking the boundary between the upper and lower plates. Several large roadcuts west of Secret Pass reveal the sheared schist, quartzite and gneiss and a platy mylonite of the core complex of the lower plate. West-dipping normal faults displace the bands of metamorphic rocks in some of the roadcuts.

Close-up of folded quartzite exposed in a roadcut along NV 229 near Secret Pass.

Hills. These sediments accumulated on the ocean floor of the foreland basin east of the Antler highland in late Paleozoic time.

East of the Elko Hills, the high peaks to the northeast are in the East Humboldt Range, with the even loftier summits of the Ruby Mountains to the southeast. Exposed in the mountains is the East Humboldt–Ruby Mountains metamorphic core complex, in which dissected and weathered exposures of late Precambrian marble, quartzite, and schist are intimately mingled with masses of sheared, mostly Mesozoic granitic rock and gneiss. These high-grade metamorphic rocks formed deep underground in the middle and lower portion of the crust. Younger rocks once covered the older metamorphic rocks, but extensional forces stretched and thinned the crust so much during Cenozoic time that the East Humboldt and Ruby Mountains region bulged upward in a large dome, bringing deep crustal rocks toward the surface. The book introduction and the narratives for NV 231 (Angle Lake) and NV 227 (Lamoille Canyon) provide additional details on the rocks and origin of the East Humboldt–Ruby Mountains metamorphic core complex, as does the side trip to Secret Pass.

About 10 miles northeast of Elko, I-80 bends due east past the northern end of the Elko Hills. In this area, the rugged Osino Canyon of the Humboldt River can be seen south of I-80. The dark rocks near the top of the canyon walls are Cenozoic rhyolite flows that weather to a brown color. In the vicinity of milepost 335, just east of the Deeth exit, I-80 crosses Marys River, one of the largest tributaries of the Humboldt River in the upper drainage basin. About 2 miles east of the Marys River crossing, I-80 crosses the main channel of the Humboldt River, but it is so small at this point that it is difficult to discern from the interstate. Rock exposures are limited in this area, but the light-colored strata seen in the low bluffs and roadcuts are Miocene sediments and tuffs of the Humboldt Formation.

Layers of Miocene sandstone, siltstone, and volcanic ash of the Humboldt Formation exposed in a roadcut along I-80 near the Deeth exit.

Wells to the Utah Border

During the time of western migration along the California Trail, the town site of modern Wells was known as Humboldt Wells in reference to the springs west of town where the Humboldt River begins. After resting and watering their stock, travelers followed the main channel of the Humboldt River west for more than 300 miles. (More information about Wells, including the powerful earthquake that affected the town in 2008, is presented in the road guide for US 93.)

East of Wells, I-80 transects a portion of the Great Basin in which thick sequences of limestone, dolomite, and shale accumulated on the continental shelf during the Paleozoic Era. These Paleozoic sediments remained mostly undeformed during the time that tectonic disturbances were creating geological chaos farther west. However, during the Cretaceous Period compressive forces related to the Sevier Orogeny ruptured the thick Paleozoic sequence into slabs and drove the great sheets of rock eastward along several major thrust faults. The main mountain building occurred in Utah. In eastern Nevada, along the west slope of the Sevier orogenic belt, sometimes called the Sevier hinterland by geologists, rocks were buried deeply enough under thrust sheets to drive widespread metamorphism, converting the original sedimentary rocks into schist, marble, and quartzite. In Cenozoic time, when extensional forces swept through the region, many of the Cretaceous thrust faults were reactivated as low-angle normal faults, along which the slabs of rock slid off one another. This process, called denudation, exhumed some of the deeply buried and intensely metamorphosed Paleozoic rocks. Some of these rocks are exposed in the Wood Hills south of I-80 east of Wells.

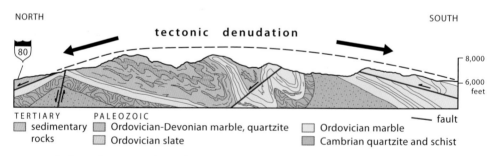

Deformed metamorphic rocks in the Wood Hills were exposed following denudation along low-angle Cenozoic normal faults. —Modified from Camilleri, 2010

While I-80 does not pass over any of the metamorphic rocks in the core of the Wood Hills, you can see tilted layers of Cenozoic sediments above the low-angle normal faults in the hills and gullies near Moor Summit. To the north of the road in the lowest saddle near Wells Peak, the highest peak in the Windermere Hills, is a low-angle normal fault dipping west beneath unmetamorphosed Permian limestone. East of the saddle, quartzite and metaconglomerate beneath this fault are of Mississippian age.

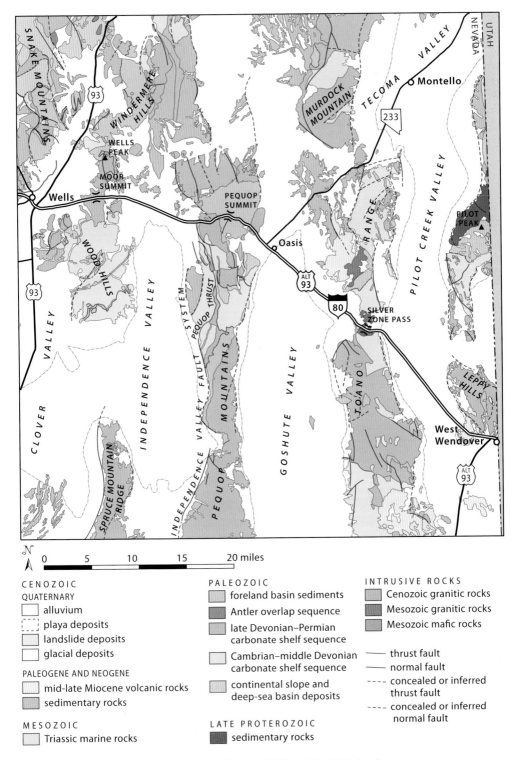

Geology along I-80 between Wells and the Utah border.

Independence Valley, a nearly enclosed basin east of the Wood Hills, is bounded on the east by the Independence Valley fault system, a set of normal faults that extends more than 30 miles along the western escarpment of the Pequop Mountains. Beneath the flat surface of Independence Valley, sand, gravel, and silt washed from the adjacent mountain has accumulated to a maximum thickness of more than 15,000 feet in the southern end of the basin. One of the faults in the Independence Valley fault system appears to have been the source of a magnitude 7 earthquake about 40,000 years ago that produced about 3 feet of displacement. On a clear day, you can see the low area on the west side of Independence Valley to the southwest of I-80. Here, Independence Valley opens into Clover Valley through a low gap between the Wood Hills and Spruce Mountain Ridge to the south. During the Pleistocene ice ages, Lake Clover submerged the floor of Clover Valley and spilled into Independence Valley through the gap. At its last peak stage, probably between 11,000 and 8,000 years ago, Lake Clover covered more than 350 square miles and submerged the floor of Independence Valley to a depth of 50 to 100 feet.

In the Pequop Mountains, deformed and metamorphosed Paleozoic rocks have been lifted to the surface from a deep crustal level. The relatively undeformed Paleozoic sedimentary rock that once overlay the deeper metamorphic rock has been displaced along the Pequop thrust fault. Significant mineralization occurs in several locations within the deep crustal rocks. The Pequop trend, one of Nevada's most recently recognized mineral belts, includes the central Pequop Mountains, as well as the southern Wood Hills.

Towering cliffs of unmetamorphosed Devonian limestone rise high above I-80 as it climbs through Maverick Canyon toward Pequop Summit. The thick limestone layers formed in the shallow seas that covered the continental shelf some 370 million years ago. I-80 follows closely an east-trending fault that has elevated the limestone cliffs south of the road several hundred feet higher than those to the north. Just west of Pequop Summit, I-80 passes into a sequence of thin-bedded limestone, shale, and sandstone strata of Mississippian age.

Rocks exposed along the northeastern flanks of the Pequop Mountains east of Pequop Summit are mostly Mississippian limestone and shale, faulted in complex patterns. In the vicinity of the Nevada Department of Transportation maintenance station (near milepost 375), low roadcuts along the highway expose east-dipping sandstone, siltstone, and black shale that accumulated during Mississippian time in a deepwater foreland basin east of the Antler highland. East of the small settlement of Oasis, the view southwest from I-80 reveals some of the mining roads and workings associated with Long Canyon, one of the principal mining centers in the Pequop trend.

The downfaulting in the Goshute Valley during Cenozoic time was more active along the eastern margin, where a prominent fault system lies along the base of the Toano Range. The normal faults have a total vertical displacement on the order of 12,000 feet. The maximum thickness of Cenozoic rocks and unconsolidated sediment under the broad Goshute Valley is more than 8,000 feet. During the Pleistocene ice ages, Lake Waring filled the Goshute Valley and lapped against the opposing slopes of the Pequop Mountains and the Toano Range. At its last peak stage of development, sometime between 10,000 and

Cliffs of Devonian limestone along I-80 at the mouth of Maverick Canyon on the west slope of the Pequop Mountains.

Rocks exposed in this roadcut along I-80 just west of Pequop Summit are thin-bedded limestone and sandstone of Mississippian age.

20,000 years ago, Lake Waring extended more than 60 miles, from about where I-80 crosses Goshute Valley southward into Antelope and Steptoe Valleys, and had a maximum depth of about 200 feet.

At exit 387, for Shafter, the low roadcuts and mounds north of I-80 are Miocene lake and stream deposits. Hills farther north consist mostly of Cenozoic volcanic rocks, including 12-million-year-old rhyolite flows that contain tiny topaz crystals.

I-80 climbs over the Toano Range at Silver Zone Pass, where you can see outcrops of Jurassic granodiorite, cooled from magma that intruded Cambrian and Ordovician limestone deep underground about 162 million years ago. East of Silver Zone Pass, the gray rocks in roadcuts north of the highway are limestone and dolomite some 480 to 460 million years old. In places, these rocks have been metamorphosed into foliated and platy impure marble, and metallic mineralization includes the formation of ores of silver, tungsten, lead, copper, zinc, and iron.

If you look northeast from I-80 as it crosses the floor of Pilot Creek Valley, you'll see 10,716-foot Pilot Peak, the highest point in the Pilot Range. Between 1845 and 1850, this landmark guided weary travelers following the Hastings Cutoff segment of the California Trail across 70 miles of the waterless Great Salt Lake Desert to springs along the eastern base of Pilot Peak. The high point is composed of hard late Precambrian to Cambrian sandstone and quartzite, and the lower slopes of the southern Pilot Range are Paleozoic limestone faulted against the older rocks.

Weathering formed pockets and cavities in the Miocene rhyolite north of I-80 a few miles west of West Wendover.

West of West Wendover, I-80 bends to the south around low ridges known as the Leppy Hills. This small, northwest-trending block is bounded by normal faults on the east and west. The bedrock is dominated by Devonian to Permian limestone and shale, overlain by or faulted against Miocene rhyolite flows. You can see the distinctive, cavernous weathering pattern of the rhyolites just north of I-80 a few miles west of the West Wendover exit. Tilted layers of Paleozoic limestone form the prominent ledges and cliffs north of the hotels and casinos in West Wendover. You can see networks of white calcite veins and masses extending through the limestone in some of the roadcuts.

East of the state border, I-80 crosses the Bonneville Salt Flats, a vast expanse of salt and mud that was the floor of Pleistocene Lake Bonneville, the largest ice age lake in the Great Basin. At its last maximum stage, about 15,000 years ago, Lake Bonneville covered 20,000 square miles of western Utah and eastern Nevada with water up to 1,000 feet deep.

US 6
California Border—Coaldale Junction
33 miles

US 6 traverses the entire width of Nevada, but segments of it run concurrently with US 95 and US 50. Only the sections of US 6 that have a single designation are included here. For other sections, see the narratives for either US 50 or US 95.

US 6 crosses the California-Nevada state line in Queen Valley and climbs to Montgomery Pass at the north end of the White Mountains. As the road climbs out of Queen Valley, a viewpoint on the south side of the road provides a good place to contemplate the geologic processes at work here. Cambrian phyllite, slate, and marble occur along the base of the White Mountains in outcrops between the Jurassic and Cretaceous granitic rocks that form the higher slopes and peaks. The light-colored rock from which the White Mountains derive their name is a Cretaceous quartz monzonite, a rock similar to granite.

View south from US 6 over Queen Valley to the north end of the White Mountains. Boundary Peak is the highest peak on the skyline. The Queen Valley fault runs along the base of the mountains.

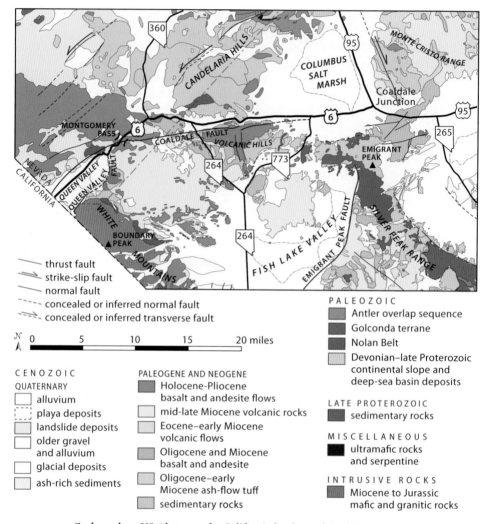

Geology along US 6 between the California border and Coaldale Junction.

Queen Valley, a fault-bounded basin, formed in response to the eastward transfer of shear stresses from the Eastern California shear zone to the Walker Lane in the vicinity of US 95. The connecting structure is the east-trending Coaldale fault zone, a zone of left-lateral strike-slip faults that US 6 parallels to US 95. Several small scarps have been mapped across Queen Valley, reflecting fault movement shifting to the Coaldale fault zone.

The Queen Valley started forming only 3 million years ago, and gravity data suggest the alluvium is 2,500 to 3,000 feet deep on its eastern end. The abrupt termination of ridges at the southeastern edge of the valley marks the Queen Valley fault, which is the northeast continuation of the north-trending White

Roadcuts along US 6 east of Montgomery Pass expose late Miocene to Pliocene light-colored tuff overlain by basaltic andesite flows. When the hot lava flowed over the tuff, it oxidized iron-bearing minerals, creating the reddish baked zone.

Mountain fault along the western edge of the White Mountains. Farther south, the right-lateral displacement along the White Mountain fault steps over to the Owens Valley fault, which generated a magnitude 8.3 earthquake in 1872.

In the Montgomery Pass area, granitic rock and older Paleozoic rocks are covered by volcanic materials, including a white to light-gray, 25-million-year-old rhyolite, one of several extensive ash-flow tuff sheets erupted here in late Oligocene time. The rhyolite is overlain by a grayish-brown Miocene andesite (about 11 million years old) attributed to volcanic activity of the Ancestral Cascade arc.

Between NV 360 and Coaldale Junction, a sequence of Paleozoic sedimentary rocks peeks out from beneath Cenozoic volcanics along the southern edge of the Candelaria Hills to the north and in some of the roadcuts on either side of the highway. Near the intersection of US 6 and NV 264, diatomite, or diatomaceous earth, is mined from several pits to the south of the highway. This soft, crumby material consists of the silica shell remains of single-celled diatoms, a form of algae, that accumulated in a freshwater lake in Miocene-Pliocene time.

West from its intersection with NV 264, US 6 passes north of the Volcanic Hills, a thick deposit of dark-gray, fine-grained basalts. The volcanics are about 3.1 million years old. The multicolored hills south of the highway consist of dark shale and slaty phyllite of Ordovician age overlain by 23- to 21-million-year-old rhyolitic ash-flow tuff. The white to pink materials are nonwelded tuffs, the brown to reddish-brown or bluish-gray rocks are welded and crystallized tuffs, and black horizons are vitrophyres, tuffs so thoroughly welded that

The varicolored rocks in the Candelaria Hills north of US 6 are composed primarily of Miocene and Pliocene volcanic rocks.

they are glassy. Near its junction with NV 773 east of the Volcanic Hills, US 6 cuts across the southern part of a pull-apart basin containing the Columbus Salt Marsh and a field of sand dunes visible north of the road.

Directly south of Coaldale Junction, you can see a thick accumulation of Miocene and Pliocene volcanic rocks in the rugged slopes rising beyond the remains of buildings in Coaldale. (The section of highway between Coaldale Junction and Tonopah is described in the US 95 road guide in this volume.)

US 6
Tonopah—Ely
168 miles

East of the historic mining town of Tonopah (discussed in the road guide for US 95), US 6 passes through double roadcuts exposing the Miocene volcanic rocks so prevalent in the southern San Antonio Mountains. A maroon-colored zone of crushed rock in the roadcut marks the trace of a normal fault. Northeast from the roadcuts, US 6 descends from the volcanic ramparts of Tonopah into the lowlands of Ralston Valley. The small hills south of the road are exposures of light-colored, ash-rich sediments of Miocene age. North of the road, these same sediments are capped by darker-brown rhyolite flows.

About 12 miles east of the NV 376 junction, near McKinney Tanks Summit, US 6 passes outcrops of 23-million-year-old, red-brown tuff, erupted from a caldera north of US 6. As the road continues toward Saulsbury Summit from the west, it passes Miocene volcanic materials ranging from lightly welded, light-colored tuff to darker andesitic flows to small plugs and knobs of rhyolite. Prominent landforms reflect the various colors of volcanic rocks: Red Peak (north of US 6), Black Butte (south of the highway east of Saulsbury Wash), and Yellow Cone (just southwest of Saulsbury Summit), all visible from US 6.

Just south of Saulsbury Summit, silver and gold ores were discovered in Miocene rhyolite and andesite of the Ellendale mining district in 1909. Mining activity was brief, declining after about 1915. Barite was discovered in the underlying Paleozoic rocks in the early 1930s, stimulating a brief wave of activity.

East of Saulsbury Summit and on the west side of Stone Cabin Valley, the view north of the highway reveals prominent west-tilted tablelands consisting of several sheets of Oligocene ash-flow tuff. Stone Cabin Valley lies near

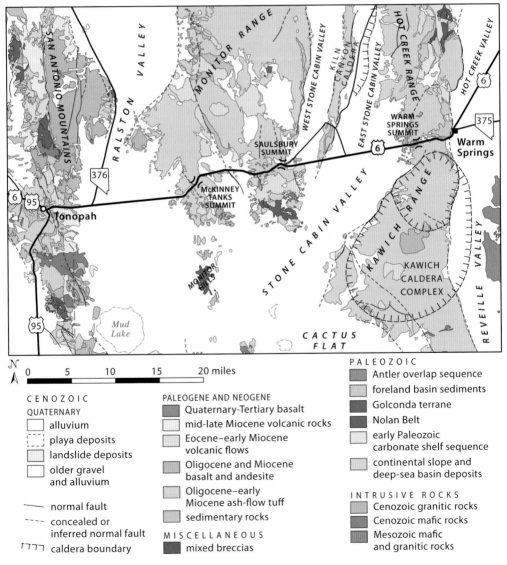

Geology along US 6 between Tonopah and Warm Springs.

the heart of the Central Nevada caldera complex, where several huge volcanic blasts created large calderas between about 36 and 23 million years ago. The Kawich Range, south of Warm Springs Summit, is dominated by tuff and other volcanic rocks related to the eruption and collapse of five nested calderas within the Kawich caldera complex. The calderas discharged at least 200 cubic miles of ash across an area no less than 12,000 square miles about 23 million years ago. North of the highway, the hills and peaks capped by black basalt are underlain by slightly older tuff that originated about 26.8 million years ago from the formation and collapse of the Kiln Canyon caldera, another component of the Central Nevada caldera complex.

At Warm Springs, groundwater with a temperature of 140°F emerges from a fault that runs along the base of the Paleozoic limestone outcrops west of US 6. Beginning in 1866, this water was used for bathing by travelers, and until the 1990s the now-abandoned site supported a gas station and bathhouse. Water at Warm Springs is highly mineralized with calcium carbonate and other minerals, suggesting that it migrates through deeply buried limestone before it surfaces.

An active normal fault along the bold eastern escarpment of the Hot Creek Range has lifted the mountain block several thousand feet relative to the valley. Layers of Paleozoic limestone and shale are exposed in the higher parts of the range, including early Paleozoic continental shelf deposits over which rocks of the Nolan Belt have been thrust from the west.

Oil exploration began in Hot Creek Valley in 2012, with oil encountered about 6,000 feet deep in Oligocene to Miocene volcanic and sedimentary rocks. The source rock for the petroleum may be even more deeply buried late Paleozoic sedimentary rocks, primarily organic-rich shale of Mississippian age. The petroleum migrated upward into the overlying porous tuffs and sandstones, where it has saturated the rock. The oil reserves could be substantial because the overall geology resembles that of Railroad Valley, a major oil-producing region 40 miles to the northeast.

On the east side of Hot Creek Valley is a series of low cuestas and hills that form the Pancake Range. The gently tilted strata of mostly volcanic rocks are arranged in stacks—the inspiration for the name Pancake Range. East of Hot Creek a rest stop on the east near the Blue Jay maintenance station provides a good view of the spectacular escarpment of Palisade Mesa in the Pancake Range. Nearly 1,000 feet of Oligocene tuff is exposed in the cliff east of the highway, and several distinctive units are easily discerned, all associated with the violent volcanic blasts related to the Central Nevada caldera complex.

Halligan Mesa, to the north of Sandy Summit, consists of east-tilted tuff layers capped by a dark-colored basalt lava flow about 10 million years old. East of Sandy Summit, Big Sand Springs Valley extends into the distance to the north as US 6 winds through the Pancake Range tablelands.

As US 6 climbs the west side of Black Rock Summit, it passes cinder cones and black basalt flows that cap older Miocene volcanic rocks. Southwest of the road, Lunar Lake playa can be seen in the distance, surrounded by basalt flows and cinder cones. Northeast of the highway at the summit, near the radio transmission tower, the blocky crags are masses of altered Paleozoic sedimentary rocks resting on, and partly embedded in, Miocene to Oligocene tuff. These

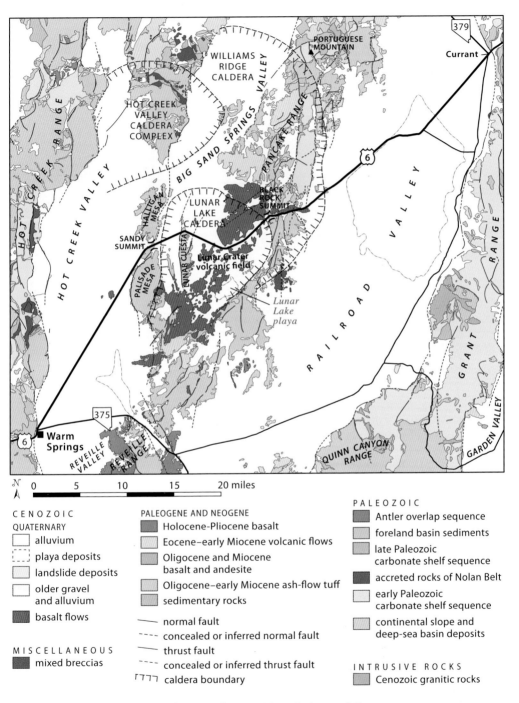

Geology along US 6 between Warm Springs and Currant.

CENOZOIC

QUATERNARY
- alluvium
- playa deposits
- landslide deposits
- older gravel and alluvium
- basalt flows

MISCELLANEOUS
- mixed breccias

PALEOGENE AND NEOGENE
- Holocene-Pliocene basalt
- Eocene–early Miocene volcanic flows
- Oligocene and Miocene basalt and andesite
- Oligocene–early Miocene ash-flow tuff
- sedimentary rocks

— normal fault
--- concealed or inferred normal fault
— thrust fault
--- concealed or inferred thrust fault
⊤⊤⊤⊤ caldera boundary

PALEOZOIC
- Antler overlap sequence
- foreland basin sediments
- late Paleozoic carbonate shelf sequence
- accreted rocks of Nolan Belt
- early Paleozoic carbonate shelf sequence
- continental slope and deep-sea basin deposits

INTRUSIVE ROCKS
- Cenozoic granitic rocks

rocks probably became associated when the walls of a caldera collapsed inward. In the summit area, roadside exposures are pinkish-brown to light-gray rhyolitic welded tuffs. A few miles to the northeast, US 6 crosses the margins of the Lunar Lake and Williams Ridge–Hot Creek Valley calderas, three overlapping calderas on the northeast margin of the Central Nevada caldera complex.

Oligocene tuff units exposed in the western escarpment of Palisade Mesa, east of US 6 in the vicinity of the Blue Jay maintenance station. The dark brown unit at the top is a welded tuff about 27.5 million years old. The well-developed system of vertical columns in the thick brown tuff formed as the hot ash cooled and contracted about 30 million years ago. Below the columnar-jointed tuff, a thin, black stripe of glassy vitrophyre represents an earlier flow of glowing ash that became densely welded. Below the black layer, a thick unit of lightly welded tuff formed from an ash-flow that came to rest at this location about 31 million years ago.

View northeast from US 6 near Black Rock Summit. The brown crags are blocks of Paleozoic rock incorporated into Oligocene to Miocene tuff near the margin of the Lunar Lake caldera.

East from Black Rock Summit, US 6 follows a black basalt flow that caps tuff and ashy rubble that accumulated near the edge of the calderas. Just southeast of Black Rock Station (Locke ranch), the highway passes between hills composed of tuff of late Oligocene age that includes a densely welded, dark-colored glassy tuff, a vitrophyre, near road level.

Railroad Valley is one of the largest interior basins in the Basin and Range Province. During the Pleistocene Epoch, Railroad Valley was the floor of Lake Railroad, the largest lake in the southern Great Basin. The most recent high stand of Lake Railroad was about 16,000 years ago, when the water was several

LUNAR CRATER VOLCANIC FIELD

About 6 miles east of Sandy Summit, US 6 intersects a gravel road leading south into the Lunar Crater volcanic field. Near this intersection, you can see very young black basalt flows and cinder cones north and south of the road. Head south to see more of this large expanse of seventy cinder cones, lava flows, and groundwater explosion craters known as maars. The outpouring of basalt lava oozed to the surface over the past few million years along a northeast-trending fissure zone that may extend as far south as the Death Valley region. This lava was hot and very fluid compared to that which fueled the caldera-forming eruptions 36 to 24 million years ago. The much younger basalt flows commonly have inclusions (known as xenoliths) of ultramafic rocks, such as dunite, that may represent deep mantle materials. Large crystals of olivine, pyroxene, and hornblende also occur in some of the basalts.

The eruptions also appear to have occurred in intense bursts separated by periods of little activity. The most recent pulse of volcanic activity took place between 1.5 and 0.5 million years ago, followed by a lull in eruptions that, other than a few exceptions, continues to modern times. Volcanic activity may return to the Lunar Craters volcanic field in the future. The magma is probably still there, deep underground, waiting for extensional stresses in the Great Basin to weaken the overlying lithosphere.

View north of US 6 in the vicinity of the Lunar Craters volcanic field of a Quaternary cinder cone and associated black basalt flow that may be as young as a few thousand years.

hundred feet deep and the waves produced subtle beach ridges and gravel spits along the shore. A variety of fish inhabited Lake Railroad, most of which became extinct when the lake disappeared at the beginning of Holocene time about 10,000 years ago. However, one small yellowish species, the Railroad Valley springfish (*Crenichthys nevadae*) still survives in the thermal springs, having adapted to hot springs concentrated at the toes of alluvial fans.

Beneath the surface of Railroad Valley, as much as 12,000 feet of alluvial sediments have accumulated above downfaulted blocks of bedrock. In 1954, Nevada's first oil was discovered in Railroad Valley at Eagle Springs, when an exploration well encountered petroleum in fractured Oligocene welded tuff more than 6,000 feet below the surface. Subsequent exploration led to more discoveries from a variety of subsurface reservoir rocks, including lake-deposited limestone and shale of Eocene age and Paleozoic marine limestone and shale. A single oil field discovered in the valley in 1983, the Grant Canyon field, tripled Nevada's oil production.

Much of the oil under the surface in Railroad Valley originates in organic-rich lakebeds of Eocene age buried at a depth where temperatures are high enough to accelerate the maturation of petroleum but not too high to break down the valuable hydrocarbons. Mississippian black shale under the valley also contributes organic matter to the oil accumulation.

On the east side of Railroad Valley, the Grant Range rises to a high point of 11,313 feet at Troy Peak, 6,500 feet above the valley floor. The bedrock includes one of the most complete sequences of Paleozoic carbonate shelf strata in Nevada, ranging in age from Cambrian to Permian. The entire rock sequence has been uplifted and tilted eastward by a normal fault along the western base of the Grant Range. Some segments of this fault system cut very young alluvial fan deposits.

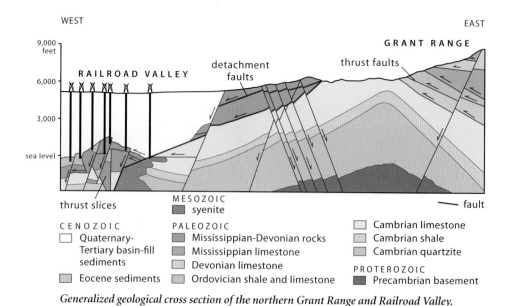

Generalized geological cross section of the northern Grant Range and Railroad Valley.

The Grant Range is broadly arched upward and deformed by several low-angle faults that cut through the thick rock succession. Some of these faults appear to be related to thrusts of the Sevier Orogeny of Cretaceous time, while others have displacement more typical of mid-Cenozoic detachment faults associated with the younger metamorphic core complexes. The detachment faults dip east and west from the axis of the Grant Range and probably continue in the subsurface of Railroad Valley, where they have been downfaulted by the range-front normal faults. The overall geologic structure of the Grant Range is similar to a metamorphic core complex, except that the exhumed rocks have not risen from such deep crustal levels.

Southeast of Currant, the reddish-brown Ragged Ridge descends from the higher parts of the Grant Range to the floor of Railroad Valley. Exposed along the eastern slope of the ridge is a thick succession of Pliocene sandstone, shale, tuff, and conglomerate overlying several east-tilted units of Oligocene to Miocene tuff.

Northeast of Currant, US 6 ascends the drainage of Currant Creek, passing exposures of Oligocene to Miocene tuff and sedimentary rocks south of the road. Northeast of the highway, the higher slopes consists of faulted Paleozoic strata, mostly limestone and dolomite of the southern White Pine Range. The contrast in rocks north and south of the highway is attributable to an east-northeasterly trending zone of geologic discontinuity that roughly follows the alignment of US 6 here. Some geologists have interpreted this zone as a strike-slip fault, part of the Pritchard Station lineament. However, recent studies of the faulting at the south end of the White Pine Range have led other geologists to conclude that this discontinuity is attributable to a low-angle detachment fault that places the Paleozoic rocks on the north against the Cenozoic strata to the south.

About 4 to 5 miles northeast of Currant, US 6 passes north of the low hills and slopes of sedimentary rock deposited in the Horse Camp basin. As extensional faulting in this part of the Great Basin developed, the downfaulted Horse Camp basin received sand, silt, gravel, and slide blocks of older rock derived from adjacent uplands. Approximately 10,000 feet of such sediment accumulated in Horse Camp basin during the Miocene and Pliocene Epochs, indicating rapid subsidence and very active normal faulting.

About 7 miles northeast of Currant, US 6 enters a narrow and winding canyon cut through Cambrian shale and limestone. Roadcuts expose thin-bedded shales containing fossils of trilobites and other primitive marine organisms. The higher cliffs are mostly thick layers of limestone deposited in warm shallow seas. An outcrop of jasperoid occurs in a fault in the Paleozoic rock about a half mile east of the intersection with Currant Creek Road. About 4 miles west of Currant Summit, US 6 passes through outcrops of the Currant stock, a granitic intrusion that formed beneath exploding volcanoes some 40 million years ago. The stock is emplaced into Paleozoic strata and is highly altered and fractured.

At Currant Summit, Oligocene tuff and ash-rich sediments are exposed in roadcuts. These volcanic rocks are faulted against gently folded Paleozoic

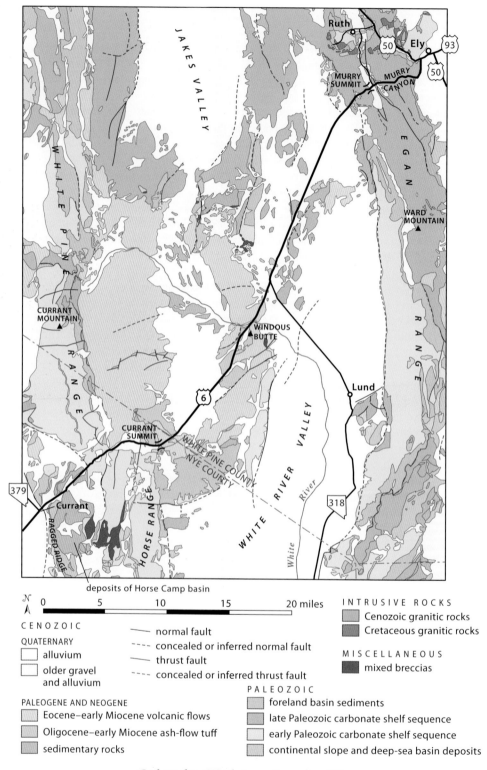

Geology along US 6 between Currant and Ely.

Map labels:

Ruth
Ely
50
93
50
MURRY SUMMIT
MURRY CANYON
JAKES VALLEY
EGAN RANGE
WARD MOUNTAIN
WHITE PINE RANGE
CURRANT MOUNTAIN
WINDOUS BUTTE
6
Lund
CURRANT SUMMIT
WHITE PINE COUNTY
NYE COUNTY
WHITE RIVER VALLEY
379
Currant
RAGGED RIDGE
318
HORSE RANGE
White River
deposits of Horse Camp basin

Legend:

N

0   5   10   15   20 miles

CENOZOIC

QUATERNARY
- alluvium
- older gravel and alluvium

——— normal fault
- - - concealed or inferred normal fault
——— thrust fault
- - - concealed or inferred thrust fault

PALEOGENE AND NEOGENE
- Eocene–early Miocene volcanic flows
- Oligocene–early Miocene ash-flow tuff
- sedimentary rocks

INTRUSIVE ROCKS
- Cenozoic granitic rocks
- Cretaceous granitic rocks

MISCELLANEOUS
- mixed breccias

PALEOZOIC
- foreland basin sediments
- late Paleozoic carbonate shelf sequence
- early Paleozoic carbonate shelf sequence
- continental slope and deep-sea basin deposits

Roadside outcrop of Cambrian shale west of Currant Summit along US 6 in the southern White Pine Range. The inset trilobite fossil is 1 inch wide.

Jasperoid, a dense silica-rich rock, typically develops along faults and fractures in limestone and dolomite.

limestone strata in the Horse Range, south of the summit. The fault is part of the Pritchard Station lineament. Near the White Pine–Nye county line, US 6 passes tuffs and lava flows of the White Pine caldera, the northernmost of the Central Nevada caldera complex.

For several miles north of the White Pine–Nye county line, the view west from US 6 is dominated by the eastern slope of the White Pine Range, a fault-block mountain of Paleozoic rock. The highest point is a craggy exposure of bare Devonian limestone. The lower slopes of the range and the undulating hills between the highway and the mountains are mostly Oligocene to Miocene volcanic rock. Though it is difficult to see from the road, a major detachment fault slices across the bedding in the Paleozoic rocks of the White Pine Range and extends into the overlying Cenozoic materials. The fault developed in the earliest Miocene Epoch, when extensional faulting began in this part of the Basin and Range Province.

About 9 miles north of the White Pine–Nye county line, the highway passes Windous Butte to the east, which consists of ash-flow tuff blown from a vent in the Central Nevada caldera complex 30 million years ago. Near the top of the butte, a dark-colored glassy vitrophyre documents the accumulation of extremely hot ash from what must have been a fiery cloud roaring across the ancient landscape.

In the vicinity of Windous Butte, light-colored tuff and ash-rich sediments are exposed in roadcuts, gullies, and low hills. The lake-deposited, ash-rich sediments contain the mineral magnesite, a magnesium carbonate, concentrated in nodules and pockets. In the 1940s, exceptionally pure magnesite was mined

Windous Butte, east of US 6, is composed of several layers of Oligocene tuff, including the dark vitrophyre at the base of the capping ledge.

from open pits east of US 6, but the operations have been inactive in recent decades.

A little more than 3 miles south of its intersection with NV 318, US 6 passes over the upper end of the White River. To the southeast, you can see the northern White River Valley receding into the distance. Though the White River is a small, discontinuous stream, it is remarkable in that it is a tributary of the Colorado River, not part of the internally drained Great Basin.

About 3 miles north of the junction with NV 318, US 6 passes through a series of hills of thin- to medium-bedded limestone of Permian age, capped in places by brownish Oligocene volcanic rocks. Beyond these hills to the west, east-dipping limestone layers of Devonian and Mississippian age compose the ridge that parallels the highway. East of the highway, the Egan Range rises to 10,936 feet at Ward Mountain, the highest peak along the nearly level skyline east of the highway. On the range's western slope, rugged exposures of Devonian limestone pass upward into terraced outcrops of Mississippian shale and limestone, and Pennsylvanian limestone makes up the top of the range. Covering the lower slopes of the Egan Range northwest of the highway, you can see the extensive tailings and heaps of waste rock from the enormous open-pit mines at Ruth.

Where US 6 crosses over the Egan Range, about 6 miles west of Ely, rocks exposed near the road in the vicinity of Murry Summit are Permian limestone, yellowish-red siltstone, and gypsum. These sediments originated in very shallow water as the Paleozoic seas that covered this part of Nevada began to recede to the west some 265 million years ago. Just east of Murry Summit, the road to Ward Mountain Recreation Area joins US 6 from the south. Here, the highway crosses a prominent down-to-the-east normal fault that displaces Paleogene sedimentary rocks against Permian limestone. The Paleogene sediments accumulated in alluvial fans and river valleys following the uplift and erosion of land elevated during the Sevier Orogeny in late Cretaceous time. These sediments accumulated in many localized basins throughout east-central Nevada, but later faulting disrupted most of them into small fault-bounded exposures similar to those near Murry Summit.

The dipping Devonian and Ordovician rocks layers in the Egan Range north of Lund are capped by more gently dipping Mississippian and Pennsylvanian rocks.

East of Murry Summit, US 6 descends through rugged, winding Murry Canyon toward Ely. Cliff-forming Pennsylvanian and Permian limestone are exposed along the road and in the upper walls of the canyon.

US 50
Lake Tahoe—Carson City—Fallon
90 miles

If you are traveling east on US 50 from California, you may feel like you've crossed over the Sierra Nevada when you reach South Lake Tahoe, but you still must cross the Carson Range, the physiographic boundary between the Sierra Nevada and Basin and Range Provinces. The bedrock in the Carson Range is primarily Cretaceous granite with some Mesozoic metamorphic rocks, essentially the same as the Sierra Nevada. US 50 passes over the Carson Range at Spooner Summit, but you can get a great look at the bedrock by taking a side trip on NV 207 to Daggett Pass. (For information about the Lake Tahoe Basin, see the road guide for NV 431.)

About 5 miles north of the resorts and casinos of South Lake Tahoe, US 50 passes directly through a Miocene volcanic neck, the scenic Cave Rock. The two tunnels were excavated in 1931 and 1958. Cave Rock gets its name from

Cave Rock, a Miocene volcanic neck, through which US 50 passes along the eastern shore of Lake Tahoe. Note the vertical jointing in the dark-colored volcanic rock. Light-tan outcrops of Cretaceous granitic rock appear on the slope to the right (east) of Cave Rock.

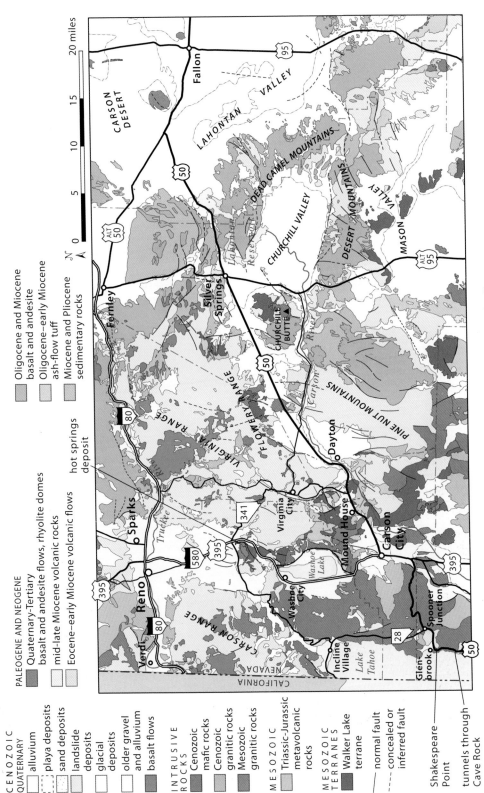

CENOZOIC
QUATERNARY
- alluvium
- playa deposits
- sand deposits
- landslide deposits
- glacial deposits
- older gravel and alluvium
- basalt flows

PALEOGENE AND NEOGENE
- Quaternary–Tertiary basalt and andesite flows, rhyolite domes
- mid-late Miocene volcanic rocks
- Eocene–early Miocene volcanic flows
- hot springs deposit

- Oligocene and Miocene basalt and andesite
- Oligocene–early Miocene ash-flow tuff
- Miocene and Pliocene sedimentary rocks

INTRUSIVE ROCKS
- Cenozoic mafic rocks
- Cenozoic granitic rocks
- Mesozoic granitic rocks

MESOZOIC
- Triassic–Jurassic metavolcanic rocks

MESOZOIC TERRANES
- Walker Lake terrane
- — normal fault
- --- concealed or inferred fault
- Shakespeare Point
- tunnels through Cave Rock

Geology along US 50 between Lake Tahoe and Fallon.

DAGGETT PASS OF THE KINGSBURY GRADE

From South Lake Tahoe, NV 207 climbs the western slope of the Carson Range via the Kingsbury Grade. The highway follows the historic Daggett Trail, which linked Genoa in the Carson Valley to the Mother Lode region of the Sierra Nevada in 1850s. The gray weathered rock in the roadcuts along NV 207 immediately east of its junction with US 50 is Cretaceous granodiorite.

Just east of Daggett Pass, roadcuts on the north side of NV 207 reveal some interesting relationships between two separate but intermingled masses of granodiorite that were emplaced at slightly different times during the Cretaceous Period as magma rose from the Farallon subduction zone. The slightly older granodiorite has more dark-colored minerals and a darker overall shade than the younger, lighter-colored granodiorite. Light-colored dikes and pods of rock streaking across both types of granodiorite represent magma that was forced into the granodiorite along fractures after it had crystallized. Some of the fracture-filling magma cooled to form aplite, a fine-grained igneous rock with very small crystals. Other veins are composed of pegmatite, an igneous rock with very large crystals of feldspar, quartz, and other minerals.

Light and dark granodiorite are intermingled in exposures along NV 207 east of Daggett Pass. In the close-up of the darker granodiorite, abundant black crystals of hornblende and biotite are sprinkled through the lighter-colored feldspar, mica, and quartz.

the several shallow caves cut on the south side of the precipice by waves during the Pleistocene ice ages. Several times during that epoch, the level of the prehistoric predecessor to Lake Tahoe was at least 140 feet higher than today. About 3.5 miles north of Cave Rock, US 50 rounds a prominent dark-colored peak known as Shakespeare Point, another volcanic neck that marks the vent of an ancient Miocene volcano.

The volcanic rocks, part of the Glenbrook volcanic center, erupted 8.7 million years ago, prior to the formation of the Lake Tahoe Basin. The mostly grayish-brown latite and andesite typically weather to dark brown, making the outcrops easy to distinguish from the lighter-colored granitic rock of the Carson Range. The volcanic rocks form craggy outcrops that tower above the highway in several places along US 50 in the vicinity of Glenbrook. Near the intersection of NV 28 and US 50, you can see knobs of brownish-gray volcanic rocks intruding and overlying the granodiorite along the mountain slopes descending to the road. Hydrothermal alteration of both the granitic and volcanic rock has produced colorful roadcuts and outcrops in this area. As hot solutions and vapors penetrated through the rock, iron-bearing minerals were altered to rusty-brown oxide minerals.

From 1861 to the late 1880s, Glenbrook was an important logging town. Tall trees from the forests surrounding Lake Tahoe were cut from the mountain slopes, floated by barge to the sawmill at Glenbrook, and cut into mining timbers that were in great demand in the Comstock mines around Virginia City to the east. As US 50 ascends the grade toward Spooner Summit from Spooner Junction, it closely follows the route of a narrow-gauge railway that transported lumber from the Glenbrook mills to the pass. From that point, the timbers were transported to the Carson Valley via a flume descending the eastern slope of the Carson Range, where they were placed on railcars for the final leg of the trip to the Comstock mining district. By the time mining operations declined in the 1880s, nearly all of the original forests surrounding Lake Tahoe had been clear-cut. The modern forests are primarily Jeffrey and ponderosa pines that have grown since the late 1800s.

From Spooner Summit to the Carson Valley, US 50 descends the eastern slope of the Carson Range, traveling almost entirely over light-colored granitic rocks of the Sierra Nevada batholith that crystallized deep underground 110 to 80 million years ago. Iron-bearing minerals in the granite weather into rusty-brown hematite, and the feldspars in the granite are converted into clay minerals, causing the granite to crumble and decay into light gray-brown granular material that accumulates at the base of the roadside exposures. In some of the roadcuts along US 50, resistant ledges of harder rock protrude through the weathered granite exposures. This rock is aplite, similar to granite in composition and origin but with a finer-grained texture that makes it more resistant to weathering. The aplite cooled from magmatic fluids migrating along fractures in the surrounding granite during, or shortly after, the time the granite was crystallizing. On the north side of US 50 halfway between Spooner Summit and Carson Valley, a small fault offsets a dark-colored dike cutting through Cretaceous granite of the Carson Range.

Roadcut near the intersection of NV 28 and US 50 along the east side of Lake Tahoe. The brownish rock is hydrothermally altered granodiorite in which iron-bearing minerals have been oxidized by hot fluids and vapors.

A resistant aplite dike cutting through weathered Cretaceous granite along US 50 east of Spooner Summit.

Carson Valley to Lahontan Reservoir

As US 50 descends the eastern slope of the Carson Range, the pine forests of the higher mountain slopes give way to the sagebrush-bitterbrush flora of the drier lowlands. This vegetation change is a classic example of the influence of the rain shadow of the Carson Range and Sierra Nevada. Precipitation east of the mountain crests is only a fraction of what is received at the higher elevations. Across the Carson Valley to the southeast rise the Pine Nut Mountains, which consist of Mesozoic plutonic rocks that have intruded older Mesozoic metamorphic rocks of the Pine Nut assemblage of the Walker Lake terrane. The Carson Range is much higher than the Pine Nut Mountains because faults along the base of the Carson Range are much more active. (See the US 395 road guide for an in-depth discussion of the Carson Valley and faulting there.)

East of Carson City, US 50 follows the valley of the Carson River to the northwest. Between Carson City and Mound House, you can see colorful outcrops of Cenozoic volcanic rocks in the upper slopes of the Virginia Range to the north. On the west side of Mound House, US 50 passes through an area where several mills were constructed in the late 1800s to process the ores mined in the Comstock district to the north at Virginia City. The mills utilized the flow of the Carson River to power ore-crushing machinery. (The geology and history of the Comstock Lode are discussed in more detail in the road guide for NV 341 and NV 342.)

Low roadcuts along US 50 expose dark-gray basalt cinders and small flows that are related to the volcanic activity in the Virginia Range. The volcanics overlie metamorphosed sedimentary rocks of Jurassic and Triassic age. In places, the Jurassic sedimentary rocks exposed in fault-bounded blocks and slices contain significant gypsum deposits.

Northeast of the junction with NV 341, US 50 and the Carson River follow a zone of left-lateral strike-slip faulting known as the Carson lineament. The rocks have been so sheared and weakened by the faulting that the Carson River was

Gypsum open-pit mine in the southern Virginia Range just north of US 50 in the Mound House area.

able to cut its canyon along the fault zone while the mountains on either side rose. As the crust stretched and the range-bounding faults developed between 10 and 3 million years ago, some areas were more actively extended than others. The Carson lineament developed to accommodate different rates of extension between the Pine Nut Mountains and the Wassuk Range to the east.

West of Dayton, US 50 bends south of Flowery Ridge, a small spur consisting mostly of Miocene andesite and dacite flows. From downtown Dayton, you can see Gold Canyon reaching into the Virginia Range to the northwest of US 50. Gold Canyon was the site of Nevada's first gold discovery in 1849, when small bits of gold were found in the sediments washed down from the higher ramparts of the Virginia Range. Such gold-rich stream sediments are called placers, and placer mining in Dayton was a booming activity in the early 1850s. When the Comstock Lode mining boom hit Virginia City, Dayton continued to thrive as a shipping, milling, and support center for the nearby mines. Remains of the Rock Point Mill, one of several mills in this area that processed Comstock Lode ore, are featured in Dayton State Park. Dayton also marks the shore of a bay in Pleistocene Lake Lahontan, from which the immense lake stretched through the lowlands to the north and east.

A low bench of waste rock north of US 50 about 2 miles northeast of Dayton marks the mouth of the Sutro Tunnel, built in 1870s to drain water from and ventilate the deep underground mines in Virginia City. Constructed over a period of nearly ten years, the tunnel was driven through 4 miles of mostly volcanic rock. The tunnel was a marvel of nineteenth-century engineering, but by the time the tunnel reached the mines, most of the largest shafts were deeper than the tunnel and the mining boom was beginning to diminish.

Near the intersection of US 50 and the Six Mile Canyon Road, a large excavation on the lower slopes of the Flowery Range is removing pumice and lightweight rhyolite from a very young, 1.5-million-year-old dome-like intrusion. The rock is used to manufacture lightweight concrete products. The rocks that make up the Flowery Range are mostly 14- to 10-million-year-old volcanic rocks, such as andesite and dacite, overlain by even younger volcanic rocks. Small-scale mining has produced more than 5,000 ounces of gold from vein deposits in the Flowery Range.

Eight miles northeast of Dayton, US 50 passes south of abandoned iron mines marked by the red-stained rocks visible on a small hill north of the highway. Some minor exploration of the iron ores here occurred in the 1950s, but there was never major production even though some 45 million tons of ore are thought to exist in the subsurface. The iron mineralization occurs in Triassic metamorphic rock that has been intruded by a body of granitic rock. A low roadcut along the highway as it passes over a rise near milepost 15 exposes the light-colored granite and the darker metamorphic rock adjacent to it.

East of the US 95A junction, US 50 passes Lahontan Reservoir, a body of water impounded by Lahontan Dam on the Carson River. This reservoir is commonly called Lahontan Lake, leading to some confusion between the reservoir and Lake Lahontan, the much larger lake that covered this part of Nevada during the Pleistocene ice ages. Shoreline terraces of the Pleistocene lake are prominent on hillsides adjacent to US 50 near the reservoir. Lahonton Dam

Shoreline terraces (horizontal lines) were carved by waves of Pleistocene Lake Lahontan on a hillside north of US 50 just west of Lahontan Reservoir.

was constructed in 1915 to capture and store Carson River water for agriculture in the Fallon area. This reservoir also receives some water diverted from the Truckee River to the north.

East of Lahontan Dam, US 50 transects a broad open plain, the southern margin of the vast lowland known as the Carson Desert. This brutally hot, dry basin stretches some 70 miles to the northeast to the Carson Sink, the natural terminus of the Carson River. Annual precipitation is less than 5 inches, and summer temperatures can soar well above 100°F. A scrappy flora of greasewood, shadscale, salt grass, and hopsage can be found in parts of the Carson Desert, but in the central playa, where the soil salinity is high, very few plants survive.

The Carson Desert was a major obstacle to the historic wagon trains following the Humboldt River in the 1800s. When immigrants reached the terminus of the river, which they had been following across the Great Basin for some 300 miles, they had two choices: head west toward the Truckee River or turn south across the heart of the Carson Desert to reach the Carson River. In either case, about 40 miles of desert had to be crossed. Ragtown, a small settlement west of Fallon, was named for the laundry of immigrants who managed to survive crossing the Carson Desert.

US 50
Fallon—Austin—Eureka—Ely
257 miles

In 1859, the US Corps of Topographical Engineers expedition led by James H. Simpson crossed the Great Basin twice, traveling west from Utah to the Carson Valley and then back to Salt Lake City. Both the inbound and outbound paths, though not identical, followed very closely the present alignment of US 50. One of Simpson's goals was to find a shorter, more direct route for wagon travel than the path along the Humboldt River. Simpson succeeded in this quest; not only was his route shorter by several hundred miles, it also offered better forage for

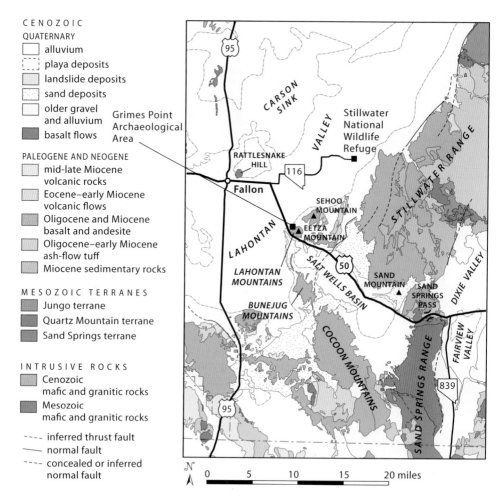

CENOZOIC

QUATERNARY

- alluvium
- playa deposits
- landslide deposits
- sand deposits
- older gravel and alluvium
- basalt flows

PALEOGENE AND NEOGENE

- mid-late Miocene volcanic rocks
- Eocene–early Miocene volcanic flows
- Oligocene and Miocene basalt and andesite
- Oligocene–early Miocene ash-flow tuff
- Miocene sedimentary rocks

MESOZOIC TERRANES

- Jungo terrane
- Quartz Mountain terrane
- Sand Springs terrane

INTRUSIVE ROCKS

- Cenozoic mafic and granitic rocks
- Mesozoic mafic and granitic rocks

- ---- inferred thrust fault
- —— normal fault
- ---- concealed or inferred normal fault

Geology along US 50 between Fallon and Sand Springs Pass.

draft animals and more abundant water. By 1860, the Pony Express utilized his westbound path in carrying the overland mail, and in 1861, the completion of the transcontinental telegraph lines, located very close to Simpson's route, helped establish a permanent path that was utilized by the Overland Mail Company from 1861 to 1869. When the Central Pacific Railroad was completed in 1869 along the Humboldt River to the north, the Overland Mail route lost much of its traffic, except for folks traveling between various mining camps and ranches through the late 1800s. These well-worn roads, especially the stretches from Fallon to Ely, were designated as parts of the historic Lincoln Highway, established in 1913, the first transcontinental road in the United States. So sparse is the human population along the modern US 50 that it has earned the nickname Loneliest Road in America, an epithet made official by an act of the Nevada state legislature in 1987.

Fallon is situated in Lahontan Valley, a broad lowland that was near the central part of Pleistocene Lake Lahontan. About 12,000 years ago this lowland was submerged beneath 450 feet of clear, cold water. After Lake Lahontan disappeared about 10,000 years ago, fertile silt, sand, and gravel deposited by the Carson River buried the lake deposits in many areas, and this alluvium provides the mineral nutrients for the rich agricultural soils here. Except in extremely dry years, the Carson River still flows to its terminus, about 15 miles north of Fallon, where a series of shallow lakes and marshes mark the final demise of the river. Most of these wetlands reside within Stillwater National Wildlife Refuge.

About 1 mile east of the Fallon city limits, US 50 passes just south of Rattlesnake Hill, a small mound of dark-colored basalt erupted onto the floor of Lahontan Valley. The basalt is similar to volcanic rock found in water wells drilled some 500 hundred feet below the valley. The basalt erupted in the Quaternary Period, after the oldest sediments of Lake Lahontan had accumulated in the basin but before deposition of the most recent Lake Lahontan sediments.

The Lahontan Mountains southeast of Fallon are composed of a thick series of Pliocene and younger volcanic rocks associated with sedimentary rocks. When Lake Lahontan reached its highest stages, the Lahontan Mountains were transformed into islands. The deep water stretched northwest from these islands for a distance of 50 miles or more. Prevailing winds howling over such an expansive lake surface generated powerful waves and currents that scoured the slopes of the islands. For this reason, Lahontan shoreline features are more prominent on the slopes of the Lahontan Mountains and the higher Stillwater Range immediately east of them than in many other slopes bordering this great ice age lake. Each one of the multiple horizontal terraces represents a time (probably thousands of years) when the ancient lake level was stable long enough for wave erosion to carve a notch into the hillside and deposit beach gravels or other sediments. Calcium carbonate deposits known as tufa are draped over the basalt bedrock at several different elevations, providing further evidence of ancient lake levels.

Geologists have carefully studied the variety of lake sediments in the Lahontan Mountains and have recognized multiple cycles of lake development and decline. The names of two peaks in the Lahontan Mountains, Sehoo and Eetza, are now used to designate specific stages in the lake's history. The Sehoo high stand occurred about 13,000 years ago, while the older but higher Eetza stand took place more than 140,000 years ago.

At Grimes Point in the Lahontan Mountains, about 12 miles southeast of Fallon, a parking lot and short trail off US 50 provide access to prehistoric rock carvings known as petroglyphs. Here, on boulders of basalt scattered around the lower slopes of the mountains, prehistoric people carved and chipped many symbols and figures into the rock by scraping off the dark-brown mineral coating known as desert varnish. This coating, which develops on rock surfaces that experience repetitive wetting and drying cycles, has a complex composition consisting of metal oxides mixed with clay minerals. Though the annual rainfall in the Grimes Point area is only about 5 inches per year, much of it comes in the form of thunderstorms that produce intense but brief and localized precipitation. After rock surfaces are moistened by thunderstorm cloudbursts, they dry quickly in the desert air, and this cycle repeats itself dozens of times each year. The recurring wetting and drying events lead to the formation of a few millimeters of dark-colored desert varnish. Hundreds or thousands of years are required for a significant layer of desert varnish to form. Such a thin coating can easily be chipped away with even primitive stone tools, exposing the lighter-colored, unweathered rock beneath.

The multiple styles of petroglyphs at Grimes Point suggest that they were probably carved over a period of time between 5,000 BC and 1500 AD. This time frame postdates the last maximum of Lake Lahontan (about 13,000 years ago), during which time Grimes Point was under several hundred feet of water. After the lake began to recede, there were probably many times when smaller lakes existed in the Carson Desert that were large enough to lap up on the lower slopes of the Lahontan Mountains. At such times, the Grimes Point Archaeological Area would have been a marshy area along the shoreline with many birds and animals.

The Grimes Point Archaeological Area also includes Hidden Cave, a pocket in the basalt bedrock about 1 mile northeast of the petroglyph area. Tufa deposits near the cave opening suggest that it probably formed from wave erosion dating back to Lake Lahontan times, some 20,000 years ago. This small cave has been excavated by archeologists several times since 1930, when thousands of artifacts were discovered that document human use of the opening as

Petroglyphs at Grimes Point. View looking northwest from the flanks of the Lahontan Mountains across the basin once submerged by Lake Lahontan and younger Holocene lakes.

a cache for food and implements. In 1940, human remains were discovered at an ancient burial site in Spirit Cave, also located in the Lahontan Mountains. These remains were originally estimated be less than 2,000 years old, but radiocarbon dating in 1996 yielded an age of 9,400 carbon-14 years (equivalent to more than 11,000 calendar years). The new date suggests that people may have been present along the shore of Lake Lahontan about the time that it began its final recession.

Southeast from Grimes Point, US 50 skirts the northern edge of the Salt Wells Basin, to the south of which lie the Bunejug and Cocoon Mountains, consisting mostly of multiple flows of Miocene basalt and andesite. The facility visible to the south of US 50, across the playa at the base of the Bunejug Mountains, is a geothermal power plant. Groundwater 250 to 700 feet below the surface at this location has a maximum temperature of 292°F. Subsurface water this hot will flash into high-pressure steam at the surface, making it feasible to produce electricity by using steam-driven generating turbines.

The salt on the surface of the playa is processed at the evaporation plant seen south of the road near the eastern end of the Salt Wells Basin. This area has been producing salt since 1863, when it was in demand for processing of silver ores in the Comstock region to the west. The salt is a renewable resource because groundwater moving up through salt-laden sediments evaporates at the surface. Today, salt produced here is used in road deicing and livestock feed.

View south from US 50 across the surface of the Salt Wells playa toward the Cocoon Mountains, in the distance.

Elsewhere in the Salt Wells Basin, another saline mineral, ulexite, a borate mineral useful in a variety of chemical products, was discovered in 1870 and produced from the lake sediments until the deposits were exhausted.

Near the eastern end of the Salt Wells Basin, US 50 passes south of a spectacular accumulation of windblown sand known as Sand Mountain, which rises some 600 feet. The dunes consist of very pure quartz sand carried to this site by strong prevailing winds that blow from the southwest, across the surface of the Salt Wells playa. As these winds are forced upward over the southern Stillwater Range, the fine sand particles settle out in the Sand Mountain dune complex as the wind loses horizontal speed. Some of the sand originates as far as 40 miles away, where the Walker River discharged into Pleistocene Lake Lahontan. Sand and silt washed into the immense lake formed a delta there, and after the lake disappeared, the unconsolidated delta sediments were easily moved by strong winds. This region still experiences strong desert sand and dust storms from time to time, and the sand in Sand Mountain is perpetually on the move. The stone remains of the Sand Springs Pony Express and stage station, which were excavated from the sand in 1976, can be visited in the Sand Mountain Recreation Area.

Just east of the entrance to the Sand Mountain Recreation Area, US 50 passes a ridge of basalt on which numerous terraces of Lake Lahontan are visible. Some of these ancient shorelines are encrusted with tufa, knobby masses of calcium carbonate precipitated from the lake water during Lake Lahontan's most recent high stand. Shoreline features are present on the hills adjacent to the highway for several more miles east from the Sand Mountain area.

At Sand Springs Pass, the platy black rocks in roadcuts on both side of the road are Triassic shales metamorphosed into shiny phyllite and slate. These metamorphic rocks are part of the Sand Springs terrane, a sequence of mostly deep-sea deposits that were deformed during accretion from the west or north. Light-colored dikes of younger rhyolite cut through the dark metamorphic rocks on both sides of the road near the summit.

Sand Mountain, north of US 50 at the southern end of the Stillwater Range.

Interactions between the older Mesozoic metasedimentary rocks in the vicinity of Sand Springs Pass and the younger igneous masses that have intruded them have led to some silver and gold mineralization. South of the road you can see the remains of the Summit King Mine on the slopes of the Sand Springs Range. This currently inactive mining area produced about $2 million worth of silver and gold between 1905 and 1951. Scheelite, an ore of the valuable metal tungsten, was also mined in this area until about 1956.

Lake Lahontan shoreline terraces on the slopes of the Stillwater Range east of Sand Mountain.

A rhyolite dike cuts across dark-colored Triassic slate and phyllite of the Sand Springs terrane on the north side of US 50 west of Sand Springs Pass.

Sand Springs Pass to Austin

From Sand Springs Pass to Austin, US 50 transects a portion of the Nevada landscape strongly affected by explosive volcanism in mid-Cenozoic time. Cataclysmic explosive eruptions blasted enormous clouds of ash and volcanic rubble across thousands of square miles. Because these eruptions preceded the normal faulting that created the modern mountain ranges, only portions of the calderas and the tuff, breccia, and lava flows that filled them are preserved here. However, geologists have reconstructed the original outlines of the ancient calderas, and there are at least a dozen near US 50 between the Stillwater Range and the Toiyabe Range. This region is also in the Central Nevada seismic belt, a northeast-trending zone of active extensional faulting that has produced some of the largest historic earthquakes in Nevada. Studies of the fault zones associated with these earthquakes have provided evidence of at least thirteen strong earthquakes since late Pleistocene time, approximately 100,000 years ago.

East from Sand Springs Summit, US 50 descends into Fairview Valley, across which you can see Fairview Peak, the highest peak to the southeast. Fairview Peak, and the entire mountain mass of which it is part, is composed of several thick units of rhyolitic tuff and rhyolite domes that filled the Fairview caldera after it was created by a massive volcanic explosion 19.5 million years ago. This elongated caldera was more than 10 miles wide in an east-west direction.

Near the intersection of US 50 with NV 839, the view north reveals the gently dipping Miocene basalt and andesite flows of the Stillwater Range overlying light-colored lakebeds, also of Miocene age. The floor of Fairview Valley is the site of an active bombing range as part of the training done at Naval Air Station Fallon. It is not uncommon to see military aircraft swoop into the valley at high speeds on simulated combat training missions.

During Late Pleistocene time, Lake Dixie existed in Dixie Valley and Lake Labou in Fairview Valley. Neither of these lakes were part of the Lake Lahontan system, as they never rose high enough to surmount Sand Springs Pass, to the west. They were, however, substantial lakes, and at their last peak some 15,000 years ago, Lake Dixie stretched north to south for more than 40 miles through the lowest part of Dixie Valley. Earlier in the Pleistocene Epoch, the lake in Dixie Valley rose high enough to merge with ancestral Lake Labou, creating a unified body of water more than 100 miles long.

East of Dixie and Fairview Valleys, US 50 passes just south of Chalk Mountain, a strikingly multicolored peak composed mostly of Mesozoic dolomite, a sedimentary rock similar to limestone. It is not chalk! The Chalk Mountain sedimentary rocks, as well as those exposed to the east in the Clan Alpine Mountains, belong to the Paradise terrane, a rock mass accreted east of the Sand Springs terrane. The dark-colored splotch on the western face of Chalk Mountain is a mass of granitic rock that intruded the dolomite and converted much of it to marble. Some mining, mainly for lead and zinc in the contact zone, occurred on the southeast side of Chalk Mountain in the 1920s.

US 50 passes through West Gate and Middlegate, narrow gaps in the southern end of the Clan Alpine Mountains. When Captain James Simpson explored

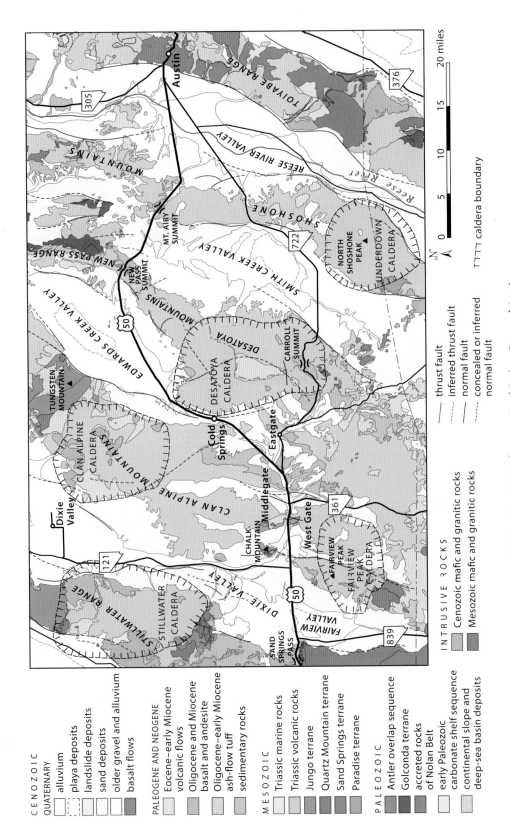

Geology along US 50 between Sand Springs Pass and Austin

CENOZOIC
QUATERNARY
alluvium
playa deposits
landslide deposits
sand deposits
older gravel and alluvium
basalt flows

PALEOGENE AND NEOGENE
Eocene–early Miocene volcanic flows
Oligocene and Miocene basalt and andesite
Oligocene–early Miocene ash-flow tuff
sedimentary rocks

MESOZOIC
Triassic marine rocks
Triassic volcanic rocks
Jungo terrane
Quartz Mountain terrane
Sand Springs terrane
Paradise terrane

PALEOZOIC
Antler overlap sequence
Golconda terrane
accreted rocks of Nolan Belt
early Paleozoic carbonate shelf sequence
continental slope and deep-sea basin deposits

INTRUSIVE ROCKS
Cenozoic mafic and granitic rocks
Mesozoic mafic and granitic rocks

thrust fault
inferred thrust fault
normal fault
concealed or inferred normal fault
ꛀꛀꛀ caldera boundary

N

0   5   10   15   20 miles

View northeast from US 50 of Chalk Mountain. The dark-colored blotch in the middle slope is a granitic intrusion into the tilted layers of dolomite. The Clan Alpine Mountains appear in the distance.

this region in 1859, he named the narrow, rocky passages his party passed through "gates." The Clan Alpine Mountains consist mostly of a thick succession of Miocene volcanic rocks related to the Clan Alpine caldera in the central part of the range. Where US 50 passes through West Gate, Triassic and Jurassic limestone and shale are exposed on the hillside and in crags on both sides of the road. These Mesozoic sedimentary rocks are cut and overlain by Miocene rhyolite tuffs and flows that make up the pillars seen from US 50 near Middlegate. Hydrothermal alteration of the older sedimentary rocks at the southern end of the Clan Alpine Mountains, probably during the intense volcanic activity of the Miocene Epoch, led to some silver, lead, and gold mineralization.

Near the junction of US 50 and NV 722, hills composed of light-colored lake sediments of Miocene age are on both sides of the highway. This clay and silt washed into small lakes between the active volcanic highlands some

11-27-20

SCARP OF THE 1954 FAIRVIEW PEAK EARTHQUAKE

About 2 miles east of the junction with NV 121, a Bureau of Land Management sign labels a gravel road leading south from US 50 as Fairview Peak Earthquake Faults. The 6-mile detour will reward travelers with a view of a 20-foot-high scarp, the ground rupture of the earthquakes that occurred on December 16, 1954. The Fairview Peak earthquake was magnitude 7.2 and was followed four minutes later by a magnitude 7.1 event on the west side of Dixie Valley to the northwest. The fault scarp along the eastern base of Fairview Peak is the product of both vertical displacement (from 7 to 20 feet) as well as horizontal movement (3 to 13 feet) during the earthquake. Many other large earthquakes have occurred on similar faults in this part of Nevada. In 1915, three strong earthquakes occurred within seven hours in the Pleasant Valley area, 50 miles north of US 50. The largest of these quakes was magnitude 7.75 and damaged structures in Lovelock and Winnemucca. In December of 1932, a magnitude 7.3 earthquake shook the uninhabited region around the Cedar Mountains, some 65 miles southeast of Fairview Peak.

11-27-20

NV 722 THROUGH THE DESATOYA CALDERA

NV 722, an even lonelier highway than US 50, loops south from US 50 before rejoining it near Austin. This scenic side trip winds along the rugged canyon of Buffalo Creek eastward as it climbs toward Carroll Summit over the Desatoya Mountains and then descends along the equally spectacular canyon of Campbell Creek to Smith Creek Valley on the east side. As it curves through the mountains, the highway crosses a 2,000-foot-thick section of ash-flow tuff that thins abruptly in all directions. It erupted from the nearby Desatoya caldera. The eruption blasted out and then filled an enormous 20-mile-long by 12-mile-wide crater with tuff about 25 million years ago. In places the rhyolitic ash-flow tuffs display columnar jointing, and where they are welded, rock fragments are flattened by the weight and heat of the hot ash.

Narrow columnar jointing in rhyolitic tuff along Campbell Creek about 4 miles east of Carroll Summit. The spacing between joints is about 8 inches. The close-up shows flattened clasts in the tuff.

This massive Miocene-age tuff, exposed 1 mile east of Carroll Summit, consists of volcanic ash and rock fragments produced during violent eruptions of the Desatoya caldera. The tuff is not welded and the matrix still appears ashy. The dark, horizontal fragment near the center of the close-up is about 1.5 inches long.

NV 722 passes just south of the playa in Smith Creek Valley, and shorelines are visible in the hills along the eastern edge of the playa, southeast of the road. The prominent vertical cliff face in tuffs to the north of the road, as it curves east to the climb over the next range to the east, aligns with the highest Pleistocene shoreline farther north. It looks like another wave-cut feature but is probably a Quaternary-age fault scarp, perhaps touched up by the waves of the Pleistocene lake.

15 million years ago. The sediments contain significant amounts of volcanic ash, from which unique minerals known as zeolites have developed. Zeolites have an atomic structure that makes them useful for water filtration, as absorbants, and as catalysts in a variety of chemical industries. The numerous pits and cuts along US 50 near its junction with NV 722 are scars of zeolite mining. Erionite and clinoptilolite, the two most common zeolite minerals in the Miocene lakebeds, formed through chemical reactions between volcanic ash particles and alkaline lake water or groundwater.

In the vicinity of the highway maintenance station at Cold Springs, US 50 passes between two large caldera complexes named for the mountains dominated by their rocks and structures: the Clan Alpine caldera on the west and the Desatoya caldera on the east. The main eruption of the Desatoya caldera occurred between 29 and 25 million years ago, while the explosive activity in the Clan Alpine Mountain to the west occurred about 25 million years ago. Some of the tuff units, formed when ash blown from these calderas settled to the surface, can be traced to the California-Nevada border and beyond. Thousands of feet of such volcanic material make up the central portions of both the Clan Alpine and the Desatoya Mountains.

The lowest (northern) end of the enclosed Edwards Creek Valley is usually dry, but shallow water sometimes collects after heavy rain or rapid snow melting. During the late Pleistocene ice ages, Edwards Creek Valley was occupied by Lake Edwards, an isolated lake about 250 feet deep at its maximum stage of development.

Hot springs associated with the range-front normal fault have hydrothermally altered volcanic rock along the foothills of the Clan Alpine Mountains. Look for light-colored masses in the slopes to the west of the highway. The chemistry of the hot water suggests that subsurface temperatures could reach nearly 350°F, hot enough for electrical power generation. Elsewhere in the Clan Alpine Mountains, relatively small bodies of Mesozoic plutonic rock were intruded into older Mesozoic sedimentary rocks before the great caldera-forming eruptions occurred. Some mineralization occurred near the margins of the Mesozoic intrusions, including the formation of tungsten ores in the region around Tungsten Mountain, the peak visible on the western skyline across the Edwards Creek Valley playa.

The rocks exposed in the canyon leading up to New Pass Summit are several different layers of 30- to 22-million-year-old tuff, some of it blown from calderas 100 miles or more away. Some of the tuffs here are weakly consolidated and crumbly, while others are firmly welded into a dense reddish-brown rock. Gold and turquoise have been mined north of New Pass Summit from narrow quartz veins that penetrate through both the tuffs and the underlying older rocks.

East of New Pass Summit, you can see Smith Creek Valley receding into the southern distance. During the late Pleistocene Epoch, Smith Creek Valley was the site of Lake Desatoya, which was larger and deeper than Lake Edwards to the west. Though these two lakes were isolated from each other in the late Pleistocene, it is possible that Lake Desatoya rose high enough in the earlier Pleistocene to spill over New Pass into Lake Edwards.

At Mt. Airy Summit, a low rise over the northern end of the Shoshone Mountains, the slopes and hills north of the highway are Oligocene and Miocene tuff. Some of the welded ash-flow tuff layers developed crude vertical columns called columnar jointing. When magma or hot ash cools uniformly and the liquid or particles contract while hardening, the loss of volume causes cracks to open that eventually penetrate the entire layer perpendicular to the cooling surface, usually the top and bottom of the layer.

The Toiyabe Range, one of Nevada's largest mountain ranges, extends from north to south more than 120 miles. The highest southern portion of the

A faulted exposure of Oligocene tuff in a roadcut along US 50 west of New Pass Summit. The light-colored tuff is weakly consolidated, while the darker colored tuff is more firmly welded. The dark rock at the left is in fault contract with the lighter tuff.

This hill, north of US 50 in the vicinity of Mt. Airy Summit, is composed of layered tuffs of late Oligocene and early Miocene age. The brown cliff in the upper slope is an ash-flow tuff with crude columnar jointing.

Range experienced glaciation during the Pleistocene ice ages, a rarity among the mountains of central Nevada. The bedrock consists of a tangled mass of mostly deformed Paleozoic (and some Mesozoic) sedimentary rocks arranged in numerous thrust slices intruded by several granitic plutons of mostly Jurassic and Cretaceous age. Thick accumulations of Oligocene and Miocene ash-flow tuff overlie the older rocks and are themselves overlain by younger basaltic flows in some places.

Austin to Eureka

Just east of its junction with NV 722, the highway passes the historic Austin cemetery and the intersection with NV 305 (discussed elsewhere in this volume), which follows the Reese River north to Battle Mountain. East of this intersection, US 50 passes through Pony Canyon, where the bedrock is Jurassic granodiorite. Roadcuts north of the road on the western outskirts of Austin expose light-gray granitic rock cut by numerous intersecting veins of quartz.

Silver ores were first discovered in Austin in 1862, only a couple of years after the great Comstock Lode mining boom in Virginia City near Reno. By 1867, eleven mills were processing ore from mines on the slopes above the town, and the population approached 10,000. At this time, most of central Nevada was unsettled, and Austin played an important role as the population center of the region. However, by 1872 the richest ores had been nearly exhausted and only two mills remained active in Austin. The historic city experienced further decline in the late 1880s, as new mining camps boomed in other parts of Nevada. The ore mined in Austin was primarily silver-bearing sulfide minerals

Light-gray Jurassic granodiorite in this US 50 roadcut just west of Austin is crossed by intersecting quartz veins.

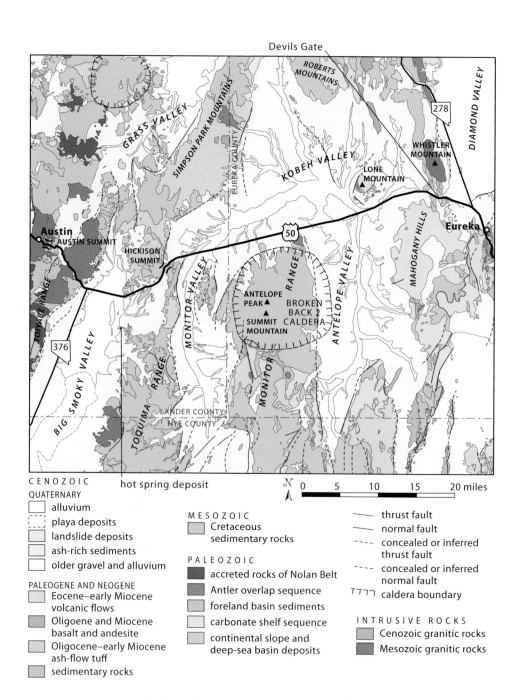

Devils Gate

ROBERTS
MOUNTAINS

DIAMOND VALLEY

GRASS VALLEY

SIMPSON PARK MOUNTAINS

EUREKA COUNTY

KOBEH VALLEY

278

WHISTLER
MOUNTAIN ▲

LONE
MOUNTAIN ▲

Eureka

Austin
AUSTIN SUMMIT

HICKISON
SUMMIT

50

MAHOGANY HILLS

TOIYABE RANGE

376

MONITOR VALLEY

ANTELOPE
PEAK ▲   BROKEN
BACK 2
SUMMIT   CALDERA
MOUNTAIN

RANGE

ANTELOPE VALLEY

BIG SMOKY VALLEY

TOQUIMA RANGE

MONITOR

LANDER COUNTY
NYE COUNTY

CENOZOIC   hot spring deposit   N   0   5   10   15   20 miles

QUATERNARY
☐ alluvium
☐ playa deposits
☐ landslide deposits
☐ ash-rich sediments
☐ older gravel and alluvium

PALEOGENE AND NEOGENE
☐ Eocene–early Miocene
   volcanic flows
☐ Oligoene and Miocene
   basalt and andesite
☐ Oligocene–early Miocene
   ash-flow tuff
☐ sedimentary rocks

MESOZOIC
☐ Cretaceous
   sedimentary rocks

PALEOZOIC
☐ accreted rocks of Nolan Belt
☐ Antler overlap sequence
☐ foreland basin sediments
☐ carbonate shelf sequence
☐ continental slope and
   deep-sea basin deposits

—— thrust fault
—— normal fault
- - - concealed or inferred
     thrust fault
- - - concealed or inferred
     normal fault
⊤⊤⊤⊤ caldera boundary

INTRUSIVE ROCKS
☐ Cenozoic granitic rocks
☐ Mesozoic granitic rocks

Geology along US 50 between Austin and Eureka.

Roadcut along US 50 west of Austin Summit exposing Jurassic quartz monzonite, a plutonic igneous rock similar to granite. The primary minerals in this rock are feldspar (white or pinkish color), hornblende and biotite (black crystals), and quartz (gray material). The close-up image is 4 inches across.

that were concentrated in the quartz veins interlaced through the Jurassic granodiorite. The granodiorite is about 157 million years old, while the vein minerals appear to have crystallized from fluids migrating along an intricate fracture system about 94 million years ago.

From central Austin, US 50 winds eastward up the north side of Pony Canyon through a series of switchbacks that pass the tailings and working of historic mines. The rocks exposed in the roadcuts are Jurassic quartz monzonite, which is similar to the granodiorite exposed along the road west of Austin, and probably part of the same large mass, but has fewer dark-colored minerals. In places, white quartz veins similar to those mined in Austin in the late 1800s, but with no significant mineralization here, cut the plutonic rock.

Near Austin Summit, ash-flow tuffs of Miocene age cap the granitic rock in several places north and south of the road. Three miles east of Austin Summit US 50 intersects the gravel Grass Valley Road, which transects more than 75 miles of spacious, remote country in Grass Valley, an elongated graben.

East of the junction with Grass Valley Road, US 50 rises over Bob Scott Summit, where most of the roadside outcrops are of the Jurassic granitic rock. About 5 miles east of Bob Scott Summit, roadcuts on the north side of the highway reveal dark-greenish or red-brown shale and quartzite of mostly Ordovician age. Magma of the granitic pluton intruded and metamorphosed these Paleozoic rocks to varying degrees. The dark Paleozoic rocks are part of the upper plate of the Roberts Mountains thrust sheet, rocks from the deep ocean that were thrust eastward during the Antler Orogeny.

US 50 loops around the southern end of the Simpson Park Mountains, named for Captain James Simpson, who scouted a route for wagons trains through this area in 1859. Roadcuts along the highway and the scattered outcrops west of Hickison Summit are 25- to 22-million-year-old volcanic tuff, likely discharged from caldera-forming eruptions to the south, but the source

Roadcut on the north side of US 50 in the Hickison Summit area. The darker mass is firmly welded Miocene tuff, while the lighter-colored rock is tuff composed of nonwelded ash. View southwest toward the Toiyabe Range.

Ash-rich lakebeds associated with Miocene tuffs of the southern Simpson Park Mountains.

has not been identified. Some of the tuff exposed here is associated with lake sediment, suggesting these rocks accumulated in a low basin between the exploding volcanoes. About a half mile west of Hickison Summit, a short side road to the north leads to the Hickison Summit petroglyph site. The engravings, which probably range in age from about 500 years ago to historic times, were carved into low cliffs and bluffs of relatively soft Miocene tuff.

East of Hickison Summit, three valleys merge into an expansive sagebrush plain. Although no permanent streams flow through this lowland, plentiful groundwater exists in the alluvial aquifers. In the vicinity of the Bean Flat Rest Area, US 50 passes just north of the Monitor Range, composed of Miocene and Oligocene tuffs, possibly related to the numerous calderas identified in the central and southern parts of the Monitor Range. To the northwest, across the expanse of Kobeh Valley, lie the northern Simpson Park Mountains, which consist of deep-sea Paleozoic sediments of the Roberts Mountains thrust sheet.

The view to the north is dominated by the Roberts Mountains, composed of a faulted block of east-dipping layers of Paleozoic limestone and dolomite of the continental shelf over which deep-sea shale, siltstone, and chert were thrust during the Antler Orogeny. The Roberts Mountains thrust fault was first mapped here in the 1950s and played an important role in the development of geologist's concepts concerning the Antler Orogeny. Since its initial discovery and mapping, the Roberts Mountains thrust and similar faults of the same age and type have been mapped in many other areas in north-central Nevada. In some places, such as in the Roberts Mountains, erosion has worn away the upper plate of deep-ocean rocks, opening windows through which the underlying shelf strata are exposed.

At the south end of the Roberts Mountains, mining operations related to the Gold Bar mining district are visible to the north of US 50. This district is part of the Battle Mountain–Eureka trend, a zone of very productive gold mines in central Nevada. The gold, discovered in 1983, occurs as microscopic grains disseminated through Devonian limestone and silty shale. Several bodies of ore have formed along high-angle faults, where hydrothermal fluids migrated through a complex network of interconnected fractures.

Near the intersection of US 50 and Antelope Valley Road, the view north is dominated by Lone Mountain, an isolated peak rising above the sagebrush plain. Best seen between milepost 17 and milepost 32, this mountain is composed of an east-dipping sequence of sedimentary rock layers that accumulated on the continental shelf in Paleozoic time. The prominent light-colored band is a very clean Ordovician sandstone called the Eureka Quartzite. The whitish peak on the left (west) side of the mountain is made of the Lone Mountain Dolomite, a reeflike mass of dolomite deposited during late Silurian time. All of these rock layers lie structurally below the Roberts Mountain thrust sheet, which has been eroded from the crest of Lone Mountain.

East of Lone Mountain and about 7 miles west of Eureka, US 50 passes through Devils Gate, a narrow notch through massive gray cliffs, especially prominent north of the road. These exposures of late Devonian limestone and dolomite are named the Devils Gate Limestone for this locality. This sediment accumulated on the shallow seafloor of the continental shelf of Laurentia just before deeper ocean sediments were thrust over them during the Antler Orogeny. Numerous small fractures are filled with white calcite deposited by water moving through the shattered limestone. Near the west end of Devils Gate, at the top of the limestone cliffs north of the road, a sill of igneous rock lies parallel to the limestone layering. The sill intruded during the Jurassic Period, some 200 million years after the limestone layers were deposited. As the sheet

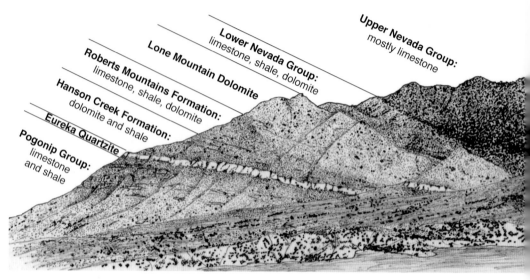

The primary formations of Ordovician through early Devonian rocks exposed on the slopes of Lone Mountain.

East-dipping layers of Devonian limestone exposed on the north side of US 50 in Devils Gate.

of magma cooled and hardened into solid igneous rock, numerous vertical fractures developed, creating crude columns generally oriented at right angles to the overall layering. The rock in the sill is alaskite, similar to granite but composed almost entirely of just two minerals, quartz and potassium feldspar. Larger bodies of such Jurassic igneous rocks are present farther north, in Whistler Mountain.

Near the intersection of NV 278 (covered elsewhere in this volume) and US 50, the view to the northeast is dominated by the Diamond Mountains, composed mostly of Mississippian sandstone, shale, and conglomerate deposited in a coastal sea (the foreland basin) just after the Antler highland emerged as land to the west.

Eureka Mining District

South of US 50, opposite the NV 278 junction, are the tailing and workings of the Ruby Hill mining complex, the principal center of activity for the Eureka mining district, where rich silver-lead-gold ores were first discovered in 1864. Ruby Hill was given its name in reference to the deep-red color of pyrargyrite, a mineral containing silver, antimony, and sulfur. This mineral is so red that it is commonly referred to as ruby silver. At first, the polymetallic ores were difficult to process and smelt due to the presence of lead. New methods of treating and smelting lead-rich ores were developed in 1869, and the Eureka & Palisade Railroad reached the area from the north in 1875, triggering a spectacular mining boom. By 1878, as many as sixteen smelters and furnaces belched out great clouds of smoke and fumes. You can still see some of the slag and other waste as US 50 passes through Eureka. After 1890, mining declined, with only spurts of production following the discovery of new ores bodies, the development of new ore treatment and processing technologies, or significant increases in market prices.

The ores discovered at Ruby Hill were found in fractured masses of Cambrian limestone and dolomite deposited on the Paleozoic continental shelf. Near the surface these ores were oxidized, producing the colorful slopes and tailings, but at depth there are massive unoxidized sulfide minerals containing silver, gold, lead, zinc, and copper. These Paleozoic rocks were not strongly affected by either the Antler or Sonoma Orogeny, but between about 122 and 116 million years ago, compressive forces of the Sevier Orogeny began to fold the rock layers into a large anticline, while several low-angle thrust faults below the folded mass developed. The folded rocks were transported eastward along the thrusts and piled up on similar undeformed strata in the Eureka region, forming a mangled heap of rock more than 50,000 feet thick. Geologists call this immense pile of bent and broken rock the Eureka culmination.

From 106 to 85 million years ago, magma intruded the Eureka culmination, forming plutons and dikes of granitic rocks that cut through the deformed Paleozoic strata and metamorphosed it. Then, in late Eocene through Oligocene time, magma surged upward. The carbonate compounds in the Paleozoic rocks were highly reactive to the magmatic gases and solutions, and the deformation and faults provided the geological plumbing through which the mineralizing fluids were transported.

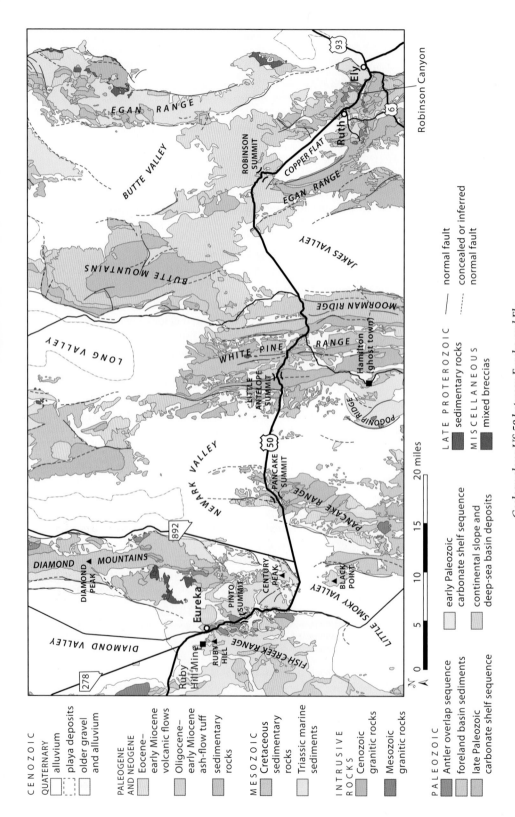

Geology along US 50 between Eureka and Ely.

CENOZOIC

QUATERNARY
- alluvium
- playa deposits
- older gravel and alluvium

PALEOGENE AND NEOGENE
- Eocene–early Miocene volcanic flows
- Oligocene–early Miocene ash-flow tuff
- sedimentary rocks

MESOZOIC
- Cretaceous sedimentary rocks
- Triassic marine sediments

INTRUSIVE ROCKS
- Cenozoic granitic rocks
- Mesozoic granitic rocks

PALEOZOIC
- Antler overlap sequence
- foreland basin sediments
- late Paleozoic carbonate shelf sequence
- early Paleozoic carbonate shelf sequence
- continental slope and deep-sea basin deposits

LATE PROTEROZOIC
- sedimentary rocks

MISCELLANEOUS
- mixed breccias

— normal fault

····· concealed or inferred normal fault

0   5   10   15   20 miles

Eureka to Ely

Knobby outcrops near the southern end of Eureka on the west side of the road are silicified and metamorphosed Ordovician dolomite and sandstone, similar to the rocks that host the ores in the deep mines around town. Farther south, the light-colored slopes and roadcuts expose weakly consolidated Oligocene tuff. South of Pinto Summit, US 50 follows Pinto Canyon. Patches and layers of white Oligocene tuff along the slopes above the road and in several road-cuts represent volcanic ash that fell to the surface from explosive eruptions that blasted tiny droplets of lava high into the atmosphere.

US 50 swings around south end of the Diamond Mountains past Century Peak, where the rocks exposed in the craggy outcrops are mostly Devonian to Pennsylvanian sediments shed from the Antler highland into the Antler fore-land basin to the east. Black Point, the dark-colored hill to the southeast, is named for its dark-colored Oligocene lava flows.

Newark Valley, split into eastern and western portions by the Pancake Range, was submerged several times under the waters of Lake Newark during the Pleis-tocene ice ages. Four cycles of lake development have been documented from older shoreline features, with the last major phase of Lake Newark culminat-ing about 13,700 years ago, precisely the time of the most recent peak of Lake Lahontan. Lake Newark submerged the floor of Newark Valley to a maximum depth of at least 230 feet.

The Pancake Range consists mostly of Mississippian- to Permian-age lime-stone and shale, overlain in places by Cenozoic volcanic rocks. At Pancake Summit, most roadcuts expose layers of conglomerate of the Diamond Peak Formation. This lithified gravel was deposited by swift rivers flowing east from the Antler highland toward a seaway that covered the foreland basin to the east in Mississippian time.

Roadcut on the east side of US 50 south of Pinto Summit. The light-colored material is tuff, while the darker rock at left is Paleozoic rock buried when the ash accumulated in Oligocene time.

This roadcut along the northern side of US 50 near Pancake Summit exposes east-tilted layers of conglomerate of the Diamond Peak Formation.

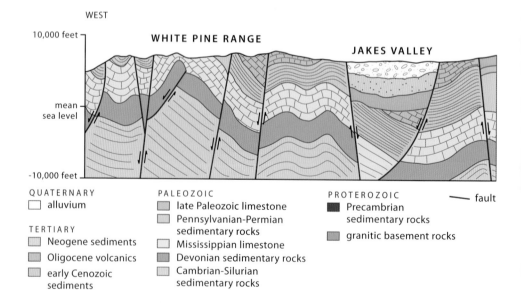

WEST

10,000 feet

WHITE PINE RANGE

JAKES VALLEY

mean sea level

-10,000 feet

QUATERNARY
☐ alluvium

TERTIARY
☐ Neogene sediments
☐ Oligocene volcanics
☐ early Cenozoic sediments

PALEOZOIC
☐ late Paleozoic limestone
☐ Pennsylvanian-Permian sedimentary rocks
☐ Mississippian limestone
☐ Devonian sedimentary rocks
☐ Cambrian-Silurian sedimentary rocks

PROTEROZOIC
☐ Precambrian sedimentary rocks
☐ granitic basement rocks

— fault

Geologic cross-section from the White Pine Range to the Steptoe Valley along US 50.

West-dipping, ash-rich sediments of Neogene age are exposed in a roadcut on the north side of US 50 in the eastern Newark Valley. These sediments accumulated in lakes, swamps, and floodplains between active volcanic centers.

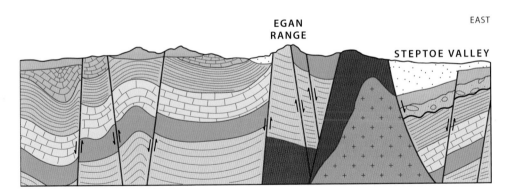

The view south from the highway is dominated by Pogonip Ridge, the westernmost of several north-south-trending ridges that collectively make up the White Pine Range. The Paleozoic sedimentary rocks of these mountains range in age from Cambrian to Pennsylvanian and total more than 18,000 feet in aggregate thickness. This sequence of limestone, shale, dolomite, and sandstone was folded in late Mesozoic time into a series of anticlines and synclines. The individual folds are too large to see from any single vantage point on US 50, but observant travelers will notice that the layers of Paleozoic rock dip in opposing directions over a distance of a few miles.

The cuts and roads seen south of US 50 on Mt. Hamilton at the south end of Pogonip Ridge are part of the Mt. Hamilton mining area. Gold, silver, tungsten, molybdenum, and copper ores were mined from skarns in shale, dolomite, and limestone metamorphosed by two different igneous intrusions. The discovery of silver ore in this area in 1867 started an impressive but short-lived rush to the Treasure Hill area just east of Mt. Hamilton. By 1885, the boom was over, and following a fire that destroyed what was left of the town of Hamilton, the community became a ghost town. The varied metamorphic rocks contain calcium-bearing minerals such as garnet, diopside, and zoisite.

US 50 crosses several ridges at the north end of the White Pine Range, where rocks generally get younger toward the east: Cambrian and Ordovician rocks underlie the western flanks, while younger Mississippian through Permian rock layers form the cliffs and slopes in the central and eastern parts of the range. Near the turnoff from US 50 to the Illipah Creek Reservoir, roadside outcrops consist of well-stratified Mississippian and Pennsylvanian limestone. As the road approaches Moorman Ridge from the west, the slopes on either side of the highway are yellowish-gray, silty limestone of late Pennsylvanian and early Permian age.

East of Moorman Ridge, US 50 crosses Jakes Valley, a relatively small enclosed basin formed primarily by normal faulting along the eastern and western sides. Around 13,870 years ago, a small, several-hundred-foot-deep lake filled much of Jakes Valley. This lake was one of the highest lakes in the Great Basin, with a surface elevation of more than 6,300 feet above modern sea level. The hills

Well-bedded Pennsylvanian limestone is exposed in these hills along US 50 near the Illipah Creek Reservoir turnoff.

northeast of Jakes Valley are mostly Oligocene andesite flows, breccias, and mudflow deposits overlying Permian limestone. Roadside outcrops along the highway west of Robinson Summit are mostly these volcanics.

East of Robinson Summit, US 50 crosses into an elongated valley known as Copper Flat. Dark-colored Oligocene volcanic rocks cap the higher hills and slopes along this portion of the highway, while roadcuts and lower outcrops expose mostly yellowish-gray Permian limestone and sandstone. From Copper Flat, the higher parts of the Egan Range are visible south of the road. They are composed mostly of Paleozoic limestone, dolomite, and shale that accumulated in shallow seawater on the continental shelf of Laurentia.

Robinson Mining District

The view south from US 50 as it passes through Copper Flat is dominated by the extensive tailings from several open pits and underground mines of the Robinson mining district, the most productive copper mining region in Nevada. The metallic ores were first discovered in 1867 by Thomas Robinson. Limited mining in the late 1800s produced minor amounts of the precious metals, but the early prospecting led to the discovery of a much larger, buried ore body particularly rich in copper-bearing minerals.

The initial copper mines were underground and extended into a zone of altered Pennsylvanian limestone adjacent to a body of Cretaceous intrusive rock. The copper-bearing sulfide minerals formed when the host limestone was invaded by the younger magma. This kind of ore deposit is a copper porphyry. The underground ores had been enriched by water leaching copper from near the surface and carrying it downward below the water table, where it was redeposited in the host rock. Most of the large underground mines closed in 1914, after which time mining intensified as several large open pits were excavated. The primary copper ore produced in porphyry deposits generally contains less than 1 percent copper, necessitating the mining of great volumes of mineralized

View southeast from US 50 of a portion of the extensive tailings heap in the Robinson mining district. Ward Mountain in the Egan Range is visible on the skyline.

rock. Much of the yellow, brown, and reddish waste rock seen in the heaps south of US 50 in Copper Flat consist of the oxidized, leached material stripped away to reach the buried low-grade ores. The open pits are not visible from US 50, but they include the Liberty Pit, the largest surface excavation in Nevada.

East of Ruth, US 50 passes though Robinson Canyon, which exposes limestone and dolomite of Mississippian and Devonian age. The dips of these rock layers change from east to west as US 50 crosses several folds. In places, these deformed sedimentary rocks have been hydrothermally altered and contain metal-bearing minerals such as pyrite, chalcopyrite, sphalerite, and galena. Where these minerals have weathered, rusty brown masses of iron, copper, and zinc oxides form, decorating the walls of Robinson Canyon.

US 50
Ely—Utah Border
64 miles

Although Ely was first settled as a stagecoach station in the 1870s, development of the town did not really begin until large-scale copper mining commenced nearby in the early 1900s. (See the previous road guide for information about the Robinson mining district, west of town.)

The bedrock between Ely and the Utah state line is dominated by limestone, dolomite, and sandstone that accumulated on the continental shelf from Cambrian through Permian time. The compressional forces of the late Cretaceous Sevier Orogeny thickened the crust, leading to the uplift of the high Nevadaplano by early Cenozoic time. Beginning in mid-Cenozoic time, east-west extensional forces swept through this region, triggering the collapse of the Nevadaplano. Between the Egan and Snake Ranges, the crust was lengthened by some 250 percent—one of the most highly extended portions of the Basin and Range Province. This stretching was accommodated along numerous normal, listric, and detachment faults.

East of Ely, the Schell Creek Range is composed mostly of Paleozoic and late Precambrian sedimentary rocks broken by a complex set of low-angle normal faults. West of Connors Pass are roadside exposures of Mississippian shale and overlying Pennsylvanian limestone separated by a low-angle fault. The limestone forms benches and cliffs on the higher slopes, while the smooth lower slopes along the highway are softer shale. Movement along the fault has deformed the shale, and you can see contorted rock in some of the roadcuts. In this part of the Schell Creek Range are several areas of copper, silver, lead, zinc, and gold mineralization. The workings visible in the foothills north of US 50 are the Taylor mining district. Silver ores were discovered here in 1872, and mining activity continued intermittently until the 1990s.

The rocks exposed near the road at Connors Pass are shattered Pennsylvanian limestones, transported here along a low-angle detachment fault that is part of the metamorphic core complex better exposed to the east in the Snake

Range. East of Connors Pass, the highway travels through a sequence of Cambrian shale that has been metamorphosed to shiny phyllite. The phyllite is cut by several bodies and streaks of white calcite and also intruded by dikes of Cenozoic rhyolitic rock.

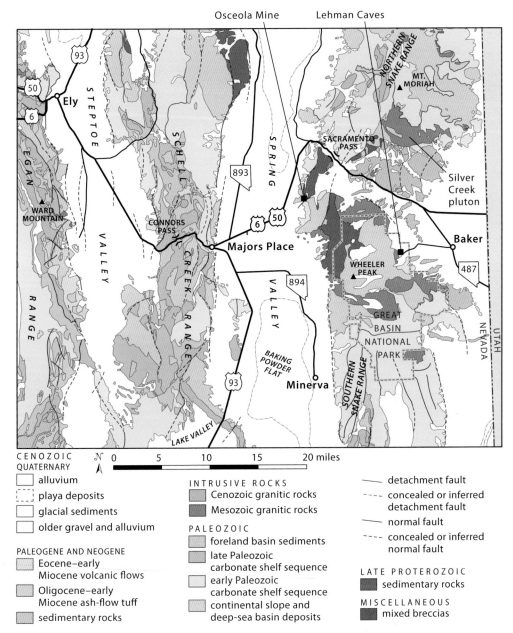

CENOZOIC
QUATERNARY
- alluvium
- playa deposits
- glacial sediments
- older gravel and alluvium

PALEOGENE AND NEOGENE
- Eocene–early Miocene volcanic flows
- Oligocene–early Miocene ash-flow tuff
- sedimentary rocks

INTRUSIVE ROCKS
- Cenozoic granitic rocks
- Mesozoic granitic rocks

PALEOZOIC
- foreland basin sediments
- late Paleozoic carbonate shelf sequence
- early Paleozoic carbonate shelf sequence
- continental slope and deep-sea basin deposits

—— detachment fault
---- concealed or inferred detachment fault
—— normal fault
---- concealed or inferred normal fault

LATE PROTEROZOIC
- sedimentary rocks

MISCELLANEOUS
- mixed breccias

N
0   5   10   15   20 miles

Geology along US 50 between Ely and the Utah border.

Deformed shale and limestone in a roadcut along US 50 on the western flanks of the Schell Creek Range.

Well-foliated Cambrian phyllite exposed in a roadcut along US 50 east of Connors Pass on the eastern slope of the Schell Creek Range.

Snake Range Metamorphic Core Complex

From Majors Place at the intersection with US 93 near the eastern foot of the Schell Creek Range, you can look east across Spring Valley to the Snake Range, a large mountain block separated into northern and southern segments by Sacramento Pass, the low area on the eastern skyline. The southern Snake Range reaches its apex at Wheeler Peak, the prominent treeless summit south of the pass. This peak, along with others along the crest of the southern Snake Range, consists of Cambrian quartzite.

The Snake Range is a classic example of a metamorphic core complex, a type of structure discussed in more depth in this book's introduction. A major low-angle fault, known as the Northern Snake Range décollement, or detachment, separates an upper plate of Paleozoic sedimentary rocks and Cenozoic volcanic rocks from an underlying plate. The Snake Range core complex developed incrementally beginning in the Eocene Epoch, about 45 million years ago, when extensional forces first became active in the region. The detachment fault, which is exposed north of US 50, emerged over the past 20 million years as extreme tensional deformation stretched the fault-bounded blocks apart.

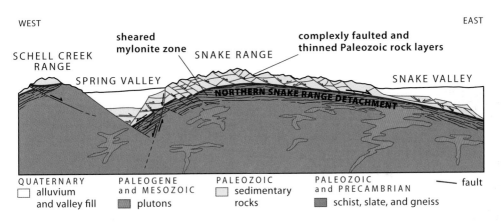

Cross section of the Snake Range, showing the Northern Snake Range detachment fault.

Where US 50 approaches the western flank of the Snake Range from Spring Valley, it bends to the north and parallels the mountain front for about 8 miles. The rocks in the Snake Range east of the north-trending section of US 50 are cliff-forming Paleozoic limestone and shale of Cambrian, Ordovician, and Silurian age, part of the upper plate of the core complex. The detachment fault is buried below these rocks, dipping to the west into the subsurface under Spring Valley. Numerous caves are visible near the base of the cliffs of Ordovician limestone. Mexican free-tailed bats inhabit some of these caves, and their accumulated droppings were mined as a source of nitrogen and phosphorus in the 1920s. When the large array of wind turbines in Spring Valley was constructed in 2012, biologists documented an alarming increase in the mortality of bats. Operations in the wind farm were later modified to minimize bat deaths caused by the spinning blades of the turbines.

Cliffs of Ordovician limestone along the western slope of the Snake Range, east of US 50 in northern Spring Valley, contain many caves and pockets produced by dissolution of the limestone.

On the eastern side of Spring Valley, US 50 bends sharply to the southeast to ascend Sacramento Pass via Turnley Canyon. In the vicinity of this bend, the barren hills to the north of the highway are outcrops of Cambrian quartzite. The higher, wooded cliffs north and east of the road are gray limestone and dolomite of Ordovician and Silurian age. These rocks are also part of the upper plate, a sequence of tilted blocks of unmetamorphosed rock transported along the underlying detachment fault. South of the road through Turnley Canyon, you can see Wheeler Peak on the skyline. Most of the rocks between the road and the high peak are late Precambrian and Cambrian sandstone and shale of the lower plate below the detachment fault, as well as Jurassic plutons. The tailing piles south of the highway are from some minor gold and tungsten mining that occurred here in the late 1800s and early 1900s. For several miles east and west of Sacramento Pass, roadcuts expose tilted layers of early Cenozoic conglomerate and sandstone. These sediments accumulated in local basins that subsided during the earliest phases of extensional faulting in the Great Basin.

About 10 miles east of Sacramento Pass, at the intersection with NV 487, you can see the Northern Snake Range detachment fault to the north. The thin, white, nearly horizontal line on the middle slope is an exposure of highly sheared rock, called mylonite, that developed along the detachment fault. Most of the rocks below the mylonite line, including those in the lower hills north of US 50, are various metamorphic rocks of the lower plate cut by a large body of granite known as the Silver Creek pluton. The age of the granite is somewhat uncertain; radiometric dates suggest a late Oligocene to early Miocene age, but the rock might actually have been reheated at this time after its initial crystallization during late Mesozoic time. Above the mylonite zone, the higher peaks consist of gray to brownish blocks and slices of unmetamorphosed Paleozoic limestone, dolomite, and shale of the upper plate.

Steeply dipping layers of early Cenozoic conglomerate exposed in a roadcut along US 50 in the Sacramento Pass area of the Snake Range.

View of the northern Snake Range northwest from US 50 near its intersection with NV 487. The thin, white, horizontal line is mylonite marking the base of the Northern Snake Range detachment fault.

Great Basin National Park

From US 50, NV 487 leads southeast to Baker, where NV 488 heads west 5 miles into the Great Basin National Park, which spans the southern Snake Range. Among the most famous geological features of Great Basin National Park are the Lehman Caves, a cavern system developed in soluble Cambrian limestone, part of the thick sequence of shallow marine sediments that accumulated on the rifted margin of Laurentia some 500 million years ago. The interconnected cavities and passageways formed much more recently through the dissolution of the limestone by groundwater migrating along cracks and crevices below the water table. After the mountains rose and the desert climate developed following the Pleistocene ice ages, the water table fell and groundwater drained from the solution cavities, making them accessible for exploration from the surface. The Lehman Caves were discovered in 1885 and were protected as Lehman Caves National Monument prior to the creation of Great Basin National Park in 1986. The National Park Service has regularly scheduled tours of the caves.

Wheeler Peak Scenic Drive winds up the mountain slopes from the Lehman Caves Visitor Center to the base of Wheeler Peak. The road ends at one of the highest campgrounds in the Great Basin, renown for its magnificent views of the night sky. Several trails lead from Wheeler Peak Campground into the backcountry of the national park, including one that clambers up the slopes to the top of Wheeler Peak, more than 3,000 feet above the trailhead.

A glacial cirque in the northeast wall of Wheeler Peak is visible southwest of the Wheeler Peak Scenic Drive in Great Basin National Park.

Wheeler Peak (elevation 13,063 feet) is composed of Cambrian quartzite, a firmly cemented and relatively pure type of sandstone. A Pleistocene glacier carved the U-shaped valley of Lehman Creek, as well as the bowl-shaped depression, known as a cirque, at the base of the northeast wall of Wheeler Peak. The only remaining glacier in the entire Basin and Range Province lingers in the shadowy floor of the cirque. This little glacier is shrinking, and its surface is normally covered with a mantle of rock that has fallen from the sheer walls ascending to Wheeler Peak. Such glaciers are difficult to study because the ice is concealed, and its movement is altered by the large rocks frozen within it. The current status of the last glacier in the Basin and Range, and how much longer it may survive, is uncertain.

US 93
Las Vegas—US 50 near Ely
233 miles

US 93 traverses Nevada from Hoover Dam at the Arizona border to Jackpot at the Idaho border. See the Las Vegas Area section of the book for Hoover Dam, Las Vegas, and I-15. Departing from I-15 at exit 64, US 93 crosses a small valley and then climbs alluvial fan surfaces between low hills composed of limestone of the Bird Spring Formation of early Permian to late Mississippian age. In the vicinity of the Silverhawk power plant, the road bends to follow a nearly north-south alignment between mountain ranges. To the west of the road, you can see several ridges of light-colored Pennsylvanian and Permian rock layers in the southern end of the Las Vegas Range, beyond which is the crest of the higher Sheep Range.

To the east, the 2,400-foot-high escarpment of the Arrow Canyon Range consists primarily of limestone and dolomite of late Cambrian to Silurian age. The prominent white band is the Eureka Quartzite of middle Ordovician age. The quartzite has been mined for silica near the base of the southern part of

East-dipping rock units from Cambrian to Silurian age are spectacularly displayed in the Arrow Canyon Range. The prominent dark-gray cliff is the late Ordovician Ely Springs Dolomite, which is underlain by the light-colored Eureka Quartzite of early Ordovician age. The dark rock of the peak at right is Silurian dolomite.

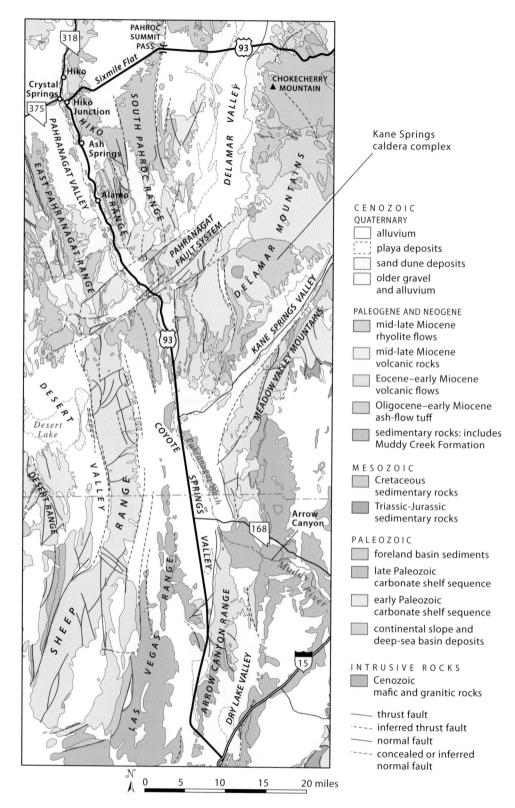

Key (legend):

CENOZOIC

QUATERNARY
- alluvium
- playa deposits
- sand dune deposits
- older gravel and alluvium

PALEOGENE AND NEOGENE
- mid-late Miocene rhyolite flows
- mid-late Miocene volcanic rocks
- Eocene–early Miocene volcanic flows
- Oligocene–early Miocene ash-flow tuff
- sedimentary rocks: includes Muddy Creek Formation

MESOZOIC
- Cretaceous sedimentary rocks
- Triassic-Jurassic sedimentary rocks

PALEOZOIC
- foreland basin sediments
- late Paleozoic carbonate shelf sequence
- early Paleozoic carbonate shelf sequence
- continental slope and deep-sea basin deposits

INTRUSIVE ROCKS
- Cenozoic mafic and granitic rocks
- —— thrust fault
- ---- inferred thrust fault
- —— normal fault
- ---- concealed or inferred normal fault

Kane Springs caldera complex

0   5   10   15   20 miles

Geologic map along US 93 between I-15 and the Delamar Valley.

the range, where it has been downfaulted to valley level. Across from the silica mine, you can find colonial corals at the south end of a limestone exposure, where a wide parking area is available.

The Arrow Canyon Range has been lifted up about 6,000 feet along a normal fault, so the rocks in it are older than the Paleozoic rocks exposed in the low hills of the Las Vegas Range to the west. The folds observed in exposures west of the highway are attributed to the deformation that occurred during the Sevier Orogeny in Cretaceous time. West-facing fault scarps formed in Pleistocene time cut older Quaternary alluvium along the base of the Arrow Canyon Range.

US 93 crosses a low divide into Coyote Springs Valley, where creosote-covered alluvial fans dominate both sides of the road. Prior to the housing crash of 2008, the valley was slated to be home to 70,000 houses and 16 golf courses. The proposed development, which would rely on groundwater, has raised environmental concerns. The groundwater feeds warm springs on the east side of the Arrow Canyon Range. The Moapa dace, a small endangered fish, is found only in these warm springs, which are the headwaters of the modern-day Muddy River.

US 93 intersects NV 168 at the north end of the Arrow Canyon Range, which slopes evenly downward to the north, like the point of an arrow, and has been buried by sediments. Along the eastern side of Coyote Springs Valley to the east of US 93 are remnants of an extensive flat surface with eroded cliffs that expose light- to reddish-tan, fine-grained deposits of the Muddy Creek Formation. Streams deposited these sediments in enclosed basins in Miocene and

Fine-grained deposits of the Muddy Creek Formation are capped by cemented stream gravel in exposures along NV 168 between US 93 in Coyote Springs Valley and I-15.

Pliocene time, before the valley drained south to the Colorado River. In Pleistocene time, the Muddy Creek sediments were dissected by the White River, which originated 150 miles to the north and flowed through Pahranagat Wash before turning eastward to cut through the topographic gap at the north end of the Arrow Canyon Range. The river cut Arrow Canyon, in places only 20 feet wide and 400 feet deep, through a fossiliferous limestone ridge. The canyon is accessed from NV 168 via a four-wheel-drive road.

North of the NV 168 intersection in the Coyote Springs Valley, you can see alluvial fan deposits that overlie and interfinger with light-colored, finer-grained sediments of the Muddy Creek Formation. Look for well-developed caliche in gully exposures crossed by the highway.

US 93 crosses the stream bed of the Pahranagat Wash just south of the intersection with a dirt road that follows Kane Springs Valley to Elgin and Caliente. About 20 miles northeast of US 93 along the Kane Springs Valley road are the remnants of the Kane Springs caldera complex, formed 14 million years ago. The Kane Springs Valley was eroded along a left-lateral oblique-slip fault that has offset this caldera complex by 3 to 4 miles. The larger portion of the caldera is in the Delamar Mountains to the north of the road, and the smaller portion (offset to the northeast) is at the northern edge of the Meadow Valley Mountains, to the south of the road.

At the northern end of Coyote Springs Valley, reddish volcanic rocks north and east of the highway overlie steeply dipping, gray Paleozoic limestones. An erosional unconformity, representing a long period of time during which the previously folded or tilted limestone units were eroded, separates the two rock types. The Sevier Orogeny, which ended around 80 million years ago, may have folded the limestone. The volcanic rocks are 25 to 15 million years old, so there had been plenty of time in the Cretaceous and early Tertiary Periods for erosion of the limestones.

An old erosion surface on steeply west-dipping gray Paleozoic limestone is covered by reddish rhyolitic volcanic rock at the north end of Coyote Springs Valley.

As US 93 approaches a narrow cut in the volcanic flows from the south, near a sign announcing the southern border of the Pahranagat National Wildlife Refuge, a basalt flow overlies welded ash-flow tuffs on the east. The prominent white bathtub ring on the lower part of the dark rock walls was left by a former lake. On the north end of the narrow cut, the highway enters a wider valley containing a series of wetlands and lakes formed by ponded spring flow and return flow from irrigation. The abundance of water in this area has caught the eye of the thirsty Las Vegas urban area, 100 miles to the southwest. The Las Vegas Valley Water District has bought ranches in the next valley to the east, the Delamar Valley, and plans to construct a water pipeline to Las Vegas if the city's current source, the Colorado River, is insufficient in the future.

The linear northern edge of the volcanic hills south of the wildlife refuge reflect a west-trending normal fault, part of the Pahranagat fault system. Between the fault and Ash Springs, Tertiary volcanics predominantly form the hills on both sides of the highway, and terrace gravels flank the modern floodplain and are exposed in roadcuts. The volcanic rock in the Alamo area is a combination of 22-million-year-old rhyolitic ash-flows from the Central Nevada caldera complex to the west overlain by tuffs erupted from younger caldera complexes to the east of the highway, such as the 14-million-year-old Kane Springs caldera.

At Ash Springs, 7 miles north of Alamo, tufa mounds occur on both sides of the road. Tufa consists of calcium carbonate precipitated from spring discharge over a long time. Ash Springs is the largest spring in the valley, with a discharge in 1988 of more than 6,000 gallons per minute and a temperature of 90°F.

Hiko Junction to Caliente

East of Hiko Junction, US 93 follows Crystal Wash through Devonian rocks of the Hiko Range. These mostly limestone and dolomite sedimentary rocks formed on the shallow seafloor of the continental shelf. Within the Devonian sequence is the Alamo Breccia, an unusual deposit consisting of large blocks of limestone, dolomite, and sandstone that were shattered by a comet or meteorite impact around 382 million years ago. The extraterrestrial object, estimated to be about 3 miles wide, slammed into the shallow seafloor, excavating a crater more than 30 miles across. Huge tsunamis transported the rubble across at least 39,000 square miles of the seafloor. In addition, large pieces of the continental shelf were dislodged and slid down the continental slope into deeper water. Based on the thickness of the Alamo Breccia, it appears that the impact site was located in Sand Spring Valley, about 60 miles northwest of Alamo. Two miles east of Hiko Junction you can see exposures of the Alamo Breccia in the drainage directly north of and adjacent to US 93.

About 3 miles east of Hiko Junction, dark-colored Devonian strata are overlain by two Miocene-age tuffs. The Hiko Tuff, a crystal-rich rhyolitic ash that weathers to bulbous forms resembling granitic exposures, was erupted 18.6 million years ago from the western end of the Caliente caldera complex, in the Delamar Mountains to the south. The 1,000-foot-thick Hiko Tuff is thicker than the overlying Kane Wash Tuff because it is closer to its source.

View north from US 93 of stratified Miocene tuffs the North Pahroc Range. The darker bands represent welded ash-flow tuffs, while the lighter-colored layers are composed of poorly welded tuff. Note the spheroidally weathering Hiko Tuff in the foreground.

East of the Hiko Range, US 93 crosses Sixmile Flat before gradually ascending to Pahroc Summit Pass, which separates the North Pahroc Range from the South Pahroc Range. These tilted fault-block mountains are composed of mostly of Silurian and Devonian strata overlain by Miocene ash-flow and air-fall tuffs. North of the pass, you can see a thick series of light-colored, weakly consolidated ash deposits interlayered with darker welded tuffs. The pass formed in a zone of east-trending strike-slip faults known as the Timpahute lineament, one of several similar zones that geologists have identified in this part of south-central Nevada. These accommodation zones allow the crust to stretch westward at varying rates to the north and south.

Delamar Valley is nearly continuous to the north with Dry Lake Valley. Playa lakebeds, with their barren surfaces of light-colored sediments and alkaline deposits, occupy the lowest points of both valleys. During the Pleistocene Epoch, the entire floor of both valleys was submerged as much as 75 feet deep under an isolated lake.

The inactive Delamar mining district, situated in the lower slopes of the Delamar Mountains, was most active between 1890 and 1902. The gold mineralization occurred in early Cambrian quartzite that had been intruded by magma during the flare-up of Miocene volcanic activity.

As US 93 begins a gradual ascent of the Burnt Springs Range (north of the road) and the Delamar Mountains (to the south), you'll see distinctive yucca plants known as Joshua trees along the road. These thickets are among the most northern occurrences of Joshua trees, which are iconic plants of the hot and stark Mojave Desert to the south. Northward from this area, the flora gradually shifts to a sagebrush-pinyon-juniper plant community better adapted to the colder conditions of the higher Great Basin Desert.

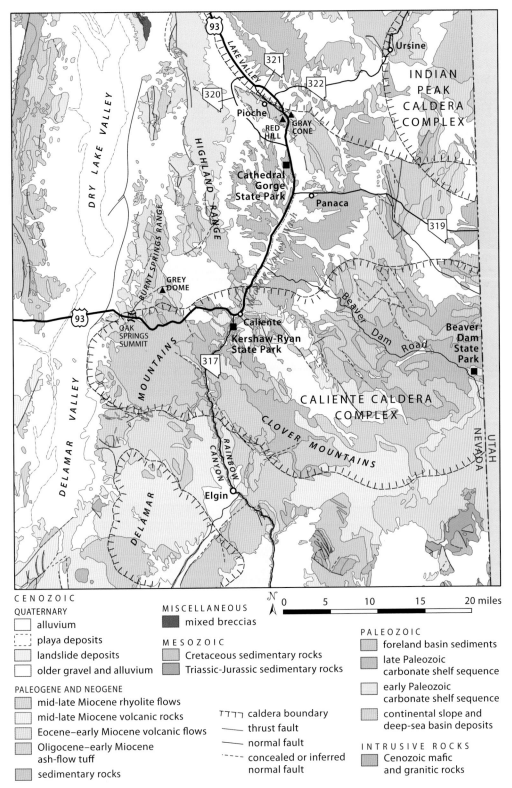

Geology along US 93 between the Delamar Valley and Pioche.

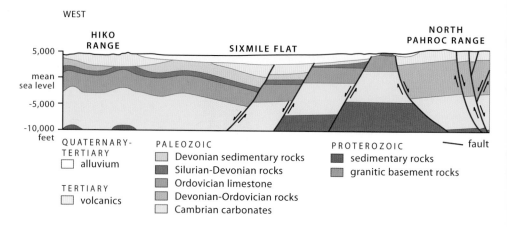

WEST

HIKO RANGE

SIXMILE FLAT

NORTH PAHROC RANGE

5,000

mean sea level

-5,000

-10,000 feet

QUATERNARY-TERTIARY
☐ alluvium

TERTIARY
☐ volcanics

PALEOZOIC
☐ Devonian sedimentary rocks
■ Silurian-Devonian rocks
☐ Ordovician limestone
☐ Devonian-Ordovician rocks
☐ Cambrian carbonates

PROTEROZOIC
■ sedimentary rocks
☐ granitic basement rocks

— fault

The conspicuous peak north of the highway is Grey Dome, composed of Cambrian limestone. Outcrops of the Cambrian rocks along the road include orange to reddish quartzite, greenish-gray shale, and medium-gray limestone deposited under shallow, warm seas that covered the continental shelf of Laurentia 525 to 500 million years ago. Fossils are fairly common in the Cambrian shales and limestones, and just east of milepost 81, a dirt road to the northwest leads to a trilobite collecting locality maintained by the Bureau of Land Management. Trilobites have been extinct for 250 million years but were the dominant arthropods of the Cambrian seafloor, which no doubt swarmed with millions of these hard-shelled relatives of modern crustaceans.

As US 93 ascends to Oak Springs Summit, it crosses the western margin of the Caliente caldera, an elongated feature that spans more than 50 miles across from west to east. The Caliente caldera consists of four smaller, nested calderas

Grey Dome, a prominent knob of Cambrian limestone, is visible north of US 93 in the Burnt Springs Range.

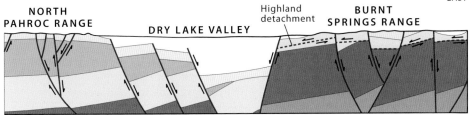

Generalized geologic cross section from Hiko to the Burnt Springs Range.
—Based on geological maps from the Nevada Bureau of Mines and Geology

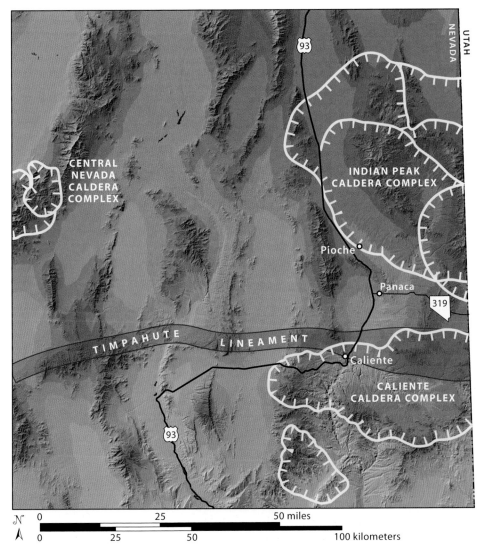

Oligocene and Miocene caldera complexes of southeast Nevada. The Timpahute lineament is a zone of strike-slip faults that accommodate extension in the region. —Modified from Sweetkind and du Bray, 2008

created by explosive eruptions that occurred 23 to 18 million years ago, during the Miocene Epoch. Each of the eruptions blasted ash across thousands of square miles, which welded and consolidated into layers of tuff. The Hiko Tuff, well exposed along US 93 west and east of Oak Spring Summit, erupted from the caldera, as did several others. Although the caldera was a depression after the eruptions, the subsequent filling with pyroclastic volcanic and sedimentary rocks and later disruption by extensional faulting and accommodation zones has altered the land surface, and no great depression is visible from US 93.

You can see spheroidally weathered outcrops of the Hiko Tuff along the road near Oak Springs Summit. About 6 miles east of Oak Springs Summit, roadcuts in Newman Canyon expose tuff, welded ash-flows, and ash-rich sedimentary deposits that filled the Caliente caldera. The light-gray layers are mostly ash deposits, while the pink to rusty layers are ash-flow tuffs. Buff to brown, ash-rich sandstones and siltstone also occur in the roadcuts. In places, you can see layers of coarse rubble consisting of large angular chunks of volcanic rocks—the debris of ancient landslides and mudflows that occurred as the northern walls of the Caliente caldera collapsed inward. Just east of milepost 91, about 2 miles west of Caliente, the highway crosses a prominent normal fault displacing the volcanic layers.

Volcanic breccia exposed in a roadcut on the north side of US 93 west of Caliente is composed of large chunks of volcanic rock mixed with ash, sand, and gravel that cascaded into the Caliente caldera as a landslide or mudflow. The higher cliff is composed of an ash-flow tuff.

RAINBOW CANYON

NV 317 intersects US 93 on the outskirts of Caliente and extends south 21 miles through Rainbow Canyon before the pavement ends at Elgin. Along the canyon walls, you can see spectacular exposures of the ash-flow tuffs and volcanic breccias that formed within the Caliente caldera, normal faults displacing volcanic rock layers, and interesting weathering phenomema. Kershaw-Ryan State Park is located in a scenic side canyon cut in the volcanic rocks just 2 miles south of Caliente.

An outcrop of Miocene tuff north of Caliente with irregular pillars produced by columnar jointing as the ash cooled and hardened.

Ranchers settled near the confluence of Meadow Valley Wash and the Clover Creek drainage in the early 1860s. After the Union Pacific railroad tracks arrived in the early 1900s, the settlement was named Caliente ("hot" in Spanish) in reference to hot springs here. The classic mission-style building in Caliente was constructed in 1923 and served as a railroad depot for many years. North of Caliente, US 93 follows the normally dry Meadow Valley Wash through a canyon cut into Miocene-age tuffs, volcanic mudflow deposits known as lahars, and associated ash-rich sedimentary rocks. Just north of Indian Cove, the canyon widens out into Meadow Valley. The wash here drains to the Muddy River and on to Lake Mead, so although this is within the Basin and Range Province, it is outside the internally drained Great Basin.

Near the intersection of US 93 with Beaver Dam Road, you can see rusty-tan lakebed deposits east of the road. Beaver Dam Road heads 28 miles southeast to Beaver Dam State Park, where dramatic exposures of volcanic tuff and rhyolite line the rugged canyon of Beaver Dam Wash along the Nevada-Utah border. More Pleistocene lakebeds are exposed around Panaca, a small farming town about 1 mile east of the highway on NV 319.

CATHEDRAL GORGE STATE PARK

Cathedral Gorge State Park, 1 mile north of the Panaca junction, was set aside in 1935 to help preserve the intricate network of gullies, crevices, spires, and mounds resulting from the erosion of soft lake sediments known as the Panaca Formation. These sediments accumulated 5 to 2 million years ago in a large lake that extended some 15 miles north into Lake Valley. Rivers draining into the lake carried substantial amounts of clay derived from the weathering of the older Miocene tuffs. The clay minerals in the sediments swell as they absorb water and shrink when they dry out, preventing the sediment from hardening into a cohesive rock. Paleontologists have discovered a great variety of fossil plants and animals in the Panaca Formation. About 2 miles north of the entrance to Cathedral Gorge State Park, US 93 passes the Miller Point Overlook, from which exceptional views of the badlands are available.

Erosion of soft Pliocene lakebeds has created a network of gullies in the badlands of Cathedral Gorge.

Pioche to Majors Place

About 5 miles north of its junction with NV 319, US 93 bends to the northwest around the Pioche Hills, winding between Red Hill to the west and Gray Cone to the east. The Pioche Hills are composed almost entirely of complexly faulted sedimentary rocks of Cambrian age, as are the higher Highland and Bristol Ranges looming in the background to the northwest. The Prospect Mountain Quartzite, the resistant rock of Red Hill, is overlain by the soft Pioche Shale and a thick sequence of limestone. The shale normally weathers to smooth slopes, while the limestone layers form cliffs and ledges in the higher parts of the Pioche Hills. Gray Cone consists of gray Cambrian limestone. Several dikes of igneous rock cut the Cambrian rocks, and Miocene volcanic rocks cover the older rocks in the southeastern part of the hills.

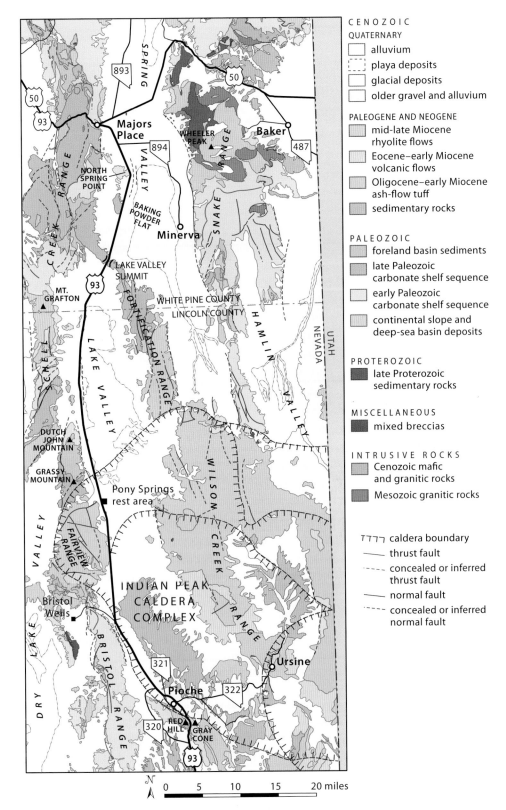

CENOZOIC

QUATERNARY
- alluvium
- playa deposits
- glacial deposits
- older gravel and alluvium

PALEOGENE AND NEOGENE
- mid-late Miocene rhyolite flows
- Eocene–early Miocene volcanic flows
- Oligocene–early Miocene ash-flow tuff
- sedimentary rocks

PALEOZOIC
- foreland basin sediments
- late Paleozoic carbonate shelf sequence
- early Paleozoic carbonate shelf sequence
- continental slope and deep-sea basin deposits

PROTEROZOIC
- late Proterozoic sedimentary rocks

MISCELLANEOUS
- mixed breccias

INTRUSIVE ROCKS
- Cenozoic mafic and granitic rocks
- Mesozoic granitic rocks

- ⊤⊤⊤⊤ caldera boundary
- ——— thrust fault
- - - - - concealed or inferred thrust fault
- ——— normal fault
- - - - - concealed or inferred normal fault

Geology along US 93 between Pioche and Majors Place.

These remains of an ore bin and tramway are along NV 321 at the south end of Pioche. Ore was transported east by buckets suspended from steel cables, to a mill east of US 93, over the hill in the distance.

Just north of Red Hill, US 93 intersects NV 321, which runs through the downtown portion of historic Pioche just west of US 93. Silver ores were first discovered in the Pioche area in 1864 in veins in the Cambrian quartzite. The silver ore was accompanied by the valuable lead-bearing mineral cerussite. By 1869, several mines were operating, thanks in part to financing from François Pioche, who purchased several claims and built a smelter to process the ore. The most intense area of mining was at Treasure Hill, the prominent mountain west of the town with dumps, head frames, and old structures scattered over its slopes. Just south of the intersection of US 93 and NV 322, the remains of an old aerial tramway cross the highway. The tramway was used primarily in the 1920s and 1930s to carry ore from Treasure Hill to a mill east of the road.

The bedrock and host rock for the silver ores around Treasure Hill is the Prospect Mountain Quartzite. Lower-grade silver ores were later discovered in shale and limestone on the southwestern side of the Pioche Hills. These deposits were more extensive than the fissure veins closer to Pioche, and the silver was accompanied by minerals bearing lead, manganese, zinc, and iron.

North of Pioche, US 93 enters Lake Valley, an extensive graben. The Wilson Creek Range on the east was uplifted along a major normal fault that runs near its western base but is mostly concealed beneath alluvial fan deposits shed west from the mountain front. The mountain block consists almost entirely of volcanic rocks related to the Indian Peak caldera complex, a set of large, nested calderas that erupted between 32 and 27 million years ago, when southeastern Nevada was part of a high, nearly level plateau. At least 3,500 cubic miles of volcanic ash was blown from the caldera, and with few mountains to block its dispersal, it spread over an area of more than 20,000 square miles. The ash sheet produced by these supervolcano eruptions is up to 3,000 feet thick within the caldera complex and thins out in all directions.

In the northern Bristol Range, ores of silver, copper, gold, and lead were discovered in the 1870s, leading to the organization of the Jackrabbit and Bristol mining districts. The ores were mostly a mixture of carbonate and sulfide minerals replacing some of the Cambrian limestone. In 1877, charcoal ovens were built at Bristol Wells to provide fuel for smelters. Though no mining activity has occurred in the Bristol Range since 1914, the now-abandoned site of Bristol Wells and the curious beehive-shaped charcoal ovens can be visited by traveling 7 miles west from US 93 on the gravel-surfaced Bristol Wells Road.

The central part of the Fairview Range, west of the highway and north of the Bristol Range, is composed of ash and lava flows that filled a portion of the western end of the Indian Peak caldera complex. Some of these tuffs are exposed in several low roadcuts along the highway as it passes the Fairview Range.

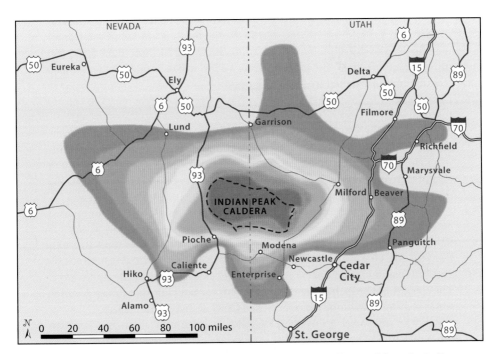

The Wah Wah Springs Tuff, one of several sheets of welded tuff erupted from the Indian Peak caldera (dashed blue line), was deposited over a large area of Nevada and Utah.
—Modified from Best, Christensen, and Gromme, 2013

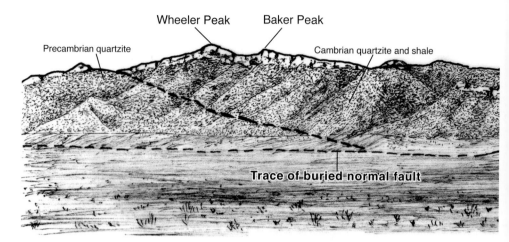

Wheeler Peak   Baker Peak

Precambrian quartzite   Cambrian quartzite and shale

Trace of buried normal fault

In the west slope of the Snake Range, seen east from US 93 across Spring Valley in the foreground, a south-dipping detachment fault separates the upper plate rocks, transported from the north, from lower plate rocks.

North of the Pony Springs rest area, you can see Grassy Mountain and Dutch John Mountain west and northwest of the road, both composed of faulted and gently tilted layers of mostly Mississippian limestone. Grassy Pass, the low saddle between the two mountains west of the highway, is eroded in the Chainman Shale, a Mississippian-age formation consisting of more than 1,000 feet of relatively soft shale and siltstone. Lake Valley, which contains at least 3,000 feet of alluvium washed from the surrounding mountains, was submerged in Pleistocene time under nearly 100 feet of water by Lake Carpenter. You can see relict shorelines on some of the lower slopes.

East of US 93, light-colored tuffs erupted from the Indian Peak caldera complex form the southern end of the Fortification Range, while gray to tan Pennsylvanian and Permian sedimentary strata form the bedrock in the northern part of the ridge. The boundary between these two types of rock represents the northern limit of volcanic rocks associated with the Indian Peak caldera.

The bedrock of the southern Schell Creek Range west of US 93 is dominated by complexly folded Cambrian through Mississippian sedimentary rocks. US 93 passes a series of springs along the toes of the alluvial fans spreading east from the Mt. Grafton area. The water issuing from these springs is between 65 and 70°F, warm but not hot enough to be used as a geothermal energy resource. The springs are probably related to a buried normal fault that forces groundwater seeping downslope from the Schell Creek Range to the surface.

US 93 climbs over a low ridge of yellow-tan Pennsylvanian and Permian limestone at Lake Valley Summit, the boundary between the internally drained Great Basin to the north and the Colorado River drainage to the south. The southern end of Spring Valley, known as Baking Powder Flat, is the expanse visible east from US 93 about 8 miles north of Lake Valley Summit. Beneath the

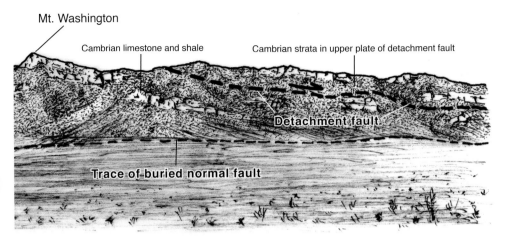

Mt. Washington

Cambrian limestone and shale

Cambrian strata in upper plate of detachment fault

Detachment fault

Trace of buried normal fault

nearly level surface of Spring Valley, some 6,000 feet of basin-filling sediments have collected above the buried Paleozoic bedrock. In Pleistocene time, cooler and wetter conditions led to the development of a large lake in the enclosed valley. At its maximum stage of development, this lake was about 250 feet deep. At least six ancient shoreline terraces have been identified around the margins of southern Spring Valley, indicating multiple cycles of lake growth and decline during the ice ages.

Across Spring Valley to the east, the Snake Range dominates the skyline, culminating in Mt. Wheeler, the second-highest peak in Nevada, at 13,063 feet. This classic fault-block mountain was uplifted by normal faulting that began in Miocene time and continues to the present day. On the western slope of the Snake Range, the location of the range-bounding faults is approximated by the lower limit of trees, where the pinyon-juniper forests give way to the sagebrush scrub of the valley floor. The bedrock of the southernmost Snake Range is mostly southeast-dipping Cambrian limestone in the upper plate of a major detachment fault. The detachment is related to the Snake Range metamorphic core complex to the north, discussed more fully in the narrative for US 50.

Near milepost 13, US 93 passes exposures of Pennsylvanian and Permian rocks in low hills west of the highway. Six miles farther north, the highway bends to the northwest in the vicinity of North Spring Point, a set of crags and hills of shattered Devonian limestone west of the road. Across Spring Valley, the reddish outcrops at the base of the Snake Range are Cambrian quartzite, while the higher cliffs are exposures of Cambrian limestone. Several bodies of Jurassic granite rock have been emplaced into the Cambrian layers of Snake Range.

US 93 joins US 50 at Majors Place. The geology between Majors Place and Ely is described in the US 50 section of this book.

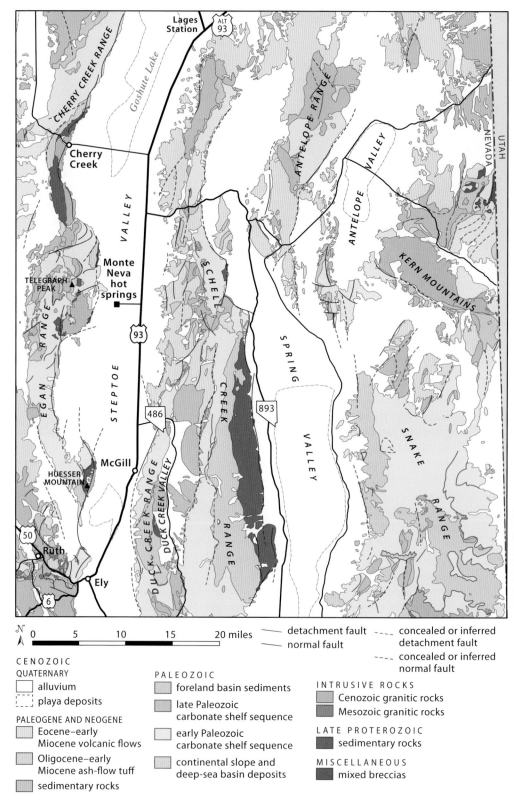

CENOZOIC

QUATERNARY
- alluvium
- playa deposits

PALEOGENE AND NEOGENE
- Eocene–early Miocene volcanic flows
- Oligocene–early Miocene ash-flow tuff
- sedimentary rocks

PALEOZOIC
- foreland basin sediments
- late Paleozoic carbonate shelf sequence
- early Paleozoic carbonate shelf sequence
- continental slope and deep-sea basin deposits

INTRUSIVE ROCKS
- Cenozoic granitic rocks
- Mesozoic granitic rocks

LATE PROTEROZOIC
- sedimentary rocks

MISCELLANEOUS
- mixed breccias

detachment fault
normal fault
concealed or inferred detachment fault
concealed or inferred normal fault

0 5 10 15 20 miles

Geology along US 93 between Ely and the junction with US 93 Alternate.

US 93
Ely—Wells—Jackpot
205 miles

A few miles northeast of East Ely, near milepost 73, US 93 passes a rest area on the west commemorating Jedediah Smith, a western explorer who passed through this area in 1827. Farther west stands Huesser Mountain, composed of intensely faulted reddish-brown quartzite and slate of late Precambrian and early Paleozoic age, cut by lighter-colored granite of Cenozoic age. To the east, the Duck Creek Range, a fault block separated from the northern Schell Creek Range by Duck Creek Valley, consists of several thrust sheets of deformed Paleozoic limestone that have been transported over shale and quartzite.

Twelve miles north of Ely, US 93 passes through the historic town of McGill, where a large mill and smelter processed ore from copper mines in the Egan Range from 1908 to 1983. In its heyday during the 1920s and early 1930s, McGill had 3,000 residents and processed 285 million tons of ore, about 95 percent of which now resides in the 4,000-acre slag and tailings field west of US 93. The large excavation at the base of the mountains east of McGill is the remnant of a limestone quarry that provided fluxing material for the old smelting process.

NV 486, the Success Loop Road, extends east through Gallagher Gap, an opening in the Duck Creek Range through which Duck Creek flows west to the Steptoe Valley. The creek has deposited an extensive alluvial fan where it enters the valley. The fan is a subtle feature from ground level but is obvious from an

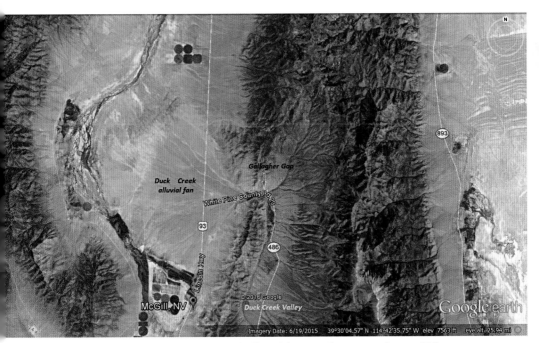

Google Earth view of the Duck Creek alluvial fan spread out across Steptoe Valley.

aerial perspective. So much sediment has accumulated in this alluvial fan that the channel of Duck Creek was forced to the west side of southern Steptoe Valley.

The Paleozoic bedrock under Steptoe Valley has been downfaulted along normal faults on either side. As much as 8,000 feet of sediment derived from adjacent mountains has accumulated in the valley, making it one of the deepest structural basins in eastern Nevada. In the 1980s, spotty oil accumulations were discovered 4,400 to 6,000 feet under the surface of southern Steptoe Valley, but no significant production of petroleum has occurred since.

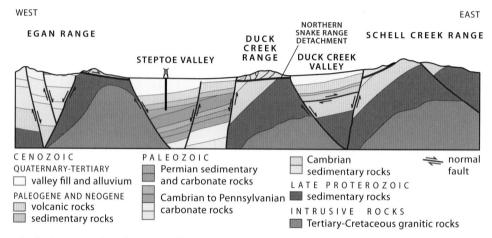

Geologic cross section of Steptoe Valley. —Based on maps from Southern Nevada Water Authority and the US Geological Survey

Much of Steptoe Valley was submerged in the Pleistocene Epoch under Lake Steptoe, an elongated 450-square-mile lake that had a maximum depth of about 350 feet. Aquatic organisms were able to move between Lake Steptoe and Lake Waring, to the north in Goshute Valley, on the rare occasion when the two lakes rose high enough to merge into one. Modern springs in Steptoe and Goshute Valleys still support genetically similar populations of small fish known appropriately as the relict dace, holdovers from the large Pleistocene lakes.

About 18 miles north of McGill, US 93 passes the road leading west toward the Monte Neva hot springs, visible west of the highway as the patch of light-colored, bleached rock and soil. These springs were a popular destination for people living in the McGill and Ely areas during the boom times of the 1920s and 1930s. The springs are no longer accessible to the public, but the deep heat reservoir has attracted attention. Recent drilling and geophysical surveys in Steptoe Valley have detected groundwater at temperatures of 250 to 390°F around 10,000 feet below the surface.

To the west of Steptoe Valley in the vicinity of the Monte Neva hot springs, the Egan Range is composed of early Paleozoic rocks intruded by 36-million-year-old plutonic bodies. Near the widest part of Steptoe Valley, US 93 passes the road to Cherry Creek, a small historic settlement situated at the base of the mountains. The rock exposed in the slope above the town is Cenozoic granitic rock that intruded into Precambrian quartzite. The mining activity for which Cherry Creek is famous occurred primarily from 1872 to the 1920s. Silver ores started the mining boom, but later discoveries of gold and tungsten ores sustained activity for many decades.

Between the Cherry Creek road intersection and Lages Station, US 93 parallels the northeast trend of the Schell Creek Range and the large normal fault along its western base. The mountain block is composed of Paleozoic limestone and shale intruded and overlain by extensive tracts of Miocene and Oligocene volcanic rocks, which make up the mounds and crags that protrude through the alluvial apron just east of the highway. About 3 miles south of Lages Station, south-dipping layers of late Paleozoic limestone crop out just east of the road.

US 93A Junction to Wells

At junction of US 93 and 93A, the southern Cherry Creek Range is visible west of the road across the northern end of Steptoe Valley. The prominent west-dipping rock layers of light-gray rock are mostly Paleozoic limestone and dolomite. The thicker, resistant limestone and dolomite layers weather into bold cliffs separated by smooth slopes of softer shale or siltstone. The northern end of the range, visible farther north, does not have prominent cliff layers because the light-tan to yellowish-brown outcrops are mostly Pennsylvanian- and Permian-age siltstone, shale, and mudstone.

North of the junction, the low roadcuts and undulating mounds along US 93 expose soft volcanic and sedimentary rocks. White to light-gray tuffs and ash-rich sediments accumulated in ancient lake basins and stream valleys in Cenozoic time, prior to development of the modern topography.

Currie was an important way station and shipping point in the early 1900s on the now-defunct Nevada Northern Railway. Shipment of copper ore north

View east from US 93 of abandoned railroad tracks in Currie and low hills capped with mid-Cenozoic volcanic rocks in the distance. The reddish excavation beyond the small house to the right is a quarry from which Jurassic sandstone has been mined for use as building stone.

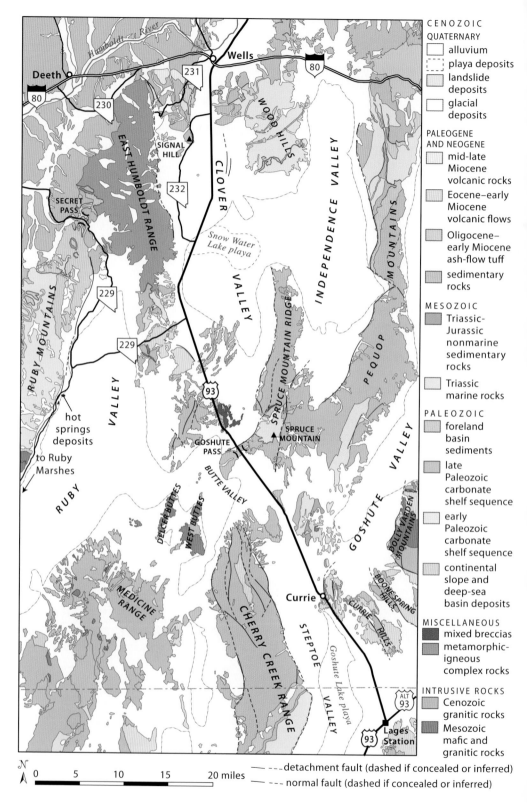

CENOZOIC

QUATERNARY
- alluvium
- playa deposits
- landslide deposits
- glacial deposits

PALEOGENE AND NEOGENE
- mid-late Miocene volcanic rocks
- Eocene–early Miocene volcanic flows
- Oligocene–early Miocene ash-flow tuff
- sedimentary rocks

MESOZOIC
- Triassic-Jurassic nonmarine sedimentary rocks
- Triassic marine rocks

PALEOZOIC
- foreland basin sediments
- late Paleozoic carbonate shelf sequence
- early Paleozoic carbonate shelf sequence
- continental slope and deep-sea basin deposits

MISCELLANEOUS
- mixed breccias
- metamorphic-igneous complex rocks

INTRUSIVE ROCKS
- Cenozoic granitic rocks
- Mesozoic mafic and granitic rocks

Deeth

Wells

Humboldt River

WOOD HILLS

EAST HUMBOLDT RANGE

SIGNAL HILL

CLOVER VALLEY

Snow Water Lake playa

INDEPENDENCE VALLEY

PEQUOP MOUNTAINS

SECRET PASS

RUBY MOUNTAINS

hot springs deposits

to Ruby Marshes

RUBY VALLEY

SPRUCE MOUNTAIN RIDGE

SPRUCE MOUNTAIN

GOSHUTE PASS

GOSHUTE VALLEY

DOLLY VARDEN MOUNTAINS

BOONE SPRING HILLS

BUTTE VALLEY

DELCER BUTTES

WEST BUTTES

MEDICINE RANGE

CHERRY CREEK RANGE

Currie

CURRIE HILLS

STEPTOE VALLEY

Goshute Lake playa

Lages Station

231 230 232 229 229 93 80 80 ALT 93 93

N

0   5   10   15   20 miles

----- detachment fault (dashed if concealed or inferred)

--- normal fault (dashed if concealed or inferred)

Geology along US 93 between the US 93A junction and Wells.

from the McGill mining area in the southern Steptoe Valley continued until the 1980s, but today the tracks are abandoned and have been removed from the road crossing. West of the highway at Currie are prominent dark-brown bluffs of andesite of Oligocene and Miocene age, similar to the volcanic rocks that form the Currie Hills to the east. Below the andesite flows in this area are orange-red sandstones of Jurassic age. The red sandstone was quarried as building stone at two localities along the base of the Currie Hills.

The rocks at Goshute Pass are Ordovician limestone, dolomite, and shale of the Pogonip Group. These rocks are metamorphosed to varying degrees, probably by the effects of a pluton of diorite emplaced into Pennsylvanian and Permian strata to the north along the Spruce Mountain Ridge. In 1869, lead and silver ores were discovered at Spruce Mountain, and a mining district was organized in the area in 1871. The ore formed along fractures in dolomite and limestone, deposited by fluids associated with the magma. Most of the mining was done by 1916.

North of Spruce Mountain, low roadcuts along US 93 expose white Miocene-age sandstone and limestone, much of which is rich in volcanic ash. You can see rugged, glaciated peaks of the Ruby Mountains to the west and northwest, across the expansive lowland of Ruby Valley.

RUBY MOUNTAINS AND RUBY MARSHES

You can head west on NV 229 to get a better view of the Ruby Mountains and go bird-watching at Ruby Marshes. NV 229 passes near the southern tip of the East Humboldt Range, not much more than a north-trending ridge of gray Devonian limestone here. The Warm Creek mining district at the south end of the ridge produced mostly zinc, lead, and silver ores from shattered and altered sedimentary rocks between 1912 and 1943.

The stunning eastern escarpment of the Ruby Mountains was uplifted at least 6,500 feet along the normal fault system at the base of the slope. Because the eastern side of the Ruby Mountain block has been lifted up, the entire range is tilted down toward the west and the highest peaks are located near the eastern slope. The bedrock of the northern Ruby Mountains is mostly deformed and metamorphosed Precambrian and Paleozoic sedimentary rocks, part

The eastern escarpment of the Ruby Mountains seen west of NV 229 from Ruby Valley.

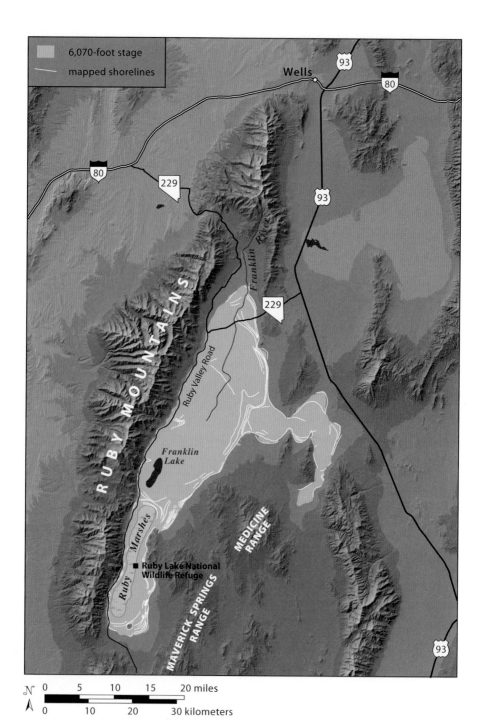

Pleistocene Lake Franklin (tan) filled the Ruby Valley about 17,000 years ago.
White lines are mapped shorelines. —Modified from Munroe and Laabs, 2013

of the East Humboldt–Ruby Mountain metamorphic core complex. You can see these rocks if you continue through Secret Pass on NV 229. See the side trip from I-80 to Secret Pass, as well as the discussion in the introduction about metamorphic core complexes.

Streams draining the mountains collect in an extensive tract of wetlands, lakes, and meadows known as the Ruby Marshes. Turn south onto Ruby Valley Road (Highway 767) to reach the wetlands. More than two hundred springs exist in the Ruby Valley, many of them aligned along the fault zone at the base of the mountain slope. During the Pleistocene ice ages, when glaciers were carving the magnificent peaks of the Ruby Mountains, Ruby Valley was inundated by Lake Franklin, which rose and fell many times with the oscillations of the Pleistocene climate. About 17,000 years ago, Lake Franklin reached its most recent maximum stage, at which time it covered 400 square miles of the Ruby Valley to a depth of 100 feet.

About 7 miles north of the intersection with NV 229, US 93 passes just west of Snow Water Lake playa, a barren plain of white silt and clay in the lowest part of Clover Valley. During the late Pleistocene ice ages, Clover Valley was inundated by at least 150 feet of water in Lake Clover. At its maximum stage, the water body penetrated eastward through the low area between the Wood Hills and Spruce Mountain Ridge to partially flood Independence Valley to the east.

In the Clover Valley, US 93 parallels the eastern escarpment of the East Humboldt Range, composed of gneiss, schist, and quartzite of the Ruby Mountains–East Humboldt metamorphic core complex. The high-grade gneiss is thought to be of Archean age, more than 2.5 billion years old. The south-dipping foliation in the core metamorphic rocks is responsible for the streaks and layers you can see from US 93 exposed in the higher slopes. The metamorphic rocks rose to the surface from deep within Earth's crust in Cenozoic time, when a thick mass of overlying rock slid off a rising dome. (For more discussion of these rocks, see the NV 231 road guide.)

Southwest from the northern intersection of NV 232, the Clover Valley Road, the conical hill protruding from the East Humboldt Range is Signal Hill, composed of Silurian and Devonian limestone in the upper plate of the metamorphic core complex. The low outcrops of reddish material between the higher parts of the East Humboldt Range and Signal Hill are Miocene rhyolite flows. The Wood Hills, to the east of US 93, consist of mostly of deformed and foliated marble, slate, and quartzite of the core complex.

Wells to Jackpot

Wells was an important rest stop along the California Trail in the mid-1800s. In the later 1800s, when the transcontinental railroad was completed, Wells became an important center of commerce for ranching and mining. On the morning of February 21, 2008, Wells was shaken by a magnitude 6.0 earthquake. Such strong temblors are not common in this part of Nevada, far east from the more seismically active areas. The epicenter of the earthquake was located a few miles northeast of Wells, but no surface fault rupture was produced during the event.

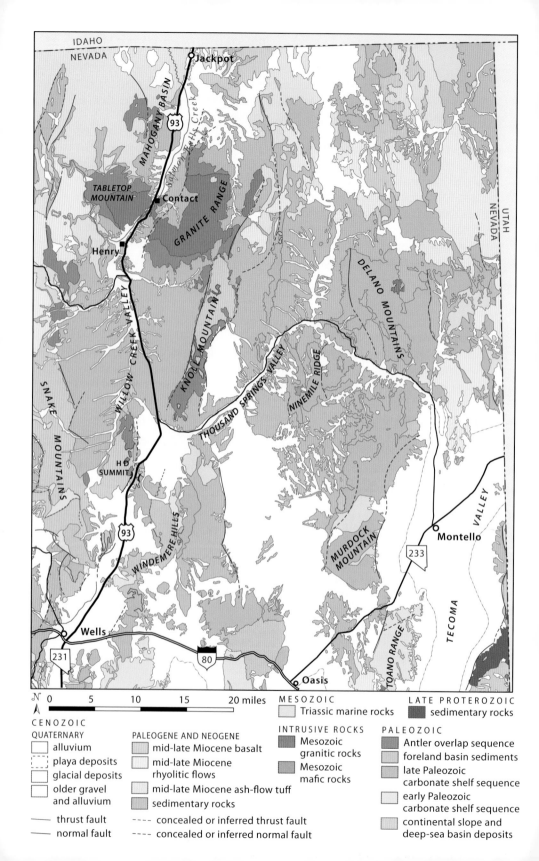

IDAHO
NEVADA

Jackpot

Salmon Falls Creek

MAHOGANY BASIN

93

TABLETOP
MOUNTAIN

Contact

GRANITE RANGE

Henry

DELANO MOUNTAINS

UTAH
NEVADA

KNOLL MOUNTAIN

WILLOW CREEK VALLEY

THOUSAND SPRINGS VALLEY

NINEMILE RIDGE

SNAKE MOUNTAINS

HD SUMMIT

93

WINDEMERE HILLS

MURDOCK MOUNTAIN

Montello

233

TECOMA VALLEY

Wells

231

80

TOANO RANGE

Oasis

N 0   5   10   15   20 miles

MESOZOIC
☐ Triassic marine rocks

LATE PROTEROZOIC
■ sedimentary rocks

CENOZOIC
QUATERNARY
☐ alluvium
☐ playa deposits
☐ glacial deposits
☐ older gravel
   and alluvium

── thrust fault
── normal fault

PALEOGENE AND NEOGENE
☐ mid-late Miocene basalt
☐ mid-late Miocene
   rhyolitic flows
☐ mid-late Miocene ash-flow tuff
☐ sedimentary rocks

--- concealed or inferred thrust fault
--- concealed or inferred normal fault

INTRUSIVE ROCKS
■ Mesozoic
   granitic rocks
■ Mesozoic
   mafic rocks

PALEOZOIC
■ Antler overlap sequence
☐ foreland basin sediments
☐ late Paleozoic
   carbonate shelf sequence
☐ early Paleozoic
   carbonate shelf sequence
☐ continental slope and
   deep-sea basin deposits

North of Wells, US 93 crosses a barren lowland between the Windermere Hills on the east and the Snake Mountains to the west, both ranges composed of Devonian through Pennsylvanian rock layers. Barite, a barium sulfate mineral useful in oil and gas drilling, occurs as a bedded deposit in some of these layers and was extensively mined starting in the 1980s.

North of H D Summit, you can see Thousand Springs Valley extending to the northeast, which carries water east to the Bonneville Salt Flats. North of where the highway crosses Thousand Springs Creek, Knoll Mountain lies east of US 93. It is composed of late Paleozoic sedimentary rocks, with its flanks partly covered by Cenozoic volcanic rock. Farther north, in the Granite Range, a large pluton of Jurassic granite is emplaced into the late Paleozoic rocks, as the name implies.

About 5 miles north of the Thousand Springs Creek crossing, the highway passes over the divide that separates the Thousand Springs Creek drainage basin from the north-flowing Salmon Falls Creek drainage. This divide marks the boundary between the internally drained Great Basin to the south and the Snake River drainage to the north, which reaches the Pacific Ocean via the Columbia River.

In the low roadcuts and mounds in this area, you can see soft white to gray, ash-rich sandstones of the Humboldt Formation of Miocene age. Near Henry, an abandoned railroad station, you can see the gorge of Salmon Falls Creek west of US 93. The creek cut this gorge into Miocene tuffs and rhyolite flows. The flat tops of the mountains west of the highway are composed of a thick Miocene rhyolite flow that caps a series of softer tuffs and ash-rich sandstones. About 4 miles northeast of the Henry site, US 93 skirts the eastern slopes of Tabletop Mountain, the top of which is capped by the same resistant rhyolite flow.

Near the site of the old settlement of Contact, brownish knobs of Jurassic granodiorite are exposed along the road. The outcrops exhibit classic spheroidal weathering, the tendency to form rounded knobs and spheres as the bedrock naturally disintegrates. Small veins of aplite, a very fine-grained igneous rock, cut through the granodiorite in some of these exposures. This plutonic igneous rock intrudes late Paleozoic limestone and has metamorphosed the older rocks into marble and schist. The name of the historic mining town reflects the concentration of copper minerals in the contact zone between the granodiorite and metamorphosed limestone. The copper ores were mined sporadically between 1895 and 1957. Lesser amounts of lead, zinc, silver, and gold were also recovered but not enough to sustain mining after the 1960s.

About 2 miles north of the Contact site, in vicinity of milepost 126, US 93 passes through a series of roadcuts exposing Miocene-age volcanic rocks broken and displaced along several small faults. The layers of volcanic tuff here range from very light-colored air-fall tuffs to darker brown ash-flow tuffs to an almost black, glassy, and firmly welded tuff known as vitrophyre. All of the ash probably originated in a single cycle of explosive eruptions to the north. Volcanic rocks of this type, along with some associated ash-rich sediments, are widespread along US 93 from this point north into Idaho.

A spheroidally weathered exposure of Jurassic granodiorite near the historic mining site of Contact on US 93.

Close view of faulted Miocene volcanic tuffs exposed along US 93 north of Contact. The black material in the upper part of the sequence is vitrophyre, a densely welded ash-flow tuff. The thinly stratified material beneath it is an ash-rich sandstone. The gray, tan, and white materials lower in the sequence are air-fall tuffs.

Roadcut along US 93 exposing ash-rich, lake-deposited sediments of Miocene age south of Jackpot.

About 10 miles south of Jackpot, the landforms are dominated by flat-topped mesas and plateaus consisting of Miocene volcanic rocks, part of the Columbia Plateau Province. This pattern is noticeably different from the alternating mountains and valleys so characteristic of the Basin and Range Province to the south. Though normal faults do exist in this area, they are more widely spaced and generally have smaller displacements than the range-bounding faults farther south.

Near milepost 138, Salmon Falls Creek crosses under US 93 and continues northwest into southern Idaho. A rest stop on the west side of the road is a good place to view the Miocene welded tuffs and rhyolite flows exposed in the bluffs on either side of the river. Crude columnar jointing, formed as the hot ash cooled and contracted, is present in some of the tuffs. Between the Salmon Falls Creek rest stop and Jackpot, 4 miles north, the roadcuts along the highway expose additional units of Miocene ash-flow tuff, rhyolite flows, and ash-rich sediments.

US 93 Alternate
US 93 at Lages Station—West Wendover
58 miles

North of its departure from US 93, US 93A heads northeast to West Wendover and I-80. The brown hills northwest of the road are the Currie Hills, and the more prominent forested mountain range farther north is the Dolly Varden Mountains, both composed of volcanic rocks that overlie and largely conceal Permian and Triassic sedimentary rocks. The Dolly Varden Mountains are heavily mineralized, and silver and copper mining has occurred at varying levels of

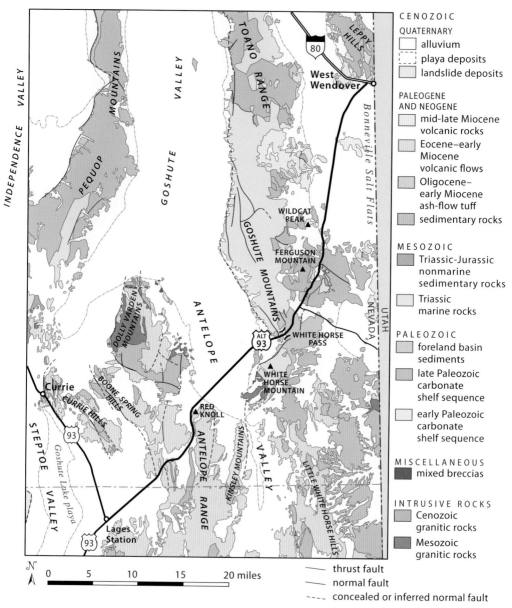

Geology along US 93A between US 93 at Lages Station and West Wendover.

intensity since the 1870s. As recently as the 1980s, major open-pit mines were still active.

As US 93A winds through the Boone Spring Hills, the roadcuts expose a variety of volcanic rocks of Miocene and Oligocene age. Especially prominent are several units of light-colored welded volcanic ash containing many small rock fragments. This kind of tuff formed when great clouds of turbulent ash

Roadcut along US 93A in the Boone Spring Hills, exposing Oligocene tuff. The pinkish-tan material is welded volcanic ash, while the larger angular pieces are fragments of rock incorporated into the ash.

flowed over the surface from some distant source, picking up angular fragments of rock in the process. Darker andesite lava flows overlie the lighter-colored tuffs on both sides of the road.

Northwest of the Boone Spring Hills, US 93A swings north around Red Knoll, a conical peak composed of dark-brown andesite. On the east side of Antelope Valley, you can see White Horse Mountain, an isolated peak at the southern tip of the Goshute Mountains. The light-colored cliffs on the slopes of White Horse Mountain are thick layers of west-dipping Devonian limestone. The folds in these layers were probably generated during the late Mesozoic Era when compressional deformation related to the Sevier Orogeny swept through here.

US 93A crosses over the southern Goshute Mountains at White Horse Pass, where roadcuts on both sides of the road expose layers of black limestone and shale that are commonly folded and faulted. These rocks are part of the Antler foreland basin sequence, marine sediments that accumulated east of the Antler highland in Mississippian and Pennsylvanian time. For several miles northeast of White Horse Pass, roadcuts along the highway expose more of the gently folded, highly fractured black limestone, rich in carbon residues.

As US 93A continues north along the eastern side of the Goshute Mountains, it passes just east of Ferguson Mountain. The layered rocks exposed on its east slopes are complexly faulted limestone of Pennsylvanian and Permian age. Ores of copper and silver were mined from the limestone sporadically from the 1880s to the 1950s. Where the highway swings past Ferguson Mountain, several

A normal fault cuts foreland basin rocks exposed in a roadcut on the south side of US 93A at White Horse Pass. The brown shaly layers to the left (east) are separated from the darker limestone layers to the right (west) by a zone of crushed rock along the fault plane. The close-up view of black limestone shows how intersecting veins of white calcite have filled the fractures.

Colorful roadcut through weathered limestone along US 93A in the Ferguson Mountain area.

of the roadcuts along US 93A expose brightly colored weathering products of the mineralized rock. The red and orange shades form as the metal-bearing limestone weathers to iron oxide and iron hydroxide minerals.

About 15 miles south of West Wendover, US 93A passes Wildcat Peak, a conspicuous knob of Miocene welded tuffs 2 miles west of the highway. North from Wildcat Peak, US 93A gradually descends toward the Bonneville Salt Flats, a vast, salt-encrusted plain that covers a large part of western Utah and extends a few miles into Nevada. The white surface is composed mostly of halite, the mineral name for common sodium chloride salt, but also contains a variety of other alkaline minerals and silt. This great plain was the floor of an immense ice age water body known as Lake Bonneville. At its most recent peak about 15,000 years ago, Lake Bonneville covered 20,000 square miles of lowlands under as much as 1,000 feet of water. The lake level stabilized long enough to carve numerous shoreline terraces on the lower slopes of hills and mountains. The dissolved salts in the water of Lake Bonneville, though hardly noticeable in the freshwater lake during Pleistocene time, accumulated as a crust on the exposed and desiccated floor of the ancient lake as the climate became warmer and drier over the past 10,000 years.

View east from US 93A of hills about 7 miles south of West Wendover. The well-developed horizontal terrace was a shoreline eroded in the volcanic rock during a stable period in the level of Lake Bonneville. The light-colored silt and clay exposed at its base are lake deposits.

US 95
Indian Springs—Beatty—Tonopah
167 miles
See map on page 53 for geology east of Amargosa Valley.

Between Las Vegas and Indian Springs, US 95 follows the trend of the Las Vegas shear zone through the Las Vegas Valley. The geologic features viewed from US 95 in the valley, including the Spring Mountains, Sheep Range, Las Vegas shear zone, and Tule Springs Fossil Beds, are discussed in the chapter for the Las Vegas area.

The Nevada National Security Site, formerly known as the Nevada Test Site, lies to the north of US 95, so the whole area northeast of US 95 between the Sheep Range and Tonopah is off limits to the public. Between 1951 and 1992,

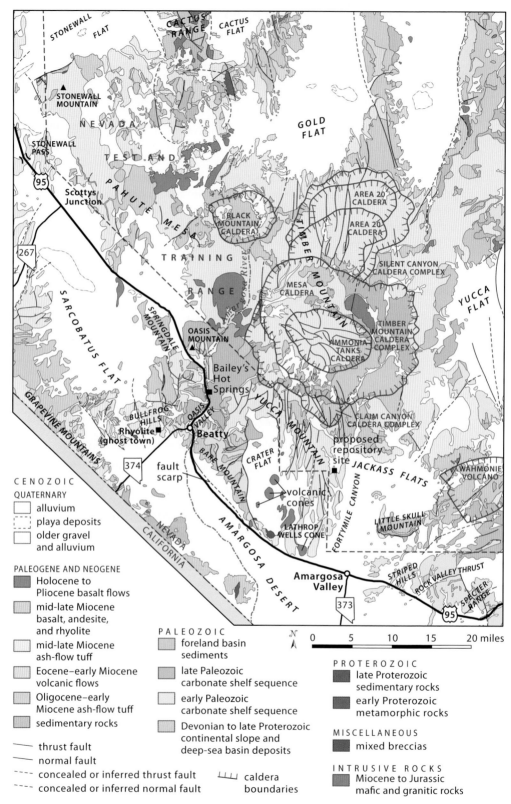

Geology along US 95 between Amargosa Valley and Scottys Junction.

about one thousand nuclear tests were conducted in the area, of which around nine hundred were underground. In the 1950s, mushroom clouds from the atmospheric tests could be seen from downtown Las Vegas.

Water emerges from springs along the north end of the Las Vegas shear zone at Indian Springs and Cactus Springs. West of the road to Mercury, US 95 heads through a narrow pass between the Spring Mountains to the south and the Specter Range to the north, both containing many faulted blocks of Proterozoic to early Paleozoic rock. Most of the hills close to the road are Cambrian carbonates. Between Cactus Springs and Amargosa Valley, US 95 is on or near the bed of the Las Vegas & Tonopah Railroad, built in 1905–07. It never got farther than Goldfield and was dismantled in 1919.

The Specter Range is separated from the Striped Hills to the north by the northeast-trending Rock Valley thrust fault, an active structure that occasionally triggers small earthquakes. The aptly named Striped Hills consist of a continuous section of late Proterozoic (on the south) to Ordovician (northernmost) rocks that are steeply dipping to overturned.

Southwest Nevada Volcanic Field and Yucca Mountain

Between the Amargosa Valley intersection and north of Beatty, US 95 skirts the southwestern margin of the Southwest Nevada volcanic field. The ridges to the northeast have the characteristically smooth profile of volcanic rock, all erupted from more than six major calderas that formed between about 15 and 7.5 million years ago. Some of the older calderas are known by only the ash-flow tuffs erupted from them, as they have been either covered by or obliterated by younger eruptions. Each caldera erupted ash-flow sheets within a 300,000- to 100,000-year time span. Eruptions of two of the larger ash-flow tuffs, the 12.8-million-year-old Tonopah Spring Tuff and the 12.7-million-year-old Tiva Canyon Tuff, occurred within a period of 100,000 years.

The Nuclear Waste Policy Act of 1982 designated that a number of locations in the United States be further studied to select one final site for the underground disposal of high-level nuclear waste from commercial nuclear power

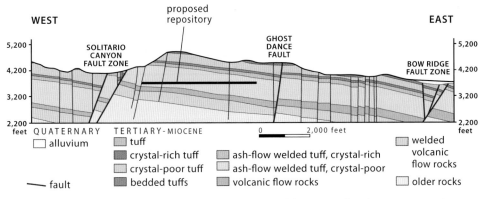

Cross section of Yucca Mountain showing the location of the proposed nuclear waste repository.
—Modified from Day and others, 1998

plants. Studies of Yucca Mountain began in 1978, and it has been referred to as the most studied piece of real estate on the planet. In 1987, Congress selected Yucca Mountain as the repository, and in 2008, a license application was submitted to the Nuclear Regulatory Commission for a permit to start construction. The project was controversial, and federal funding was eliminated in 2010, leaving the repository plans in limbo.

Yucca Mountain is one of several north-trending ridges north of US 95 consisting of layers of welded to nonwelded tuff. The ridges have a gentle eastward tilt because steeply west-dipping faults along their western edges tip the blocks downward on their eastern side. The repository was to be situated on a relatively intact block between two north-trending faults that exhibit some displacement in Quaternary time. Of equal or greater concern is the proximity of the active Death Valley fault zone in California. Also, Quaternary-age cinder cones in Crater Flat, to the west of the Yucca Mountain crest, show there was volcanic activity here as recently as 60,000 years ago.

The tunnels intended to house the waste canisters are roughly 1,000 feet below the ground surface and 1,000 feet above the water table. Groundwater flows from the Yucca Mountain area southward to the Amargosa Valley, where the closest down-gradient people live, and where the radionuclides could potentially contaminate water wells. However, any potential migration of radionuclides would be tens of thousands of years in the future, as they would need to first breech the repository barriers, then migrate 1,000 feet downward through the unsaturated zone between the repository and the water table, and subsequently move down-gradient about 20 miles with the groundwater flow.

Amargosa to Beatty

Just east of the Amargosa Valley junction is Gate 510, one of the two entry points into the Nevada National Security Site. Looking north along that paved road about 5 miles, you can see Little Skull Mountain with its 10-million-year-old basalt. A magnitude 5.6 earthquake occurred there on June 29, 1992, one day after the magnitude 7.3 Landers earthquake in the Mojave Desert in California. One of the last gold rushes in Nevada occurred in 1928 at Wahmonie, a mining camp northeast of Little Skull Mountain. Would-be prospectors arrived at camp with small houses on trucks—the original RVs—after the discovery of high-grade silver-gold ore. The camp is now within the security site and off-limits.

North of Amargosa Valley, you can see Pliocene and Quaternary basalt lava flows and cinder cones and a small dune field. Lathrop Wells Cone, mined for red cinders, is a half mile north of US 95 between mileposts 36 and 37. North and south of the red cinder cone are ridges of tuff. You can sneak a peek at several other cones from milepost 40, where a gap in the low hills north of the highway allows a view across Crater Flat toward Yucca Mountain in the distance. About 2 miles south of the highway is a dune field known as the Big Dune.

The Amargosa Desert stretches along the west side of US 95 from Amargosa Valley to Beatty. Beneath the Amargosa Desert floor is a 2- to 4-mile-thick section of stream and lake sediments, volcanic ash deposits, and local lava flows. Lake marls and silts mapped around the margins of the Amargosa Desert indicate that a lake, or spring-fed marshes and isolated ponds, occupied some of the

Carrara Formation

Zabriskie Quartzite

Bare Mountain consists of mostly Cambrian units, from the Wood Canyon Formation at its base up through the Zabriskie Quartzite, Carrara Formation, Bonanza King Formation, and Nopah Formation. Numerous faults cut the rock layers.

area 4 million years ago and possibly more recently. Mammoth remains have been found in the lakebeds.

The Amargosa River flows southeast through the western part of the valley to end in Death Valley. Prior to 4 million years ago, the river was confined to the enclosed basin of the Oasis Valley north of Beatty. Sometime between 4 and 0.5 million years ago, the Amargosa Narrows was carved through bedrock at Beatty, and the two valleys became an integrated drainage. Not until 150,000 to 100,000 years ago did the combined Oasis Valley–Amargosa Valley system breach a drainage divide near Eagle Mountain, the lone triangular peak seen looking southwest across the Amargosa Desert, and enter California.

Bare Mountain, the prominent boldly banded mountain to the north of the highway between milepost 46 and milepost 56, is composed of mainly Cambrian rock layers. The reddish cliff-former near the base is Zabriskie Quartzite. Between milepost 52 and milepost 53 is a turnoff to Carrara (a ghost town), established in 1913 to service a marble quarry in the Carrara Formation. On the east side of Bare Mountain are the Daisy and Diamond Queen Mines, where fluorspar was mined in the 1950s from breccia in the Nopah Dolomite of Cambrian age. Fluorspar is another name for fluorite, a calcium fluoride mineral useful in metallurgy, glassmaking, ceramics, and the chemical industry.

As US 95 begins to curve around the north end of Bare Mountain, watch for a prominent, 12- to 15-foot-high fault scarp that cuts the lower part of the alluvial fan east of US 95. It is quite noticeable at milepost 55 and milepost 56. US 95 crosses the usually dry Amargosa River just south of the Amargosa Narrows.

Beatty to Tonopah

Beatty is the only surviving town from the mining boom of the early 1900s in the Bullfrog mining district to the west of town. Gold and silver deposits are in fissures and veins in rhyolitic ignimbrites of Miocene age. Rhyolite, a ghost town about 4 miles west of Beatty, is named for the rock hosting the rich ores. In the mid-1980s, large open-pit excavations and heap leaching sites were established just south of Rhyolite.

On the east side of Beatty are spectacular volcanic rocks in various colors, part of the Southwest Nevada volcanic field. North of Beatty, US 95 follows the mostly buried Oasis Valley fault, a major breakaway fault that dips west and northwest beneath the intensely faulted Miocene volcanic rocks of the Bullfrog Hills west of the road. A breakaway fault is where normal and listric faults merge at depth into a low-angle fault, tilting the overlying fault blocks. Layers of landslide rubble interbedded in the volcanics probably originated from steep fault scarps, shaken loose during earthquakes that must have accompanied the intense extensional faulting between about 16 and 9 million years ago.

About 5 miles north of Beatty, a series of hot springs along the floor of the Oasis Valley sustain green vegetation and trees. These springs are probably related to faults here. The water issuing from alluvium at Bailey's Hot Springs, just east of the road, has a temperature of 109°F, and geochemical evidence suggests that subsurface water may be as hot as 278°F.

Between Beatty and Goldfield, tuffs and volcanic ash erupted from calderas in Miocene time dominate the landscape. They overlie Precambrian to Cambrian rocks, which are exposed here and there. In places, even younger volcanics, flows of basalt and andesite, cap the tuff. These resistant rocks form mesas, including Pahute Mesa, east of Scottys Junction, and Malpais Mesa, southwest of Goldfield. At Stonewall Pass, the crumbly stratified rock along the highway is ash-rich sandstone and conglomerate deposited in ancient lakes and streams. Stonewall Mountain, a prominent dome-shaped peak uplifted along a northeast-aligned normal fault, consists of Miocene volcanics that formed within a local caldera. Silver and gold ores were discovered here in 1904 but were depleted by about 1915. The low hills northwest of the NV 266 junction are the Cuprite Hills, named for a copper oxide mineral. The brownish-tan slopes are outcrops of late Precambrian and Cambrian sandstone, siltstone, shale, and limestone overlain by layered Miocene volcanic rocks.

Gold ores were first discovered in the Goldfield area in 1902, and within a few years intense mining activity was well underway in the hills east of the town. Peak production occurred in 1910, when between 15,000 and 30,000 people lived in Goldfield. In the 1980s, tailings and waste rock from the old mines, along with some ore from open pits, was processed at Goldfield, but the production was comparatively small. Overall, the mines in the Goldfield district have produced a staggering 140 tons of gold, 50 tons of silver, and 18,000 tons of copper. Production figures for most mining districts are usually in ounces.

The ore-bearing veins occur in altered andesite. Starting about 22 million years ago, the andesitic magma oozed up into fractures around the periphery of an ancient caldera. Oxidation of the iron sulfide minerals in the altered volcanic rocks produces the red and brown splotches that are visible in the yellowish hills east of Goldfield.

About 20 miles north of Goldfield, isolated hills to the north and east of the highway are composed of primarily of Miocene volcanic and sedimentary rocks. Eight miles south of Tonopah, US 95 passes west of Klondike Peak, the most prominent of several knobs of brown rhyolite of Miocene age visible just east of the highway. Two miles farther north, the highway bends to the northeast around the base of Hasbrouck Peak, the slopes of which bear roadcuts and tailings

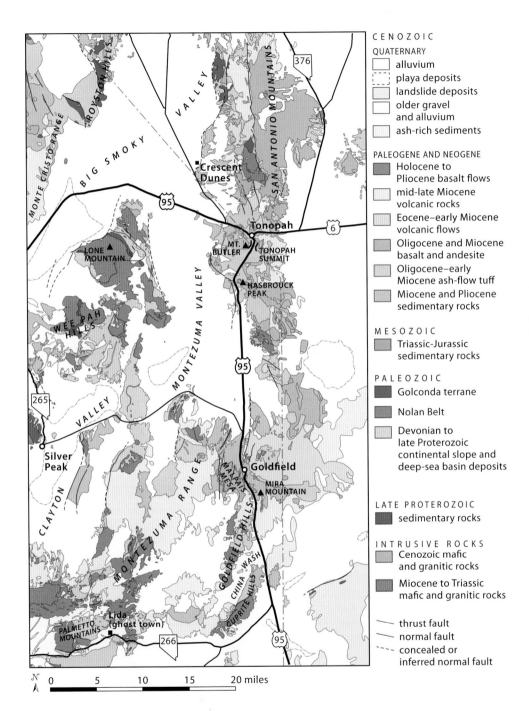

CENOZOIC

QUATERNARY

- [ ] alluvium
- [ ] playa deposits
- [ ] landslide deposits
- [ ] older gravel and alluvium
- [ ] ash-rich sediments

PALEOGENE AND NEOGENE

- Holocene to Pliocene basalt flows
- mid-late Miocene volcanic rocks
- Eocene–early Miocene volcanic flows
- Oligocene and Miocene basalt and andesite
- Oligocene–early Miocene ash-flow tuff
- Miocene and Pliocene sedimentary rocks

MESOZOIC

- Triassic-Jurassic sedimentary rocks

PALEOZOIC

- Golconda terrane
- Nolan Belt
- Devonian to late Proterozoic continental slope and deep-sea basin deposits

LATE PROTEROZOIC

- sedimentary rocks

INTRUSIVE ROCKS

- Cenozoic mafic and granitic rocks
- Miocene to Triassic mafic and granitic rocks

— thrust fault
— normal fault
--- concealed or inferred normal fault

Geology along US 95 between Goldfield and Tonopah.

piles from old mineral prospects. The light-colored bedrock of Hasbrouck Peak is middle Miocene to early Pliocene tuffs and associated sediments, inter-layered with thin, brownish lava flows. Along the grade rising toward Tonopah Summit from the south, the view to the west and north from US 95 is domi-nated by Mt. Butler, the highest of several knobs and domes of Miocene vol-canic rocks in the Tonopah area. The light-colored lower slopes of Mt. Butler are tuffs and ash-rich sandstones, while the brown crags near the transmission towers at the summit are rhyolite and dacite flows.

US 95
Tonopah—Hawthorne
103 miles
See map on page 237 for geology west of Tonopah.

Tonopah is situated among several peaks and domes of 20- to 16-million-year-old volcanic rocks at the southern end of the San Antonio Mountains. Mt. Butler, located south of the downtown area with communications towers on its summit, consists of a large dome-shaped mass of dacite, a felsic volcanic rock very similar to rhyolite. To the northwest of Mt. Butler, the smaller mound decorated with the white T is Brougher Mountain, another dacite dome. Southwest of town, Siebert Mountain is capped by a dacite flow that overlies white tuff and ash-rich sedi-mentary rocks. On the northeast side of Tonopah, Mt. Oddie, the light-colored mountain with tailings piles and mining structures at the base, is another plug of Miocene rhyolite, as is the reddish-hued Ararat Mountain just north of it.

Early Paleozoic sandstone, shale, and limestone lie buried under the volca-nics. So much magma rose through these older rocks in Miocene time that it is likely much more magma cooled into plutonic igneous rock deep under the volcanic pile. Associated magmatic fluids were probably involved in depositing the ores that made Tonopah one of Nevada's most illustrious historic mining

Panoramic view of Tonopah south from Mt. Oddie toward the dacite domes of Mt. Butler (left), Siebert Mountain (center), and Brougher Mountain, bearing the large white T.

districts. Silver ores, discovered in 1900, were contained in crosscutting veins developed along fractures and faults in the Miocene volcanic rocks. Some of the veins were as wide as 40 feet and contained minerals bearing gold, copper, zinc, and tungsten, in addition to the silver. The historic buildings downtown, the mining museum, the old head frames and structures on the slopes, and the rusting machinery and tailing piles all reflect Tonopah's mining heritage.

West from Tonopah, the combined US 95/US 6 crosses the vast lowlands at the extreme southern end of the Big Smoky Valley. A small sandy area called the Crescent Dunes has formed near the western slopes of the San Antonio Mountains about 8 miles northeast of the highway. The dunes, formed by the prevailing winds blowing across the bare surface of the Big Smoky Valley, are sometimes difficult to see from the road.

Just west of the Crescent Dunes stands the Crescent Dunes solar energy project. The 600-foot-high heat-collecting tower dominates the view north across Big Smoky Valley, especially in the daytime, when the sunlight creates a brilliantly luminous flare hovering above the desert floor. This innovative plant, completed in 2015, uses molten salt to capture and transfer the sun's heat energy. The molten salt also stores heat efficiently, allowing the plant to produce power through its heat-exchange system after the sun sets.

To the southwest of the highway is Lone Mountain, an isolated peak consisting mostly of Cretaceous granitic rock. On the western flanks of Lone Mountain, the intrusive contact between the granite pluton and late Precambrian to Cambrian sedimentary rocks is discernible from the highway. The west-dipping Precambrian and Cambrian strata consist of brown sandstone and phyllite and tan dolomite, while the underlying granite is light gray and massive, forming the high point.

On the east side of Big Smoky Valley, US 95 skirts the base of the Monte Cristo Range, low hills composed of colorful exposures of Miocene volcanic and sedimentary rocks, around 15 million years old. In the deeply eroded hills south

Exposures of Miocene volcanic rocks south of Coaldale Junction on US 95. Darker rocks are basalt and andesite flows, while lighter-colored rocks are mostly tuff and ash-rich sediments. Brown ledges are predominantly composed of welded ash-flow tuff.

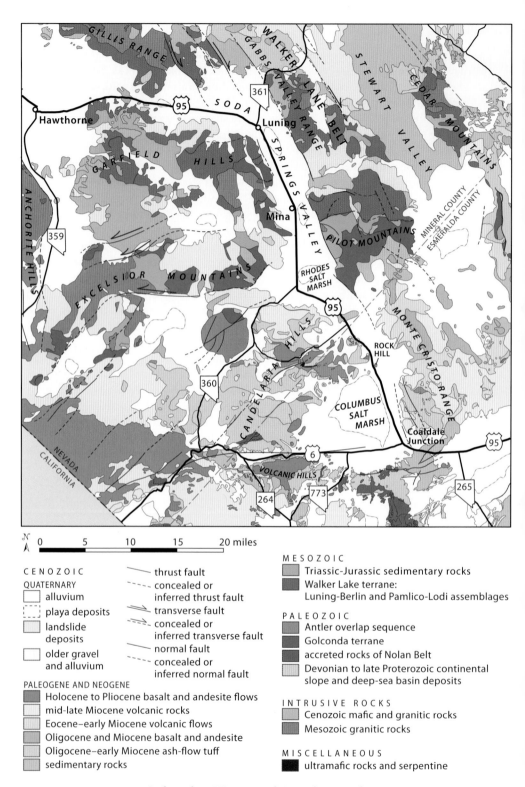

CENOZOIC

QUATERNARY

- ☐ alluvium
- ⬚ playa deposits
- ☐ landslide deposits
- ☐ older gravel and alluvium

PALEOGENE AND NEOGENE

- Holocene to Pliocene basalt and andesite flows
- mid-late Miocene volcanic rocks
- Eocene–early Miocene volcanic flows
- Oligocene and Miocene basalt and andesite
- Oligocene–early Miocene ash-flow tuff
- sedimentary rocks

— thrust fault

--- concealed or inferred thrust fault

⇒ transverse fault

⇒ concealed or inferred transverse fault

— normal fault

--- concealed or inferred normal fault

MESOZOIC

- Triassic-Jurassic sedimentary rocks
- Walker Lake terrane: Luning-Berlin and Pamlico-Lodi assemblages

PALEOZOIC

- Antler overlap sequence
- Golconda terrane
- accreted rocks of Nolan Belt
- Devonian to late Proterozoic continental slope and deep-sea basin deposits

INTRUSIVE ROCKS

- Cenozoic mafic and granitic rocks
- Mesozoic granitic rocks

MISCELLANEOUS

- ■ ultramafic rocks and serpentine

Geology along US 95 west of Tonopah to Hawthorne.

of the abandoned outpost of Coaldale, multicolored volcanic and sedimentary rocks of Miocene to Pliocene age are exposed. Northwest from Coaldale Junction, the broad playa of Columbus Salt Marsh can be seen west of the highway, beyond which are the colorful volcanic strata of the low Candelaria Hills.

As US 95 passes north of Columbus Salt Marsh, it enters a zone of northeast-trending, left-lateral strike-slip faults that offset the prominent right-lateral faults of the Walker Lane by about 30 miles. This zone, known as the Mina deflection, is named for the small town through which US 95 passes about 30 miles north of Coaldale Junction. Columbus Salt Marsh is in a pull-apart basin, a lowland resulting from the alignment of faults in the Mina deflection, rather than a simple graben resulting from normal faults.

Eight miles northwest of Coaldale Junction, US 95 passes Rock Hill, a small knob of late Paleozoic (and perhaps early Mesozoic) conglomerate, probably shed from the southeastern portion of the Antler highland in Pennsylvanian and

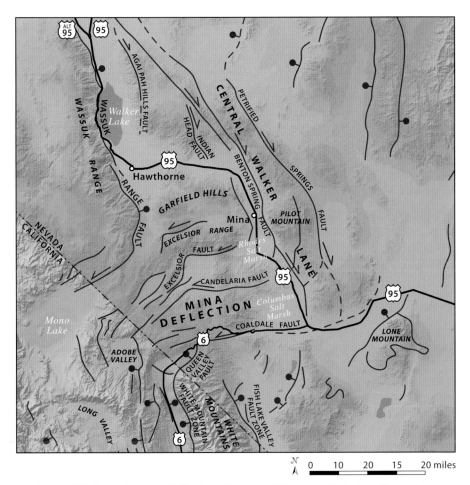

Left-lateral faults in the Mina deflection offset the Walker Lane faults 30 miles to the west. Ball and bar on downdropped side of normal fault. —Modified from Faulds and Henry, 2008

Permian time. These coarse sediments overlie older Cambrian- to Devonian-age shale, chert, and limestone that accumulated in a deep ocean basin west of the Antler highland.

At Redlich Summit, the complexly faulted deep-ocean sediments overlain by the late Paleozoic sandstone and conglomerate are capped by Miocene volcanic rocks. North of Redlich Summit, near the Mineral-Esmeralda county line, a dirt road leads west toward the Candelaria mining district, the tailings of which can be seen west of the highway. These mines were most active in the 1860s to the 1880s, producing silver, along with some minor production of gold, lead, zinc, and antimony.

The oldest rocks in the Candelaria Hills consist of deformed chert and shale of Ordovician age thrust from the west, probably during the Antler Orogeny. These strata are overlain by Permian to Triassic sandstone and conglomerate, which in turn are overthrust by a mangled and metamorphosed sequence of oceanic sediments and volcanic rocks. Numerous dikes of Jurassic igneous rock cut though the entire complicated sequence, and it appears that much of mineralization occurred when the dike rocks were emplaced as magma.

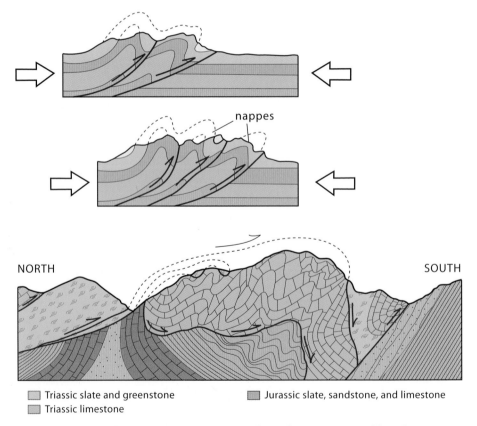

Triassic slate and greenstone   Jurassic slate, sandstone, and limestone
Triassic limestone

Thrust faults and nappes (top) created the complex geologic structure visible in the western side of the Pilot Mountains.

Near the junction of US 95 and the Candelaria Road, the Pilot Mountains come into view to the northeast. Several thrust sheets of contorted layers of gray Triassic limestone and slate have been shoved over the underlying Triassic and Jurassic slate, sandstone, and volcanic rocks of the Gold Range assemblage. Toward the south end of the Pilot Mountains, another package of deformed slate and dark gray volcanic sediments is thought to be related to the Golconda terrane and ranges in age from Permian to Triassic. These deformed terranes are internally faulted and separated from each other by extensive thrusts, which are also folded into great looping geological structures known as nappes.

The main axis of the Excelsior Mountains to the west of US 95 has an east-west alignment that is unusual for the Great Basin area and reflects a number of northeast-trending strike-slip faults along the southern end of the range related to the Mina deflection. The oldest rocks in the north-tilted mountains are Permian and Triassic oceanic sediments and volcanic rocks of the Golconda terrane, overlain by Jurassic sandstone, shale, and conglomerate of the Gold Range assemblage. Younger covering materials, mostly Oligocene and Miocene volcanic rocks, are widely distributed in the lower hills to the north. Extensive and varied mineralization of these rocks led to the organization of several historic mining districts in the Excelsior Mountains beginning in the 1860s, including the Silver Star, Gold Range, Mina, and Excelsior districts. Ores of silver, gold, tungsten, lead, copper, uranium, antimony, manganese, and beryllium have all been produced.

In the Soda Springs Valley, northwest-trending strike-slip faults of the Walker Lane are superimposed on extensional normal faults that elevate the hills and mountains. The strike-slip faults have as much as 10 miles of displacement. The Gabbs Valley Range, northeast of Luning, is described in the narrative for NV 361.

View west from US 95 north of Mina in the vicinity of Black Butte Mine in the Garfield Hills. The dark-colored rocks are mafic oceanic igneous rocks of Permian age in the Golconda terrane, faulted against lighter-colored layers of Permian to Triassic chert, slate, and limestone.

A roadcut on the south side of US 95 along the northern slopes of the Garfield Hills exposes andesitic flows and volcanic breccia of Miocene age. Note the fault on the western end of the roadcut, to the right.

The Garfield Hills, southwest of Luning, are mostly composed of intensely folded and metamorphosed Triassic and Jurassic limestone, slate, sandstone, and volcanic rocks of the Walker Lake terrane (Pamlico-Lodi assemblage), intruded by Cretaceous granitic rocks. The Mesozoic bedrock is capped by Miocene volcanic rocks, consisting chiefly of andesite and basalt flows inter-bedded with layers of tuff and breccia. Silver, gold, lead, and copper ores have been mined since the late 1800s in the Black Dyke Mountain area of the eastern Garfield Hills. To the west, veins and pods of gold, silver, lead, and copper ores in the Pamlico Canyon area on the western side of the hills were intensively mined from the 1880s to about 1930.

US 95
Hawthorne—Fallon—I-80
105 miles

Hawthorne is situated at the south end of the Walker Lake basin, which is bounded on the west by the abrupt eastern escarpment of the Wassuk Range, a product of active normal faulting. The Wassuk Range fault zone, at the base of the slope just west of the highway, extends about 50 miles from south of Haw-thorne to the northern tip of the Wassuk Range. Uplift of the Wassuk Range began 15 to 12 million years ago, occurring in several pulses of rapid displace-ment punctuated by periods of little fault activity. Alluvial fans spreading from the eastern base of the central Wassuk Range are displaced by as much as 130

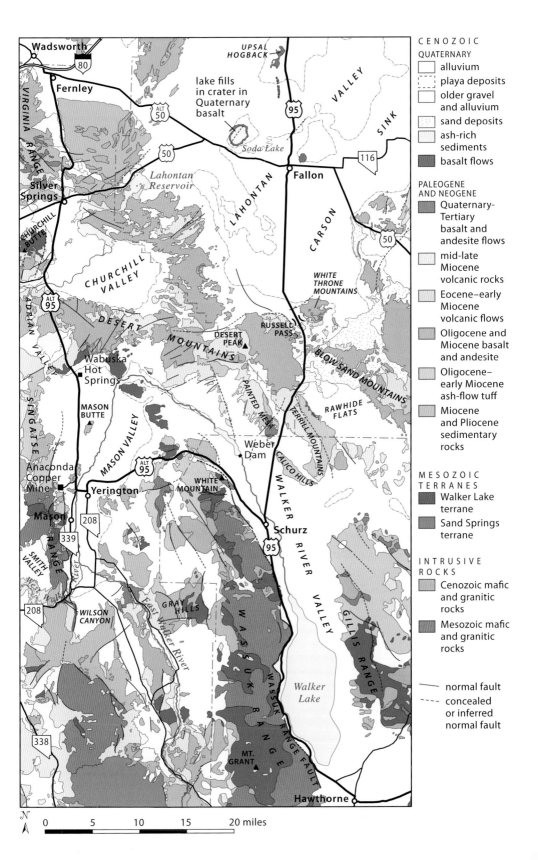

CENOZOIC
QUATERNARY
- alluvium
- playa deposits
- older gravel and alluvium
- sand deposits
- ash-rich sediments
- basalt flows

PALEOGENE AND NEOGENE
- Quaternary-Tertiary basalt and andesite flows
- mid-late Miocene volcanic rocks
- Eocene–early Miocene volcanic flows
- Oligocene and Miocene basalt and andesite
- Oligocene–early Miocene ash-flow tuff
- Miocene and Pliocene sedimentary rocks

MESOZOIC TERRANES
- Walker Lake terrane
- Sand Springs terrane

INTRUSIVE ROCKS
- Cenozoic mafic and granitic rocks
- Mesozoic mafic and granitic rocks

— normal fault
--- concealed or inferred normal fault

Wadsworth
Fernley
VIRGINIA RANGE
Silver Springs
CHURCHILL BUTTE
ADRIAN VALLEY
SINGATSE RANGE
Wabuska Hot Springs
MASON BUTTE
Anaconda Copper Mine
Yerington
Mason
SMITH VALLEY
WILSON CANYON
WEST WALKER RIVER
EAST WALKER RIVER
GRAY HILLS
WHITE MOUNTAIN
MASON VALLEY
DESERT MOUNTAINS
PAINTED MESA
DESERT PEAK
RUSSELL PASS
CHURCHILL VALLEY
Lahontan Reservoir
UPSAL HOGBACK
lake fills in crater in Quaternary basalt
Soda Lake
Fallon
LAHONTAN VALLEY
CARSON SINK
WHITE THRONE MOUNTAINS
BLOW SAND MOUNTAINS
RAWHIDE FLATS
TERRILL MOUNTAINS
CALICO HILLS
Weber Dam
Schurz
WALKER RIVER
WASSUK RANGE
WASSUK RANGE FAULT
MT. GRANT
Walker Lake
GILLIS RANGE
Hawthorne

0   5   10   15   20 miles

feet by normal fault scarps. Recent trenching studies along the fault zone suggest that the rate of displacement over the last 10,000 years is about 0.05 inch per year. This may sound very small by human standards, but the total cumulative displacement on the Wassuk Range fault zone has lifted the mountain block to an elevation as high as 11,239 feet at Mt. Grant, the highest point on the ridge northwest of Hawthorne.

The Walker Lake basin is located in the middle of the Walker Lane, a broad northwest-trending zone of right-lateral strike-slip faults formed by the northwesterly movement of the Pacific Plate against the edge of the North American Plate. Within this part of the Walker Lane, the crust is being sheared to

Satellite image of Walker Lake, bounded by the west-tilted Wassuk Range to the west (left) and the Gillis Range to the east (right). The Walker River enters Walker Lake from the north. —NASA

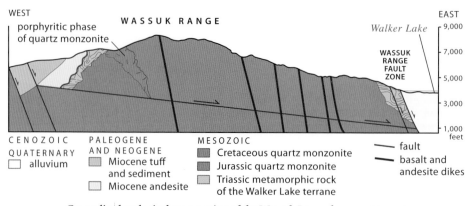

Generalized geological cross section of the Wassuk Range from west to east.

the northwest at a rate of about 0.2 inch per year. Several of these strike-slip faults slice across the floor of the Walker Lake basin just east of the range-front normal fault zone.

The Wassuk Range is predominantly granitic, composed of several plutonic bodies that weather differently. The Walker Lake granite forms the craggy cliffs, whereas both the upper and lower third of the mountain are granodiorite, which weathers to smooth slopes. Older Jurassic and Triassic metavolcanic and sedimentary rocks, the Pine Nut assemblage of the Walker Lake terrane, are visible as darker-colored masses along the lower slopes. These older rocks originated in a volcanic arc and marine basin and were later deformed and accreted to the edge of the ancient continent. Several roadcuts along US 93 west of Walker Lake expose these older accreted rocks, now hydrothermally altered. The Gillis Range, to the east of Walker Lake, is composed of bedrock similar to that of the Wassuk Range, except that the cover of Cenozoic volcanic rocks has not yet been eroded away, especially on the northern end of the range.

Walker Lake is the terminus of the Walker River, one of the major permanent streams in the western Great Basin, sustained year-round by snowpack melting from the high peaks of the Sierra Nevada. The surface of Walker Lake hovers around 3,930 feet above sea level but fluctuates in rhythm with climatic changes that influence the inflow of water from the Sierra Nevada and rate of evaporation. Prior to 1882, when farmers began withdrawing river water to irrigate crops upstream in Mason Valley, the lake stood 150 feet higher. The salinity of the lake is now about eight times greater than it was in the late 1800s, and some native species of fish, such as the endangered Lahontan cutthroat trout, can no longer survive in the lake.

During the Pleistocene ice ages, the Walker Lake basin was filled with the southernmost arm of Lake Lahontan. When the lake level was high, water connected with other arms of the Lahontan system through Mason and Adrian Valleys to the north. The most recent high stage culminated about 15,000 years ago, when the water in the Walker Lake basin rose to an elevation of about 4,360 feet, some 400 feet higher than the current lake. During middle Pleistocene time, from 350,000 to 150,000 years ago, an earlier lake cycle led to an even larger lake, more than 600 feet deeper than modern Walker Lake. Shoreline terraces along the west side of Walker Lake record the various levels of these lakes. You can see drapes and masses of tufa, calcium carbonate precipitated from the water of the ancient lakes, along US 95 and on the lower slopes of the Wassuk Range as the highway skirts the western edge of Walker Lake.

From the north end of Walker Lake, US 95 continues toward Schurz, closely following the historic shoreline of Walker Lake. As the lake level has fallen during the past decade, the river has more deeply incised its stream channel between Weber Dam, northwest of Schurz, and Walker Lake. West of the highway, banded exposures of rocks of the Walker Lake terrane make up the base of the mountain slope.

US 95A branches west from the main road just south of the small town of Schurz, home to the Walker River Paiute Tribe. (See the road guide for US 95 Alternate.) North of Schurz, US 95 passes through hilly terrain of Oligocene and Miocene volcanic rocks dominated by tuffs, ash-rich sedimentary rocks, and

Tufa deposits drape over this boulder of metavolcanic rock along the western side of Walker Lake adjacent to US 95.

andesitic lava flows. Weathered exposures of these rocks can be colorful, a characteristic that no doubt inspired the name Calico Hills for one knoll northeast of Schurz. A little farther north, Painted Mesa can be seen west of the highway.

About 12 miles north of Schurz, US 95 climbs through the hilly slopes of the Terrill Mountains and skirts the western side of Rawhide Flats. In this area, the slopes north of the highway are capped by dark-colored lava flows on which several horizontal Lake Lahontan shoreline terraces are visible. After rising to Russell Pass, US 95 descends into the vast Lahontan Valley, the natural terminus of the Carson River and one of the largest subbasins of Pleistocene Lake Lahontan. At its peak stage of development, the water submerging Lahontan Valley was more than 700 feet deep.

Between 3,000 and 8,000 feet of sediment has collected in the broad basin since the beginning of Pleistocene time. This mostly unconsolidated material contains abundant groundwater distributed in numerous subsurface aquifers. The soils formed at the surface are uncommonly rich, and given the abundance of water in the otherwise dry region, the Lahontan Valley is one of Nevada's most important agricultural regions. (See US 50 for more on the Fallon area.)

About 14 miles north of Fallon, US 95 passes just east of Upsal Hogback, a low ridge composed of very young cinders of basaltic volcanic rock blasted from a shallow crater a short distance to the north. The explosion occurred

Upsal Hogback, west of US 95 and north of Fallon, is capped by a layer of dark-colored basaltic cinders.

during late Quaternary time, probably less than 25,000 years ago, when magma rising toward the surface encountered groundwater that instantly flashed into volatile steam. The magma was propelled from the crater as small blobs of molten rock that cooled in flight to produce the basalt cinders. Soda Lake, about 10 miles to the southwest, is a similar steam explosion crater and may have formed along a buried fault that extends beneath Upsal Hogback.

North from the Upsal Hogback, US 95 passes across the portion of the Carson Sink known as the Forty-Mile Desert, a name that originated during the great western migration along the California Trail in the 1800s. Immigrants bound for California had to leave the Humboldt River near its terminus in the Humboldt Sink to the north and cross 40 miles of parched and barren land before arriving at either the Carson River to the south or the Truckee River to the west. Pleistocene Lake Lahontan shoreline terraces are prominent on the eastern slopes of the Hot Springs Mountains, west of US 95.

Six miles south of I-80, US 95 makes a bend to the northeast around the Mopung Hills, a low ridge that extends from the West Humboldt Range to the northeast. You can see several large gravel pits south of the road. These deposits accumulated as gravel bars along the ancient shoreline of Pleistocene Lake Lahontan.

US 95 Alternate
Schurz—Yerington—Fernley
65 miles
See map on page 245.

From its junction with the main route of US 95, US 95A passes northwest around White Mountain before curving west through the northern foothills of the Wassuk Range. White Mountain takes its name from the exposures of light-colored granitic rock on its slopes. As US 95A swings past White Mountain, you can see the channel of the lower Walker River north of the highway. In the bluffs exposed along the river bottom, layers of gravel, silt, and sand record the development of middle Pleistocene lakes that preceded the most recent stands of Lake Lahontan.

The hills at the north end of the Wassuk Range are rhyolitic ash-flow tuffs and associated sedimentary rocks of Miocene age. As US 95A rises to a low summit, the rhyolite flows along the road are overlain by light-colored alluvium and lake deposits. West from the Wassuk Range summit, US 95A descends into Mason Valley and Yerington.

The oldest rocks in the Singatse Range, west of Mason Valley, are Triassic and Jurassic sedimentary and metavolcanic rocks of the Walker Lake terrane. Several masses of magma intruded into the older rocks, some crystallizing into granitic rock about 169 million years ago, in Jurassic time. Some of these igneous rocks have large crystals of feldspar embedded in a matrix of smaller crystals. During the Oligocene and Miocene Epochs, thick sequences of ash-flow tuff, andesitic lava flows, and volcanic rubble spread across the erosion surface, much of it erupted more than 100 miles to the southeast in the vicinity of the Toquima Range. Some of the underground magma surging upward formed dikes and veins that cut across the older rocks. When extensional forces began to stretch the crust in later Miocene time, about 19 million years ago, normal faults cut the Singatse Range into several major rotated blocks.

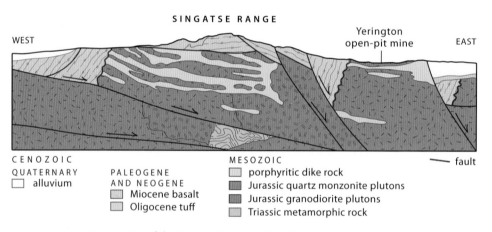

Cross section of the Singatse Range and the Yerington open-pit mine.

The magmatic activity produced mineralizing solutions that formed ore-bearing veins. Ores were first discovered in the Yerington area in 1865, when copper sulfate minerals, distinctive due to their vivid bluish color, were noticed on the western side of the Singatse Range. By 1900, several additional discoveries of these "bluestone ores" were made in the region. In the 1950s, more extensive but lower-grade copper ores were discovered. Large open-pit operations targeting this porphyry copper deposit at Yerington commenced in the 1960s, and this mine became one the largest copper-producing sites in the world at its peak of activity. After 1978, global market conditions led to low copper prices and the end of large-scale mining in the Yerington area. Some estimates have suggested that there may still be more than 20 billion pounds of copper in

The Yerington open-pit copper mine on the eastern slope of the Singatse Range in 2015. The Walker River flows just east of the mine, and the outskirts of Yerington can be seen in lower part of the photo. US 95A passes through the center of Yerington, just out of view.

the low-grade ores of the Yerington district. Gold and gypsum have also been mined in the Singatse Range.

Enormous piles and mounds of tailings and waste rock removed from the open pit can be seen west of US 95A as the road passes through Yerington. The inactive open pit is now flooded, and some of the polluted water leaks into the shallow aquifers carrying water beneath the surface of Mason Valley. In the 1970s, the US Geological Survey discovered a plume of groundwater containing arsenic, mercury, lead, copper, zinc, and chromium migrating from the mine areas. Preliminary work has been done to intercept the contaminant plume and prevent it from reaching drinking and irrigation water wells in Mason Valley. Continued monitoring and mitigation work will be necessary in the future to contain the groundwater plume, as well as windblown dust carrying heavy metal contaminants.

North of Yerington, US 95A passes through Mason Valley, a broad and heavily cultivated basin irrigated by the Walker River. About 6 miles north of Yerington, US 95A passes west of Mason Butte, a fault-bounded mound of Mesozoic granitic rocks cut by several andesitic dikes. At the north end of Mason Valley is the small settlement of Wabuska, which was much larger during the height of mining activities in the Yerington district. The hot springs northeast of the town are concentrated along a northeasterly aligned zone of faults that coincides with the northern margin of Mason Valley. The groundwater circulates deeply enough along fault zones to be heated to temperatures exceeding 200°F, after which is moves upward into unconsolidated gravel and sand, where it

WILSON CANYON

About 11 miles south Yerington, NV 339 meets NV 208, which crosses through the southern Singatse Range through Wilson Canyon, a gorge carved by the West Walker River. The rugged, 3-mile-long canyon is famous for the bold outcrops of light-colored tuff and ash-rich sandstone that weather to a rusty pinkish brown. The ash and sediments originally accumulated in a broad and densely forested river basin in Miocene time, prior to the development of the modern landforms. Fossil (petrified) wood fragments are fairly common in the sedimentary rocks of Wilson Canyon and nearby parts of the Singatse Range and Smith Valley to the west.

View east along NV 208 and the West Walker River at the western entrance to Wilson Canyon. Note the rusty red of the weathered rock in the close-up of light-gray tuff.

can be encountered at a relatively shallow depth. In 1984, these hot springs became the site of the first geothermal power plant in Nevada. The depth of the geothermal wells is generally less than 500 feet. You can see some of the power facilities northeast of the highway as it begins to climb the southern slopes of the Desert Mountains.

The Desert Mountains are composed primarily of Miocene and Pliocene volcanic rocks and interbedded sediments totaling more than 5,000 feet in thickness. These rocks are relatively soft and poorly exposed, except in some of the roadcuts along the highway north of Wabuska. The view west is across Adrian Valley toward the northern Pine Nut Mountains. During the Pleistocene Epoch, the ancestral Walker River periodically flowed through Adrian Valley into the Carson River and Lake Lahontan.

North from Silver Springs, US 95A climbs a steep grade through the eastern foothills of the Virginia Range. Roadcuts along this section of the highway expose Miocene and Pliocene tuffs and ash-rich sediments, capped in places by dark-colored basalt flows.

US 95
Winnemucca—Oregon Border
74 miles

US 95 crosses the Humboldt River in central Winnemucca and continues north along the east side of Winnemucca Mountain, a thick succession of siltstone, shale, and limestone of the Jungo terrane. These rocks accumulated in a marine basin offshore of the western edge of North America in Triassic to Jurassic time and then were thrust eastward as part of the Fencemaker thrust belt. The Jungo terrane rocks are intruded by a small body of late Jurassic plutonic rock on the southeast side of Winnemucca Mountain. Interactions between the older sedimentary rocks and invading magma have led to some gold, silver, and iron mineralization in the Winnemucca Mountain area.

East of US 95, the Little Humboldt River flows south through Paradise Valley to meet the main channel about 2 miles east of the highway. Paradise Valley is a narrow graben that developed as extensional faulting in this part of the Great Basin began about 17 million years ago. Total displacement on the faults bounding the valley varies from 6,000 to 15,000 feet. As much as 7,000 feet of sediment that eroded from the surrounding highlands has accumulated in the central part of Paradise Valley.

About 10 miles north of Winnemucca, US 95 passes through a portion of the Winnemucca dune field, which covers more than 300 square miles of southern Paradise Valley and Silver State Valley to the west. The sand is blown here primarily from vast tracts of Lake Lahontan sediment to the west. The drifting sand periodically blocks the channel of the Little Humboldt River, leading to the development of a shallow lake north of the dune field at times of abundant runoff.

East of Dutch Flat, which is the floodplain of the Little Humboldt River north of the dunes, is the Hot Springs Range, formed mostly of the Dutch Flat terrane. This sequence of argillite, chert, limestone, and siltstone of Cambrian through Devonian age includes a unique feldspar-rich sandstone known as the Harmony Formation. The sandstone contains Precambrian zircon grains too old to have

View to southwest of sand encroaching on US 95 north of Winnemucca.

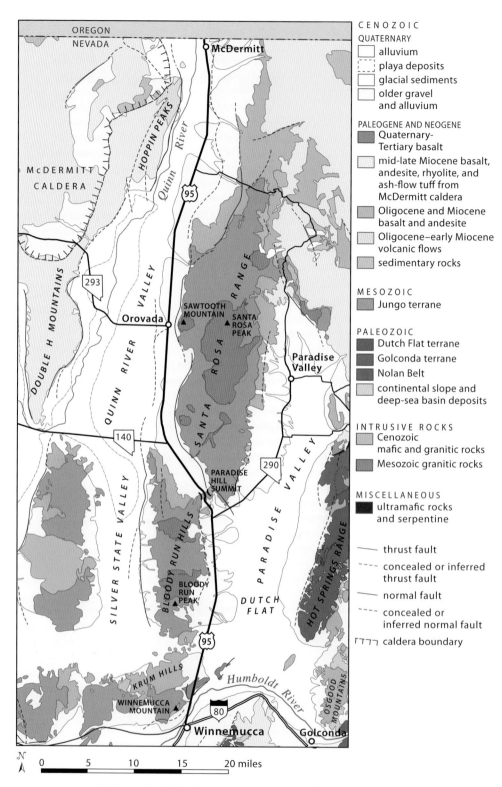

Geology along US 95 between Winnemucca and the Oregon border.

been derived from any nearby source rock in North America. It must have been derived from an unknown exotic continental mass. The Dutch Flat terrane was accreted to North America during late Paleozoic and Mesozoic time.

North from the Winnemucca dunes area, US 95 runs along the eastern base of the southern Santa Rosa Range, known locally as the Bloody Run Hills, then crosses to the west side of the mountains at Paradise Hill Summit. Like Winnemucca Mountain farther south, the Santa Rosa Range is composed primarily of late Triassic to early Jurassic ocean basin rocks of the Jungo terrane that weather into soft slopes or isolated brown outcrops on the mountain face. These rocks are mostly dark-colored mudstone and sandstone that were deformed and metamorphosed to slate, quartzite, and phyllite. Bodies of magma intruded the older rock in Cretaceous time, part of a great surge of magma from the Farallon subduction zone in northwestern Nevada. The age, texture, and chemistry of the 100-million-year-old granitic rocks indicate they are related to the granites of the central Sierra Nevada.

Excellent views of the bold western escarpment of the Santa Rosa Range dominate the scenery east of the highway in the Quinn River Valley. The prominent normal fault, mostly buried under alluvium along the base of the mountains, became active about 10 million years ago and has since displaced the mountain and valley blocks by more than 25,000 feet, while simultaneously tilting the mountain block to the east. Geologists estimate than 2 to 4 miles of rock have been removed by erosion following the uplift of the Santa Rosa Range.

The higher peaks of the Santa Rosa Range are light-colored granitic rock. East of US 95 in the vicinity of Orovado, the Santa Rosa Range reaches its highest point at Santa Rosa Peak. West of this peak and just east of US 95 near Orovada, Sawtooth Mountain is another small pluton of granitic rock intruded

Sawtooth Mountain, east of US 95 near Orovado, is a small intrusion of Cretaceous granitic rock. It intruded brownish Triassic-Jurassic metasedimentary rock of the Jungo terrane, visible on the lower slopes, especially at right.

through the Triassic metasediments. The normal fault along the west-facing escarpment of the mountain block is exposed along the lower slope of Saw-tooth Mountain. This fault descends under the Quinn River Valley to the west at an angle of about 40 degrees and to a depth of more than 8,000 feet. Brown to tan Miocene volcanic rocks are widespread on the lower western slopes of the northern Santa Rosa Range.

Around 20 million years ago, andesite and basalt flows erupted from fissures associated with extensional faulting. Then, about 18 million years ago, the Yel-lowstone hot spot began producing calderas, and the volcanic activity shifted to a more explosive style. The McDermitt caldera, an oblong depression extending about 28 miles from north of the Nevada-Oregon border to the northern slopes of the Double H Mountains to the south, erupted 16 million years ago, when the hot spot was directly below this part of the North American continent. Ash and lava accumulated within the caldera and over the surrounding terrain to a thickness exceeding 1,500 feet. The volcanic sequence is composed mostly of rhyolite tuffs, welded to various degrees, along with flows, domes, and dikes of rhyolite or latite. These rocks can be seen west of the highway in the low hills known as the Hoppin Peaks. The Yellowstone caldera activity shifted east as the North American Plate moved west over the hot spot.

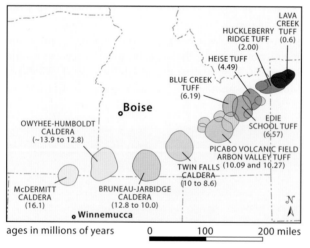

The trace of the Yellowstone hot spot moved east as western North America migrated west across the hot spot over the past 18 million years. The hot spot originated about 16 million years ago near McDermitt.

US 395
California Border—Reno—Topaz Lake
85 miles

US 395 roughly parallels the eastern escarpment of the Sierra Nevada, pass-ing through a series of fault-controlled valleys. North-trending normal faults bound the mountain ranges, and several prominent northwest-trending, right-lateral strike-slip faults, components of the northern end of the Walker Lane, control the orientation of elongated valleys, such as Honey Lake Valley in

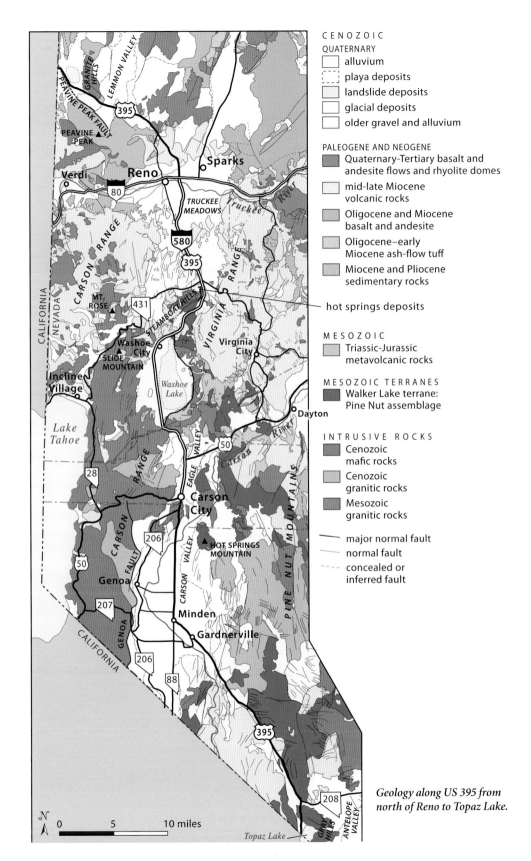

CENOZOIC
QUATERNARY
- alluvium
- playa deposits
- landslide deposits
- glacial deposits
- older gravel and alluvium

PALEOGENE AND NEOGENE
- Quaternary-Tertiary basalt and andesite flows and rhyolite domes
- mid-late Miocene volcanic rocks
- Oligocene and Miocene basalt and andesite
- Oligocene–early Miocene ash-flow tuff
- Miocene and Pliocene sedimentary rocks
- hot springs deposits

MESOZOIC
- Triassic-Jurassic metavolcanic rocks

MESOZOIC TERRANES
- Walker Lake terrane: Pine Nut assemblage

INTRUSIVE ROCKS
- Cenozoic mafic rocks
- Cenozoic granitic rocks
- Mesozoic granitic rocks

- major normal fault
- normal fault
- concealed or inferred fault

Geology along US 395 from north of Reno to Topaz Lake.

PEAVINE PEAK FAULT
GRANITE HILLS
LEMMON VALLEY
395
PEAVINE PEAK
Verdi
Reno
Sparks
80
TRUCKEE MEADOWS
Truckee River
CARSON RANGE
580
395
MT. ROSE
431
STEAMBOAT HILLS
VIRGINIA RANGE
Washoe City
Virginia City
SLIDE MOUNTAIN
Incline Village
Washoe Lake
Lake Tahoe
Dayton
28
CARSON RANGE
EAGLE VALLEY
50
Carson River
PINE NUT MOUNTAINS
50
CARSON VALLEY
Carson City
206
HOT SPRINGS MOUNTAIN
GENOA FAULT
Genoa
207
Minden
Gardnerville
206
88
395
208
GRAY HILLS
ANTELOPE VALLEY
Topaz Lake
CALIFORNIA
NEVADA
CALIFORNIA

N

0   5   10 miles

California. Finally, northeast-trending left-lateral strike-slip faults also occur in this area and are largely responsible for the northeasterly flow of the Truckee and Carson Rivers. Most of these faults are still active, and this region of western Nevada has experienced many historic earthquakes, including a dozen or so with magnitudes of 6.0 to 6.9 since the late 1800s.

South from the California-Nevada state line, US 395 skirts the western edge of White Lake, a playa that lies in Cold Springs Valley, a fault-controlled, enclosed basin between Peavine Peak to the west and the Granite Hills to the

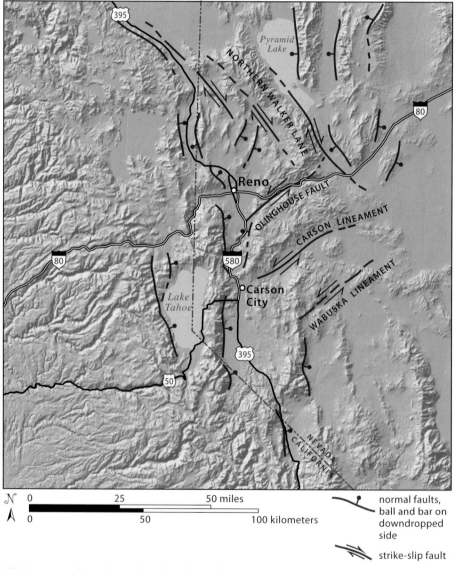

US 395 crosses through a region of north-trending normal faults, northeast-trending left-lateral strike-slip faults, and northwest-trending right-lateral strike-slip faults.

east. Silt and alkaline minerals cover the generally dry surface of White Lake, but sometimes it contains temporary bodies of shallow water after rainstorms or rapid melting of snow. The Granite Hills east of White Lake are composed mostly of Cretaceous granitic rocks intruded into a thick and varied sequence of older Jurassic volcanic rocks. Peavine Peak, the prominent mountain visible south of US 395, is a massive pile of mostly Jurassic volcanic rocks that are metamorphosed to varying degrees, probably by the intrusion of granitic magma in the Cretaceous Period. The altered metavolcanic rocks are cut in many places by veins of ore minerals containing copper, iron, silver, and gold. Local mining of these ores began in the 1860s, but there no large-scale operations currently active.

Peavine Peak was uplifted along the northwest-trending Peavine Peak fault beginning around 3 million years ago. Recent faulting has produced a noticeable scarp at the base of mountain's sheer eastern face. Geologists dug trenches across segments of the Peavine Peak fault in two places to study fault movement. Displaced soil and sediment layers in these trenches suggest that this fault has produced four or five surface-rupturing earthquakes over the past 6,000 to 8,000 years. The prehistoric earthquakes could have been in the magnitude 7 range.

About 13 miles north of Reno, US 395 descends south into Lemmon Valley in which Silver Lake, another normally dry playa, lies just east of the highway. The flat, low-lying surface, now covered with urban sprawl, is somewhat deceptive. Several intersecting faults displace the basement rocks in the valley surface

Trenches (center distance) were dug to study the normal fault along the base of the eastern slope of Peavine Peak west of US 395.

by varying amounts. The valley-filling sediments, which are up to 2,400 feet thick, contain several important aquifers that provide groundwater for the rapidly growing population in the valley. In the year 2000, three times more water was pumped from the Lemmon Valley aquifers than was naturally replaced.

A few miles north of downtown Reno, US 395 passes through low hills before descending onto the broad floor of the Truckee Meadows. The colorful rocks in the roadcuts along the highway are mostly hydrothermally altered andesite, erupted about 16 million years ago as part of the Ancestral Cascades. The hydrothermal alteration produced silicified breccias, whitish alunite from the acidic breakdown of feldspars, and cream-colored clay minerals, such as illite and smectite, that expand when they absorb water. Oxidation of sulfide and iron-bearing minerals in the volcanic rocks produced some of the red, brown, and lavender hues in the colorful outcrops along the highway.

Truckee Meadows to Steamboat Hills

Reno and the surrounding communities lie in a valley known as the Truckee Meadows, a complex downfaulted half-graben separating the Virginia Range on the east from the Carson Range on the west. The downfaulting began in this area around 3 million years ago. As the basin subsided, as much as 3,000 feet of sand, silt, and gravel collected in the sinking lowland. This mostly unconsolidated fill was deposited by rivers carrying glacial outwash sediment, by winds blowing fine sediment into the valley, and in lakes and spring-fed ponds that developed at various times on the valley floor. (See the I-80 road guide for more on the Truckee Meadows.)

The Carson Range is composed mostly of light-colored granitic rock, about 70 million years old, capped with darker-brown Miocene volcanic rock. The highest peak in the range is Mt. Rose, the summit of which is composed of a saddle-shaped mass of the brownish volcanic rocks. To the east of the highway, the Truckee Meadows are bordered by the Huffaker Hills and the Virginia Range, both consisting mostly of Miocene volcanic rocks such as andesitic and rhyolitic flows and tuffs.

Near the junction with NV 431, US 395 (also designated as I-580 here) bends around the eastern slopes of the Steamboat Hills, composed of very young andesitic volcanic flows and rhyolite domes. The magma erupted between about 2.5 and 1 million years ago, in the Pleistocene Epoch. Residual subsurface heat associated with the young crystallized magma underground has made the Steamboat Hills one of Nevada's best-known geothermal energy resource areas. The name Steamboat was reportedly given to these hills for the noise and clouds of steam and hot water that issued from several natural vents. Facilities related to the production of geothermal power and pipes transporting steam and hot water are on both sides of US 395/I-580 for several miles as it swings through the Steamboat Hills.

Scientific investigation of the geothermal power potential of the Steamboat Hills began in the 1950s, and by the 1980s, commercial development was underway. By 2016, at least six power plants were producing more than 70 megawatts of electricity. As subsurface steam and hot water were withdrawn for power development, the surface springs became less active and the once-popular mineral bath resorts have mostly vanished from the area.

The underground water in the Steamboat Hills flows from the adjacent mountain slopes into the shattered rock along a complex set of intersecting faults. Subsurface heat raises its temperature to more than 440°F at a depth of 3,000 feet beneath the surface. As the hot groundwater naturally makes its way to the surface, highly reactive acidic gases are released from the steam and penetrate into the surrounding rock. These hydrothermal fluids bleach the bedrock and form clay and zeolite minerals, leaving behind a chalky, crumbly residue. Metal sulfide minerals also form from this alteration, and subsequent oxidation of these minerals produce the red, tan, and brown shades seen on the flanks of the Steamboat Hills. Where the hot springs discharge at the surface, silicon and oxygen derived from the bedrock are deposited as a hard variety of silica known as sinter. Over time, the sinter accumulating from several fault-aligned hot springs form large, sloping aprons of sinter-cemented materials. US 395/I-580 is constructed just below the largest of three sinter terraces draping the Steamboat Hills as it passes southward toward Washoe Valley.

Washoe Valley

About one-quarter of the flat floor of Washoe Valley is submerged by Washoe Lake, except in very dry years. Washoe Lake receives inflow primarily from streams draining the eastern slope of the Carson Range. Washoe Valley is a downfaulted basin formed over the past 5 million years or so by tensional stresses that stretched the crust in this part of northwestern Nevada. The fault at the base of the Carson Range to the west has much larger and more recent displacement than those on the east side of the valley. Thus, the subsurface bedrock beneath the flat valley floor is tilted significantly to the west and basin-filling sediments are thickest on that side of the valley. Nearly 2,000 feet of unconsolidated sediments have accumulated in Pleistocene and Holocene time, including deposits from landslides that periodically plummet down the steep slopes to the west and from glacial outwash streams during the ice ages.

The view west from the northern end of Washoe Valley is dominated by Slide Mountain, which rises nearly 1 mile above the valley floor. On the steep south-facing slopes of upper Slide Mountain, you can see several bare scars where landslides have broken loose. In addition to the prominent range-front normal fault, several northeast-trending faults slice through the granitic bedrock, cutting the weathered bedrock into a mass of slabs and blocks that can be dislodged by earthquake vibrations, heavy rain, or deep snow. Geological studies of the landslide rubble along the foot of the Carson Range below Slide Mountain suggest that at least nine major landslides over the past 50,000 years have produced the scars.

The most recent major landslide at Slide Mountain occurred in May 1983, when the heavy snowpack was rapidly melting due to unseasonably warm spring weather. Meltwater saturated the fractured granite of the upper mountain slope, eventually triggering a slide of 40 to 50 acres of rock, soil, and vegetation down the drainage of Ophir Creek. This rubble, technically known as a debris flow,

View west from US 395 in Washoe Valley to landslide scars on Slide Mountain in the Carson Range. The drainage in the foreground is Ophir Creek, through which rock rubble from numerous landslides has passed eastward onto the valley floor.

overran two small lakes as it slid toward Washoe Valley and picked up additional material as it moved downslope at nearly 20 miles per hour. At the mouth of Ophir Creek, the debris flow spread out into a flood of rock, soil, and water as high as 30 feet. The debris flow destroyed several homes and killed one person before it finally came to rest along the edge of US 395. Future landslide events are likely given the chance of earthquakes and extreme weather in this area.

Just southeast of Lakeview Summit, US 395 passes through rounded outcrops of Cretaceous granitic rock, the same rock that makes up the bedrock of the Carson Range to the west.

Carson Valley and the Genoa Fault

Eagle Valley and Carson Valley originated through downfaulting along the Sierra Nevada frontal fault system, a group of major normal faults along the eastern side of the Sierra Nevada. The Carson Range to the west has been elevated some 7,500 feet by the Genoa fault zone, one of Nevada's most active faults. Many large earthquakes have occurred here since faulting began several million years ago, with at least two powerful earthquakes (magnitude greater than 7.0) in the past 1,800 years. Geologists estimate that a recurrence of such an earthquake today could result in nearly a half billion dollars of property and utility damage. Because faulting has been most active on the western side of the valley, the basin-filling sediments are thickest adjacent to the Carson Range, up to 5,000 feet thick in places.

GENOA FAULT SCARP

When lighting condition are right, usually in the mid to late afternoon, a prominent scarp as much as 50 feet high can be seen along the base of the Carson Range from US 395. You can see this scarp up close by driving west on Muller Lane (NV 757) just north of Minden. At the T intersection, turn north on Foothill Road (NV 206) and follow it along the base of the Carson Range to a gravel quarry just west of the road. The fault plane on the uplifted block was exposed when the alluvial gravel was removed during quarrying. The bedrock here is Cretaceous granitic rock, but along the fault it has been crushed and bleached into a white crumbly material that bears little resemblance to the sparkling gray bedrock seen elsewhere in the Carson Range. Grooves on this exposed fault scarp, a feauture known as slickensides, formed as rock on one side of the fault slid against rock on the other side of the fault. The scarp is the product of many earthquakes, the youngest of which probably occurred 500 to 600 years ago.

A prominent fault scarp exposed in a gravel quarry west of NV 206 at the base of the Carson Range. Note the small remnant of alluvial gravel still covering part of the scarp at right.

Across Foothill Road to the east from the exposed fault scarp, the lush vegetation and marshy ground mark the general location of Walleys Hot Springs. These historic springs, which have attracted visitors since the mid-1800s when the old Emigrant Trail passed through the area, issue from faults related to the scarp. Both cold and warm water springs occur here, as well as farther to the north along the base of the Carson Range. If you continue north on NV 206, you will follow the Genoa fault zone past the historic settlement of Genoa. The Genoa fault is located about where the gently sloping alluvial plain gives way to the steeper and more rugged slopes of the Carson Range foothills. West of the road, you can see small ridges, which are scarps cutting the recently deposited alluvium.

The Carson River flows north through the Carson Valley from its headwaters in the high peaks of the Carson Range. A complex system of ditches and canals distributes water from the Carson River to more than 40,000 acres of irrigated farmland situated around Minden and Gardnerville. In addition, significant amounts of groundwater are pumped for agriculture. Because the Carson River flows through an arid region, the withdrawal of water in Carson Valley reduces the stream flow. The falling water table, the result of groundwater overpumping, enhances seepage from the river channel, sapping even more water from the Carson River.

As it approaches Carson City, the Carson River bends to the northeast along the eastern side of Eagle Valley, following the northeasterly trending Carson lineament, a zone of left-lateral strike-slip faults. The hot springs in this part of the valley are associated with high-angle, large-displacement normal faults that allow groundwater to seep downward into the hotter subsurface environment. Saratoga Hot Spring is located at the western base of Hot Spring Mountain, a fault-bounded mass of Jurassic and Triassic metavolcanic and sedimentary rocks.

Along the base of the Carson Range, the vegetation and trees often appear to be clumped together and aligned parallel to the lower mountain front. The pulverized rock generated along the Genoa fault acts like a subsurface dam to groundwater flowing through alluvial gravel and sand toward the valley to the east. Where it encounters the fault, groundwater is forced toward the surface, producing either springs or a shallow water table that supports the relatively lush growth of plants on the otherwise arid slope.

Pine Nut Mountains and Topaz Lake

Bordering the east side of Carson Valley is the main part of the Pine Nut Mountains, a north-trending fault block elevated and tilted to the west by normal faulting along the eastern side. The overall western tilt of the range is evident in the gradual slope that descends into Carson Valley, a strong contrast to the abrupt escarpment of the Carson Range to the west. The bedrock of the Pine Nut Mountains is dominated by Cretaceous granitic rock that has been emplaced into older Jurassic and Triassic metamorphic rocks of the Walker Lake terrane. Overlying the Mesozoic bedrock is a thick succession of Oligocene and Miocene volcanics associated with the Ancestral Cascade arc and semiconsolidated sedimentary rock of late Miocene and younger ages. The sedimentary rocks include sandstone rich in volcanic ash, siltstone, diatomite, shale, and conglomerate that was originally deposited in ancient streams, floodplains, lakes, and ponds prior to the development of the modern topography. In the southern Pine Nut Mountains, 2.5-million-year-old sedimentary rocks have produced fossils of such exotic creatures as large camels, horses, mastodons, sloths, and zebras, along with more familiar vertebrates such as otters, wild dogs, and rodents. South of Gardnerville, US 395 gradually ascends the foothills of the Pine Nut Mountains, intersecting the California-Nevada border on the west side of Topaz Lake.

Prior to the construction of levees and dams between 1922 and 1937, Topaz Lake was a very small marshy pond isolated from the north end of Antelope

View southeast from US 395 overlooking Topaz Lake on the California-Nevada state line. Antelope Valley is the low basin in the distance, just behind the Gray Hills that form the lake's eastern shore.

Valley by a low divide consisting of alluvium deposited by small streams flowing from the Sierra Nevada to the west. After the impoundments were constructed, water was diverted into the basin from the West Walker River, which flows just east of the modern lake. The water stored in Topaz Lake is used for irrigation downstream in Smith and Mason Valleys to the northeast. The size and depth of Topaz Lake varies over time and is influenced by both climate and the rate of diversion of water from the West Walker River.

The Topaz Lake basin is situated between the Gray Hills to the east, Wild Oat Mountain to the north, and the eastern escarpment of the Sierra Nevada to the west. Northeast-trending faults cut through the metavolcanic bedrock of Wild Oat Mountain, while north-trending faults related to the Sierra Nevada frontal fault system parallel the base of the mountain front to the west. These active faults originated a few million years ago when tensional stresses migrated to this area of the western Great Basin. In January 2013, a swarm of sixteen small earthquakes shook the lake basin. The earthquakes ranged in magnitude from 1.1 to 3.7 and occurred 2 to 5 miles below the surface.

NV 140
US 95—Denio—Oregon Border
109 miles

West of US 95, NV 140 crosses Gallagher Flat, a low plain in the broad Quinn River Valley. The Quinn River flows southwest from southeastern Oregon to the Black Rock Desert playa. For most of its 110-mile length, the Quinn River is an intermittent stream, carrying significant amounts of water only in the spring months or after cloudbursts. Alluvial fans, well-developed along the foot of the Santa Rosa Range, consist of coarse, river-deposited sediment that grades into finer-grained sand and silt toward the valley bottom. Very fine-grained silt and clay settle out of the water of shallow ephemeral lakes that occasionally develop in the lowest part of Gallagher Flat.

During the Pleistocene Epoch, part of Lake Lahontan inundated the Quinn River Valley, and at its highest levels, water from the Quinn River Valley spilled through the natural gap to flood the Kings River Valley and Desert Valley. Remnant populations of the Lahontan cutthroat trout, holdovers from ice age Lake Lahontan, still inhabit tributaries in the upper Quinn River basin, though many populations have been lost through hybridization with introduced trout or reduction of habitat.

The Double H Mountains, the tilted tableland north of the highway on the west side of the Quinn River Valley, consist primarily of Miocene volcanic strata interlayered with some sedimentary materials. To the south, the rocks of the northern Slumbering Hills are deep-sea deposits of Triassic age similar to those exposed in the Santa Rosa Mountains (see the US 95 road guide), capped in places by late Cenozoic volcanic flows. West of the gap between the Slumbering Hills and the Double H Mountains to the north, NV 140 continues across a broad sagebrush plain. Although the south-flowing Kings River, a tributary to the Quinn River, only occasionally has water, substantial amounts of groundwater are present beneath the valley.

North of where NV 140 crosses the Quinn River, the highway passes between the Bilk Creek Mountains to the north and the Jackson Mountains to the south. Beneath a cover of Miocene andesite flows, the bedrock in the Jackson Mountains is a complex, deformed sequence of late Paleozoic to early Mesozoic rocks known as the Black Rock–Jackson terrane. These rocks include limestone, chert, siltstone, shale, and fragmental volcanic rocks that originally formed in a deep ocean basin adjacent to a volcanic island arc. In Jurassic and Cretaceous time, the terrane was accreted to the margin of North America, and the deep-sea sedimentary rocks were folded and thrust eastward along faults related to the Luning-Fencemaker thrust belt. Interactions between the older, deformed sedimentary rocks and the intrusion of igneous bodies in Jurassic and Cretaceous time produced some mercury mineralization in the northern Jackson Mountains. Most of the mining activity here occurred in the mid-1900s. Rocks of the Black Rock–Jackson terrane also occur in the southern tip of the Bilk Creek Mountains, but there they are mostly covered by Miocene rhyolite flows and volcanic breccia.

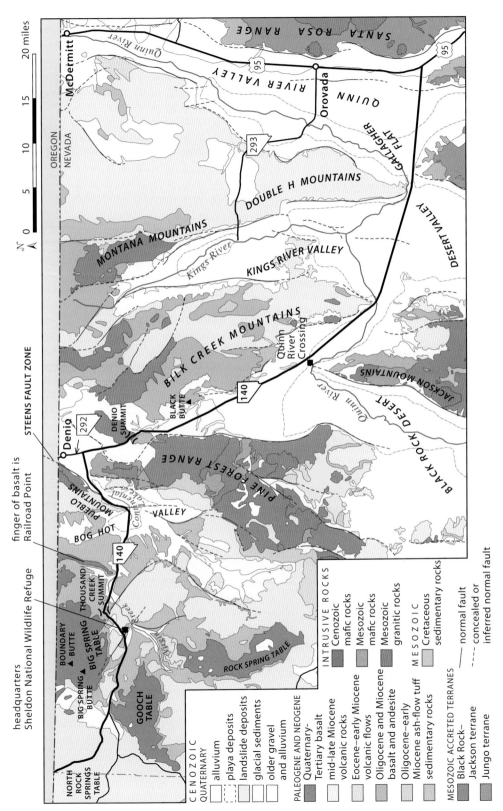

Geology along NV 140 between US 95 and the Oregon border.

WEST   EAST

TRIASSIC–EARLY JURASSIC: 245–195 million years ago

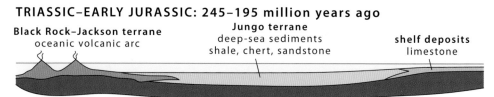

Black Rock–Jackson terrane
oceanic volcanic arc

Jungo terrane
deep-sea sediments
shale, chert, sandstone

shelf deposits
limestone

MIDDLE-LATE JURASSIC: 175–150 million years ago

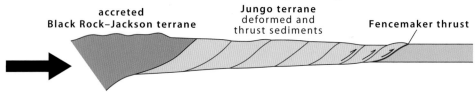

**accreted
Black Rock–Jackson terrane**

Jungo terrane
deformed and
thrust sediments

Fencemaker thrust

MIDDLE-LATE CRETACEOUS: 100–70 million years ago

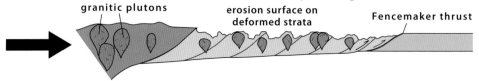

granitic plutons

erosion surface on
deformed strata

Fencemaker thrust

The Black Rock–Jackson terrane was an island arc that accreted to northwest Nevada in Jurassic time. —Modified from Wyld, 2002

About 3 miles northwest of the Leonard Creek rest area, NV 140 passes just north of Quinn River Crossing, a historic site where trails crossed a broad, relatively shallow section of the Quinn River. At about this point, the Quinn River bends sharply to the southwest and continues into the Black Rock Desert, a broad lowland consisting of several interconnected basins and playas. The sink for the Quinn River is situated in the lowest part of the Black Rock Desert, about 55 miles southwest of Quinn River Crossing, but the river only occasionally carries water that far.

North of the Quinn River Crossing, NV 140 follows along the western foothills of the Bilk Creek Mountains. To the west and southwest, across the valley of Deep Creek, is the Pine Forest Range, consisting of Paleozoic and Mesozoic metamorphic rocks associated with the Black Rock–Jackson terrane, intruded by large plutons of light-colored Cretaceous granitic rock. The Pine Forest Range is elevated along a normal fault at the base of the eastern escarpment, and the entire mountain block is tilted to the west. Even though the tensional stresses related to the normal faulting began 10 million years ago, faulting has intensified over the past 5 million years and the mountain ranges in this region are still rising relative to the valley floors.

Several hot springs in this area are part of the Black Rock Desert belt of hot springs that trends southwest from the Alvord Desert of Oregon to Pyramid Lake in western Nevada. This geothermal activity is related to the young volcanic activity and the intensity of recent and ongoing faulting. Howard Hot Spring lies along the range-bounding fault at the foot of the Bilk Creek Mountains, and Dyke Hot Springs lies along the fault adjacent to the Pine Forest Range.

At Denio Summit, Cretaceous granite is overlain by Oligocene and Miocene andesite and basalt lava flows and tuffs. Black Butte, a prominent dark-colored outcrop of basaltic rocks lies east of the highway and south of Denio Summit. The volcanic rocks in this area commonly contain small bits of opal that weather out and wash down the mountain slopes.

Denio Junction to Continental Lake

Denio, the only permanent settlement for nearly 80 miles in any direction, is a few miles north of Denio Junction on NV 292. Denio was settled in 1885 and became an important waypoint on the historic wagon roads and trails linking the mining centers near Winnemucca to those of southern Oregon and Idaho.

NV 140 extends west from Denio Junction toward the Pueblo Mountains, a tilted fault block lifted along its eastern side by a high-angle normal fault. Part of the Steens fault zone, the fault extends more than 120 miles north into southeastern Oregon and is one of the most prominent normal faults in the northwest Basin and Range Province. Displacement and tilting along this fault forms the bold eastern escarpment visible from NV 140.

The steep eastern escarpment of the southern Pueblo Mountains seen west from NV 140 in the vicinity of the Continental Lake playa. The tilted Miocene volcanic and sedimentary rocks were uplifted along the Steens fault zone, which is concealed beneath the cones of rock rubble at the base of the escarpment.

Large basalt boulders along NV 140 near the edge of Continental Lake were probably shaken from the cliffs capping the Pueblo Mountains by earthquakes associated with the Steens fault zone. —Photo from US Geological Survey, Scientific Investigations Map 2952

The valley east of the range is drained to the south by Pueblo Slough, an intermittent stream that terminates in an alkaline playa known as Continental Lake. Some 20,000 to 16,000 years ago, this valley was inundated by Alvord Lake, which extended north into southeastern Oregon. At its maximum stage, the lake was between 100 and 200 feet deep in the Continental Lake area. Ancient shoreline features are present on the lower mountain slopes surrounding Pueblo Slough but are subtle and sometimes difficult to spot from the highway. NV 140 skirts the western edge of Continental Lake as it approaches the southern tip of the Pueblo Mountains, and you can see large basalt boulders on both sides of the highway here. These boulders probably were shaken loose from the ridge-capping basalt during powerful prehistoric earthquakes and rolled down the steep escarpment to the floor of Pueblo Valley. Displaced soil and sediment layers in trenches dug across the Steens fault zone by the US Geological Survey between 2003 and 2007 provided evidence for at least three strong earthquakes (magnitude 6.6 to 7.1) between about 12,000 and 4,000 years ago.

At the southern tip of the Pueblo Mountains, NV 140 turns west, passing through Bog Hot Valley, named for Bog Hot Springs, which is situated, along with several other nearby hot springs, on the west side of the Pueblo Mountains. Additional hot springs are clustered along active range-bounding normal faults south of NV 140. When the weather is cold enough, steam rising from some of these springs is visible in the distance both north and south of the highway. At least two sets of normal faults intersect in the area of Bog Hot Valley, providing numerous avenues for surface water to descend into the hot subsurface, where is it heated and then rises back up again.

Tablelands, Opals, and Fossils in Sheldon Refuge

Between Bog Hot Valley and Oregon, NV 140 passes through the Sheldon National Wildlife Refuge, a vast tract of high desert habitat. Landforms in the refuge are dominated by flat-topped plateaus and cuestas composed of relatively soft layers of middle to late Miocene tuffs, ash, and sediment capped by harder, dark-colored basalt flows. Over the past few million years, normal faults have cut the horizontal layers into tablelike blocks, including Railroad Point, Big Spring Table, Gooch Table, and North Rock Springs Table.

Railroad Point, north of NV 140, is the southern end of a tilted tableland consisting tuffs, ash, and sedimentary rocks capped by a thin, dark-colored basalt flow. The 1.2-million-year-old basalt is known as the Mesa Basalt for its presence as the caprock in many of the tablelands along NV 140.

About 3 miles west of Railroad Point, NV 140 starts up the steep incline known as Dufurrena Grade, which culminates at Thousand Creek Summit at the top of Big Spring Table. Roadcuts reveal layers of Miocene volcanic and sedimentary rocks that cover most of this region. The volcanic units are generally light-colored unconsolidated ashes, crumbly air-fall tuff, and thicker, reddish to pale-brown ash-flow tuffs. Near the top of the plateau, resistant basalt flows cap the relatively soft sedimentary layers.

The volcanic tuffs originated from several violent caldera-forming eruptions that occurred in northwest Nevada starting about 16 million years ago, prior to the onset of intense normal faulting that created the modern landscape. This volcanic activity was probably related to the development of the Yellowstone hot spot under North America. The remnants of several calderas have been identified in the region, including the McDermitt caldera to the east and the Virgin Valley caldera to the west.

The sedimentary rocks interbedded with the volcanic tuff deposits consist of fine-grained sandstone, shale, diatomite, and clay that accumulated in streams, ponds, lakes, and marshes in the Miocene lowlands. Lenses of coarse sand and gravel were deposited by rivers. Some of the fine-grained shales contain carbonized plant residues along with abundant fossil wood, leaves, twigs, bark, and seeds. These fossils have helped scientists reconstruct the flora of the mid-Miocene forests that were present and repeatedly buried under volcanic ash. These forests consisted of fairly dense stands of spruce, cedar, oaks,

Roadcut on the north side of NV 140 near Thousand Creek Summit exposing layers of Miocene tuff, ash, and sediment composing Big Spring Table. At the top center of the photo, the dark-colored rocks are the capping basalt flows of late Miocene age.

sycamores, maples, and firs, with aquatic vegetation such as willows, reeds, and cattails clustered around the lakes and marshes. The lakes were swarming with diatoms, single-celled algae with cell walls composed of silica. Some of the sediment that accumulated on the floors of the ancient lakes consisted almost entirely of the silica remains of diatoms—now a rock called diatomite.

West of Thousand Creek Summit, roadside exposures are mostly weakly consolidated ash-rich sedimentary rocks. To the south, across the 500-foot-deep Thousand Creek Gorge cut through more-resistant welded tuffs, the low-lying area is the valley of Virgin Creek. In 1906, paleontologist John C. Merriam from the University of California–Berkeley visited the Virgin Valley to investigate reports of fossil bones weathering out of the ash-rich sediments. By 1911, Merriam had collected enough fossils from dozens of localities in the Virgin Valley to describe an incredibly diverse array of vertebrates that inhabited this part of Nevada during the Miocene Epoch. The Virgin Valley fauna, as it became known, included horses, camels, rhinoceros, elephants, rodents, doglike predators, and several extinct mammals utterly unlike any known from the modern world. Sheldon National Wildlife Refuge, famous for protecting modern animals, is also a place where paleontologists have learned a great deal about their Miocene predecessors.

The Virgin Valley is also famous for beautiful specimens of opal that occur in some of the tuffs and ashes. There are several active opal mines in the valley, along with commercial collecting sites where visitors can pay a fee to hunt for the iridescent stones. Opal is a noncrystalline form of hydrated silica. When silica-rich water flows into cracks, cavities, or pockets, tiny microscopic masses of silica can harden from a gel-like substance. These grains are not crystals,

Opal from the Virgin Valley.

but when the tiny hydrated silica masses are well ordered, light waves passing through them are subject to diffraction, or bending. The sparkling iridescence of opal is the result of the diffraction of light waves into different color bands (wavelengths) as they pass through the translucent material.

Some of the fossilized (petrified) wood preserved in the Miocene sediments has been opalized through the precipitation of silica in the open spaces of the original wood tissues. Such opalized wood can have spectacular colors and be impressive in size. The largest mass of opal recovered from the Virgin Valley area was reported to have been a 130-pound chunk of fossilized wood. Silicified volcanic ash sometimes produces pieces of black opal, an especially striking form known for the brilliant rainbow iridescence that emanates from the nearly black stone. Black fire opal from the Virgin Valley has been officially designated as Nevada's state precious gemstone.

The abundance of opal in the volcanic and sedimentary rocks of the Virgin Valley reflects a convergence of favorable geologic circumstances. Recall that the host rocks include diatomite, which is composed almost entirely of silica. In addition, the tuffs and volcanic ash deposits are of mostly rhyolitic or andesitic composition, containing 60 to 70 percent silica. Water moving through these deposits would inevitably dissolve some of this silica and eventually become saturated with it. The dissolution of silica would have been enhanced by the high temperatures of water either shortly after their burial or later from the many hydrothermal springs in the area. Finally, as tuffs are compacted and harden from the original accumulation of volcanic ash, it is common for cracks, pockets, and cavities to develop, providing spaces for the opal to be deposited by silica-laden water moving through the rock.

Southwest from NV 140 near the Dufurrena rest area, you can see the east end of Gooch Table. Like many of the fault-bounded plateaus in this area, the 1.2-million-year-old Mesa Basalt caps the top of Gooch Table, while the softer,

The east end of Gooch Table southwest of NV 140 near the Dufurrena rest area. Note the dark-colored basalt capping the softer, light-colored tuffs and ash-rich sediments exposed on the lower slopes.

ash-rich Miocene sediments below are eroded into smooth slopes cut by a network of gullies and rills. Several miles farther west, several flat-topped buttes, also capped by hard lava flows, are visible to the north, including Boundary Butte and the larger Big Spring Butte. As NV 140 climbs north toward the Nevada-Oregon border, the view southeast from the highway reveals extensive Gooch Table and the hardened basalt flow that caps it.

NV 225
Elko—Idaho Border
100 miles

NV 225 heads northwest from I-80 in Elko at exit 301, and in about 9 miles it passes over the southern end of the Adobe Range, composed of folded Paleozoic sedimentary rocks of the Diamond Peak Formation. This thick sequence of gray shale, rusty tan conglomerate, and limestone accumulated in a foreland basin associated with the Antler highland about 340 million years ago, in Mississippian time. The different types of rock reflect changing conditions in the foreland basin as it subsided and collected sediment. A dark-colored shale, deposited in a relatively deep ocean, is exposed in roadcuts and a quarry along the highway as it ascends the southern flank of the Adobe Range. Farther northwest, toward the summit, ledges of hard sandstone and reddish conglomerate are exposed along the roadsides. The layers of gray limestone were deposited on a shallow seafloor and commonly contain fossils of crinoids (related to modern sea lilies), brachiopods (clam-like shellfish), and primitive corals that thrived in the shallow tropical seas of early Mississippian time.

North of Adobe Summit, NV 225 descends through hilly terrain toward the valley of Susie and Dorsey Creeks. Rocks exposed along the road are volcanic and ash-rich sedimentary rocks deposited above the deformed Paleozoic rocks when volcanic activity commenced in this part of northern Nevada about

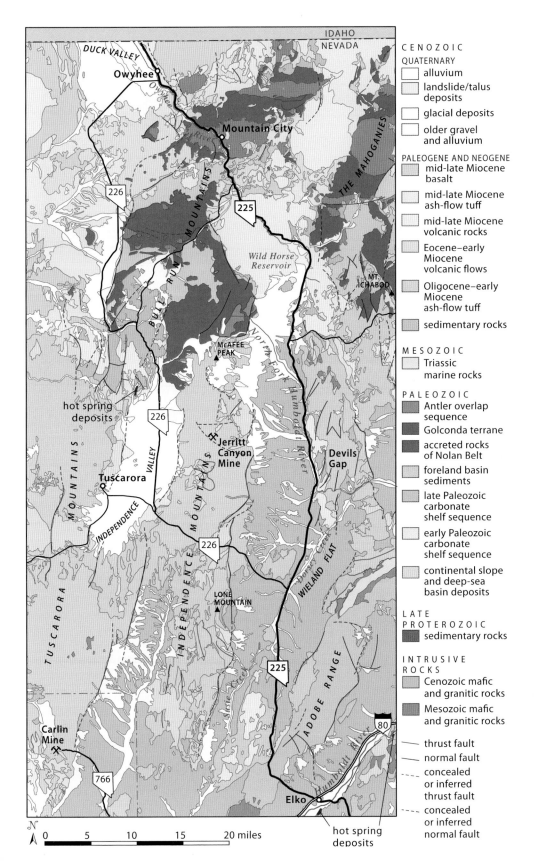

CENOZOIC

QUATERNARY
- alluvium
- landslide/talus deposits
- glacial deposits
- older gravel and alluvium

PALEOGENE AND NEOGENE
- mid-late Miocene basalt
- mid-late Miocene ash-flow tuff
- mid-late Miocene volcanic rocks
- Eocene–early Miocene volcanic flows
- Oligocene–early Miocene ash-flow tuff
- sedimentary rocks

MESOZOIC
- Triassic marine rocks

PALEOZOIC
- Antler overlap sequence
- Golconda terrane
- accreted rocks of Nolan Belt
- foreland basin sediments
- late Paleozoic carbonate shelf sequence
- early Paleozoic carbonate shelf sequence
- continental slope and deep-sea basin deposits

LATE PROTEROZOIC
- sedimentary rocks

INTRUSIVE ROCKS
- Cenozoic mafic and granitic rocks
- Mesozoic mafic and granitic rocks

— thrust fault
— normal fault
--- concealed or inferred thrust fault
--- concealed or inferred normal fault

IDAHO
NEVADA

DUCK VALLEY

Owyhee

Owyhee River

Mountain City

226

225

Wild Horse Reservoir

BULL RUN MOUNTAINS

THE MAHOGANIES

MT. ICHABOD

McAFEE PEAK

North Fork Humboldt River

hot spring deposits

226

Jerritt Canyon Mine

Devils Gap

Tuscarora

INDEPENDENCE VALLEY

INDEPENDENCE MOUNTAINS

WIELAND FLAT

Dorsey Creek

226

LONE MOUNTAIN

TUSCARORA MOUNTAINS

ADOBE RANGE

225

Sloan Creek

Carlin Mine

766

80

Humboldt River

Elko

hot spring deposits

N

0   5   10   15   20 miles

Mississippian limestone from the southern Adobe Range with fossils of crinoids, marine invertebrates that constructed stalks composed of circular plates, like a stack of tires. Most of the fossils in this limestone are segments of the stalk, or individual circular plates.

43 million years ago and intensified about 35 million years ago. Violent volcanic blasts were centered around the Tuscarora Mountains to the west. Many dikes and plutons of Eocene igneous rock formed underground as magma rose through older rock toward the volcanic centers. The magma produced the heat and chemically active fluids and vapors that hydrothermally altered rock and deposited gold in the many mining districts in this region, including the Carlin Mine, west of here.

The view west of NV 225 is dominated by the north-trending Independence Mountains, which consist of Ordovician-age deep-sea rocks thrust over younger Paleozoic limestone and dolomite during the Antler Orogeny. The thick sequence of Paleozoic sedimentary rocks in the Independence Mountains was strongly altered and mineralized when the rocks were intruded by magma in Eocene time. The Independence trend, a band of north-trending gold deposits in sedimentary rocks, similar to the Carlin-type deposits, has produced more than 6 million ounces of gold, more than half of which came from the area surrounding the Jerritt Canyon Mine.

About 3 miles south of the intersection with NV 226 (the Tucscarora junction), NV 225 passes east of Lone Mountain. The Merrimac (originally called Lone Mountain) mining district was organized in the 1870s, and several large mines produced lead, zinc, gold, and silver until the early 1950s. The ruins of the old mining camps are scattered around the slopes and canyons.

North of the NV 226 intersection, roadcuts in low hills reveal various Cenozoic tuffs and ash-rich sedimentary rocks. About 12 miles north of the junction,

NV 225 meets the North Fork Humboldt River, which turns east here and flows through a break in the hills known as Devils Gap. You can see dark-colored lava flows east of the road in the area of Devils Gap.

The North Fork Humboldt River, just to the east of the highway between Devils Gap and the North Fork maintenance station, has carved picturesque gullies and canyons through rugged spires and knobs of the Jarbidge Rhyolite, which erupted about 16 million years ago in mid-Miocene time. This enormous outpouring of felsic lava, which is associated with the development and eastward migration of the Yellowstone hot spot, erupted from a volcanic center around the Jarbidge Mountains about 35 miles to the northeast. Though it commonly weathers to dark brown, fresh surfaces of the rhyolite are light tan and studded with isolated crystals of quartz and feldspar.

The North Fork Humboldt River has its headwaters in the north end of the Independence Mountains. McAfee Peak, the highest point in the range at 10,438 feet, hosted glaciers during Pleistocene time. Just 5 miles north of the North Fork maintenance station, NV 225 crosses the drainage divide separating the internally drained Great Basin and the northwest-directed drainage of the Owyhee River, a tributary of the Snake River in southern Idaho.

The spires of rock adjacent to the North Fork Humboldt River east of NV 225 are composed of the Miocene-age Jarbidge Rhyolite. In the close-up, note the brown weathering residue on the surface and the tiny crystals of quartz and feldspar in the light-colored volcanic rock. The bright crystal in the center is 1 centimeter long.

Flow banding in Miocene rhyolite exposed in a roadcut along NV 225 south of Wild Horse Reservoir.

White feldspar crystals in felsic volcanic rock near Wild Horse Reservoir.

Miocene volcanic mudflow (lahar) deposits near Wild Horse Reservoir.

South of Wild Horse Reservoir, roadcuts along the highway expose rhyolitic lava flows, volcanic mudflow deposits, and tuffs, all part of the Jarbidge sequence. Some of the lava flows exhibit flow banding that developed when the thick, viscous lava oozed over surface irregularities prior to hardening. The mudflow deposits contain large blocks and boulders of rhyolite and other volcanic rocks in a matrix of ash, sand, and silt. Such volcanic mudflows are known as lahars, an Indonesian term for the fast-moving and highly destructive torrents of hot mud generated when volcanoes erupt violently. Some of the volcanic rocks exposed in roadcuts near Wild Horse Reservoir are sprinkled with white crystals of feldspar in a dark-gray, noncrystalline matrix. Northwest of the Wild Horse Dam, NV 225 follows the narrow canyon cut by the Owyhee River through resistant crags of the Jarbidge Rhyolite.

Gold- and silver-bearing veins adjacent to igneous bodies were discovered in the area around Mountain City in 1869. Bodies of Cretaceous quartz monzonite, a plutonic igneous rock similar to granite, intruded Paleozoic shale and limestone, now metamorphosed to phyllite, slate, and marble. In the 1930s copper ores were discovered in Ordovician slate, and from 1932 to 1947, the Mountain City mines were among the largest copper-producing sites in Nevada. Tungsten, uranium, and antimony deposits were located in the 1950s, but only minor production of these metals ever occurred. Most of the mines became inactive after the 1950s, and today the small community is a virtual ghost town.

Round masses of spheroidally weathered quartz monzonite are exposed in a roadcut along NV 225 north of Mountain City. In the close-up, the small black crystals are hornblende and biotite, and the light-colored groundmass is mostly crystalline feldspar.

About 3 miles north of Mountain City, near the southern boundary of the Duck Valley Indian Reservation, knobby outcrops and roadcuts along the highway are 90-million-year-old quartz monzonite. Northward from the exposures of the plutonic rock, tuffs, andesitic breccias, and dark-colored basalt flows of middle to late Miocene age appear along the highway.

At Owyhee, about 4 miles south of the Nevada-Idaho border, the valley of the Owyhee River broadens as it slopes north into the Snake River Plain of southern Idaho. Volcanic rocks erupted from vents to the north and east, mainly between about 12 and 6 million years ago, make up the tablelands surrounding Owyhee. The upper surfaces of the mesas and plateaus are hard basalt flows, a resistant caprock above softer layers of tuff, andesite, and volcanic breccia.

NV 227
Elko—Lamoille Canyon
32 miles
See map on page 135.

NV 227, a short trip from Elko to the end of the Lamoille Canyon Road, offers some of the most spectacular alpine scenery in Nevada, along with interesting roadside geology. From the intersection of Idaho Street and 5th Street in downtown Elko, 5th Street extends southeast and becomes NV 227 as it begins its winding ascent over the Elko Hills, which consist of folded Mississippian to Permian sedimentary bedrock cut by numerous thrust faults. Eocene volcanic and sedimentary rocks of the Elko Formation overlie the deformed Paleozoic strata, particularly in the southern part of the Elko Hills crossed by NV 227. At Elko Summit, a roadcut exposes lake deposits of the Elko Formation.

In addition to lakebeds, the Elko Formation includes river-deposited conglomerate, thin beds of volcanic ash, and felsic lava flows. These sediments, more than 2,000 feet thick, accumulated 43 to 37 million years ago in a 60-mile-wide basin that opened during an early phase of Basin and Range extension. Pulses of rapid subsidence led to the development of deep lakes, punctuated by more stable intervals during which coarse, river-deposited sand and gravels became more predominant. The upper part of the Elko Formation is rich in organic sediments, such as black, carbon-rich shale and low-grade coal. Some of the fine-grained rocks are so rich in organic matter that synthetic crude oil was produced from them for a short time near Elko. A diverse array of clams, snails, algae, and ostracods, small crustaceans sometimes called seed shrimp, lived in the lake.

From Elko Summit, you have a great view across the town of Spring Creek to the Ruby Mountains, one of the highest fault-block mountain systems in Nevada. Normal faults on both the east and west sides of the range have displaced the central block upward to elevations reaching as high as 11,387 feet at Ruby Dome, the loftiest peak in the Ruby Mountains. Along with the East Humboldt Range to the north, this mountain range is part of a large metamorphic core complex, a complicated mixture of metamorphic and igneous rocks

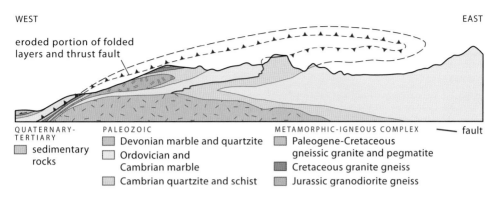

WEST

EAST

eroded portion of folded
layers and thrust fault

QUATERNARY-
TERTIARY
☐ sedimentary
rocks

PALEOZOIC
☐ Devonian marble and quartzite
☐ Ordovician and
Cambrian marble
☐ Cambrian quartzite and schist

METAMORPHIC-IGNEOUS COMPLEX
☐ Paleogene-Cretaceous
gneissic granite and pegmatite
☐ Cretaceous granite gneiss
☐ Jurassic granodiorite gneiss

— fault

Generalized geological cross section of the north wall of Lamoille Canyon from the mouth of the canyon eastward to the south bend in the paved road. —Modified from Snoke and others, 1997

that has been lifted at least 20 miles from deep within Earth's crust, where temperature and pressure conditions are extreme. The metamorphic rocks—schist, phyllite, marble, and gneiss—were originally sedimentary rocks deposited in late Precambrian and early Paleozoic time. The core rocks of the Ruby Mountain began to rise from deep within Earth's crust in Eocene time, about 40 million years ago, and continued rising as extensional forces intensely stretched the crust in the Miocene Epoch, some 20 million years ago. Under these stretching forces, great sheets of rock slid away from the rising dome in the Ruby Mountains area along low-angle normal faults.

Unlike most mountains of the central Great Basin, the Ruby Mountains were extensively glaciated at least twice during the past 100,000 years. The earliest time was the Lamoille glaciation, a cold interval that peaked between about 140,000 and 66,000 years ago in the late Pleistocene Epoch. A younger period of glacial development, the Angel Lake glaciation, occurred between about 22,000 and 14,000 years ago. During these glacial times, the glaciers in the Ruby Mountains were the largest and most extensive accumulation of ice anywhere in the Great Basin. During the most recent Angel Lake glaciation, more than 130 individual glaciers existed in the Ruby Mountains and East Humboldt Range. The higher parts of these mountains exhibit many of the classic landforms associated with alpine glaciation, including U-shaped canyons, jagged peaks known as horns, shallow basins called cirques, and sharp saw-toothed ridges referred to as arêtes. At lower elevations where the glacial ice melted, sediment released from the ice formed heaps, mounds, and ridges of moraine, a mixture of boulders, sand, and silt transported by and deposited from glaciers.

About 1 mile west of the small settlement of Lamoille, the Lamoille Canyon Road (Forest Road 660) joins NV 227 and extends 13 miles southeast up the canyon. East of the NV 227 intersection, the Lamoille Canyon Road ascends a slope of glacial sediments from the older Lamoille glaciation. South of the road, two elongated lateral moraines deposited during this earlier glaciation emerge from the mouth of Seitz Canyon. Inside of these larger moraine ridges, smaller

View southeast from NV 227 of the lateral moraines at the mouth of Seitz Canyon, which opens from the Ruby Mountains west of Lamoille Canyon. The larger paired ridges were deposited during the older Lamoille glaciation. The smaller lateral moraine ridge inset against the larger ridge to the right was deposited during the later Angel Lake glaciation.

accumulations of glacial sediment document the later and less extensive Angel Lake glaciation.

About a half mile east of the entrance road to Ruby Dome Ranch, the Lamoille Canyon Road rises up a slope that marks the scarp of one of the normal faults that form the range-front escarpment. The fault offsets late Pleistocene glacial deposits and is probably still active. As the road enters the mouth of Lamoille Canyon, the V-shaped profile of the valley, more typical of stream erosions, suggests that glacial ice did not frequently extend this far down the canyon. The downcutting of Lamoille Creek in response to the elevation of the mountain block along the fault appears to have been more important than glaciers in excavating the lower portion of the valley. In contrast, the moraines at the mouth of Seitz Canyon, to the west, extend well beyond the mountain front, suggesting that the rivers of ice in that location were longer and larger. More ice would likely have formed in the drainage basin of Seitz Canyon, which is larger and higher than Lamoille Canyon.

Roadside outcrops through the lower portion of Lamoille Canyon are mostly sheared gneiss, schist, and marble of the metamorphic core complex, cut in places by veins and pockets of granitic igneous rock. The metamorphic rocks in this part of the canyon are mostly of Cambrian and Ordovician age and originated as shale and limestone strata deposited in shallow marine conditions. Relict contorted layering can still be seen in some of the exposures of these severely metamorphosed rocks.

Roadcut on the north side of the Lamoille Canyon road exposing deformed gneiss, schist, and marble of the metamorphic core complex.

About 3 miles up Lamoille Canyon from the mouth, near an interpretive sign and pullout on the south side of the road, the valley of the Right Fork Lamoille Creek opens to the south. Prior to about 60,000 years ago, during the Lamoille glaciation, ice from glaciers moving down the main valley and the Right Fork valley merged at about this point. The valley of Right Fork is a hanging valley because its floor is a few hundred feet higher than the main valley. During the later Angel Lake glaciation, less than 20,000 years ago, the main glacier in Lamoille Canyon did not reach the mouth of the Right Fork. The glacier filling the hanging valley at this time extended a short distance onto the floor of the main canyon and deposited the prominent ridge of lateral moraine that extends into the main valley from the eastern side of the mouth of the Right Fork. Lamoille Creek is forced toward the north side of the canyon by this ridge of moraine and has cut a rugged, narrow gorge just south of the road.

Southeast of the mouth of the Right Fork, the road continues to ascend the main canyon along the north side of Lamoille Creek. Here, the magnificent U-shaped gorge was shaped by multiple cycles of glaciation. Several hanging valleys, some of which sustain waterfalls in the spring and early summer, can be seen on both sides of the canyon. In the vicinity of the Thomas Canyon Campground, the rocks exposed in the sheer canyon walls are a complex mingling of gneiss, schist, and quartzite; Cretaceous and Eocene granitic rocks; and dikes of coarse-grained pegmatite and Miocene andesitic rocks. Many light-colored sills and dikes of igneous rocks cut through the generally darker-colored

The broad U-shaped cross section of upper Lamoille Canyon was developed during multiple cycles of Pleistocene glaciation.

metamorphic rocks. The intensely deformed and metamorphosed older rocks are not commonly exposed elsewhere in Nevada. In the East Humboldt–Ruby Mountains core complex, we get a very rare opportunity to observe the effects of extreme conditions of temperature and pressure acting on rocks with a long history of deformation.

The walls in the upper part of canyon are mostly Precambrian and Cambrian quartzite and gneiss, cut by large bodies of light-colored granitic rock. The pavement terminates at the Roads End parking lot at an elevation of about 8,800 feet above sea level. From this parking lot, the Ruby Crest Trail leads into the higher parts of Lamoille Canyon and the Ruby Mountains. Outcrops along this trail a few hundred yards from the parking lot are dominated by banded and foliated gneiss cut by light-colored dikes of pegmatite.

NV 231
Wells—Angel Lake
12 miles

NV 231, known as the Angel Lake Road, begins at its intersection with Humboldt Avenue in Wells just south of I-80. This 12-mile-long scenic byway ascends the northeast slope of the East Humboldt Range, culminating at Angel Lake, nestled in a glacial basin among bold exposures of the core of the East

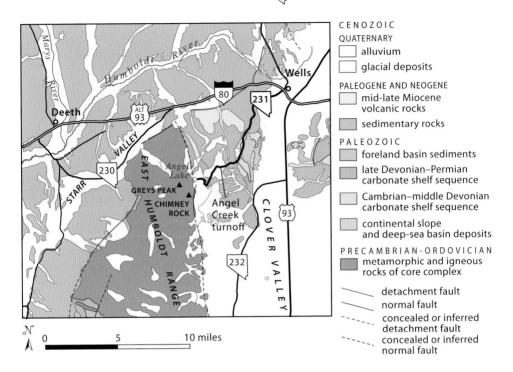

CENOZOIC
QUATERNARY
- alluvium
- glacial deposits

PALEOGENE AND NEOGENE
- mid-late Miocene volcanic rocks
- sedimentary rocks

PALEOZOIC
- foreland basin sediments
- late Devonian–Permian carbonate shelf sequence
- Cambrian–middle Devonian carbonate shelf sequence
- continental slope and deep-sea basin deposits

PRECAMBRIAN-ORDOVICIAN
- metamorphic and igneous rocks of core complex

— detachment fault
— normal fault
----- concealed or inferred detachment fault
----- concealed or inferred normal fault

Geology of the East Humboldt Range.

Humboldt–Ruby Mountains metamorphic core complex. See the discussion in the introduction for a primer on metamorphic core complexes.

About 3.5 miles southwest of Wells, NV 231 passes a roadcut exposing conglomerates of the lower part of the Humboldt Formation. Rivers that flowed through the region 15 to 10 million years ago deposited the gravels. West of the road are brown, knobby exposures of 15- to 14-million-year-old rhyolite that formed when lava was injected into the contact between the Humboldt Formation and overlying layers. The rhyolite was part of a widespread pulse of magma that affected this part of Nevada in Miocene time.

As the roads climbs the northeastern slope of the East Humboldt Range, low roadcuts on the east expose tan to yellowish metasedimentary rocks that are probably of late Precambrian to Ordovician ages. These rocks were sheared, heated, and deformed during the formation of the metamorphic core complex in Cenozoic time. Because many of the rocks in this sequence were originally limestones, they are now calcite marbles with a strongly foliated appearance. The siltstones and sandstones have been altered to quartzite and schist.

The eastern face of the East Humboldt Range comes into view to the west as the road levels out south of its initial steep ascent from Wells. The rocks exposed in the high country to the west are a complex mixture of metamorphic rocks of the core complex. The tree-covered slope below the rugged peaks is relatively unmetamorphosed Mississippian to Permian sedimentary rocks that

Roadside outcrop of conglomerate of the Miocene Humboldt Formation along the east side NV 231 as it ascends the lower slopes of the East Humboldt Range south of Wells.

Well-foliated schist and slate of the metamorphic core complex along the east side of NV 231 in the East Humboldt Range.

overlie the metamorphic core but have been severely deformed by faulting and displacement. The low-lying foothills expose Tertiary sedimentary rocks and brownish-colored volcanic rocks, mostly rhyolite. The surface that originally separated the overlying brittle rocks from the underlying high-grade metamorphic complex has been offset by high-angle normal faults. Chimney Rock, a prominent, dark-colored peak on the skyline, is composed of gneiss that forms the core of a large-scale fold that is difficult to see from this perspective.

View west of the eastern escarpment of the East Humboldt Range from the middle section of NV 231. The highest cliffs are exposures of metamorphic rocks in the core of the complex, while the lower slopes are mostly severely faulted Paleozoic and Cenozoic rocks of the upper plate. The prominent triangular peak left of center is Chimney Rock.

At the turnoff to the Angel Creek Campground, note the long boulder ridge south of the road and boulder surfaces just west of this ridge. These piles of rubble are glacial moraine that accumulated along the edge of the melting ice. During the Pleistocene Epoch, a glacier melted here following one of the earlier cold intervals, known as the Lamoille glaciation, based on evidence from Lamoille Canyon in the nearby Ruby Mountains. The road winds across such glacial deposits for the next few miles, exposing the very distinctive unsorted sediments in the roadcuts.

As the road climbs higher through a series of steep switchbacks, numerous roadcuts expose Paleozoic limestone (mostly of Permian age) that is relatively unmetamorphosed but intensely shattered. These rocks are located above the metamorphic basement of the East Humboldt core complex.

The highway ends at Angel Lake, which lies within a cirque carved by glaciers during one or more cycles of activity in the Pleistocene Epoch. This locality is the source of the name of the Angel Lake glaciation, the most recent period of cold conditions in the Great Basin, which occurred between 22,000 and 14,000 years ago. At that time, a mass of ice several hundred feet thick flowed out of the Angel Lake basin for a distance of about 3 miles to the east. The long, vegetated ridge north of the Angel Lake Campground is a lateral moraine deposited as the most recent Pleistocene glacier melted back from a lower elevation. The top of this ridge approximates the minimum thickness of the mass of ice.

Roadcut along NV 231 exposing a Pleistocene glacial moraine. Note that this rubble deposited from melting ice is not layered and is poorly sorted in terms of particle size.

View east across Angel Lake of the headwall of the cirque carved by Pleistocene glaciers. Rocks exposed in the cliffs beyond the lake are mostly schist and banded gneiss of Precambrian through Ordovician age. In the close-up, note the white vein of quartz and feldspar cutting through the rock parallel to the banding.

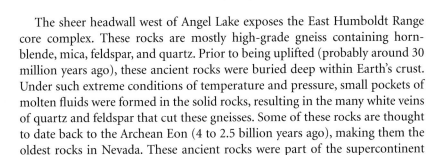

The sheer headwall west of Angel Lake exposes the East Humboldt Range core complex. These rocks are mostly high-grade gneiss containing hornblende, mica, feldspar, and quartz. Prior to being uplifted (probably around 30 million years ago), these ancient rocks were buried deep within Earth's crust. Under such extreme conditions of temperature and pressure, small pockets of molten fluids were formed in the solid rocks, resulting in the many white veins of quartz and feldspar that cut these gneisses. Some of these rocks are thought to date back to the Archean Eon (4 to 2.5 billion years ago), making them the oldest rocks in Nevada. These ancient rocks were part of the supercontinent Rodinia.

Small masses of light-colored granite containing cream-colored feldspar, translucent quartz, and tiny black flakes of biotite cut through the metamorphic rocks in several places. Radiometric dating of these igneous rocks suggests that they crystallized from magma around 30 million years ago, making them substantially younger than the metamorphic rocks they cut. A few dikes of darker-colored basalt cut through the rocks exposed in the headwall of the Angel Lake cirque. These igneous rocks probably formed when magma oozed up along fractures and hardened in place around 15 million years ago.

NV 266 and NV 264
US 95—Fish Lake Valley
60 miles

NV 266 traverses Lida Summit en route to Oasis, California, where you can either continue north to US 6 on NV 264 in Fish Lake Valley on the east side of the massive White Mountains or head west on CA 168 over Westgard Pass between the White Mountains and Inyo Mountains.

Between US 95 and the intersection with NV 774, NV 266 crosses alluvial deposits bordered on the north by Cambrian metasedimentary rock of the Nolan Belt, an accreted terrane. Despite the higher grade of metamorphism here than in rocks of similar age to the east, geologists have determined they were deposited in an oceanic reef environment. This terrane extends north and west through the Silver Peak area.

Gold Point, 7 miles south on NV 774, is situated along the edge of hills eroded in Proterozoic and early Paleozoic rocks, intruded in places by Jurassic granitic plutons. In 1868 the town was named Lime Point after the lime deposits found there, and then it became Hornsilver when the discovery of hornsilver (a silver chloride) in 1905 resulted in a boomtown with two hundred buildings. In 1932, with the discovery of gold, the town got its present name. With the closing of area mines during World War II, it became another essentially deserted Nevada mining town. Around 1970 individuals began to buy and restore the old structures, and today it has become a destination for those seeking a vestige of early Nevada history.

East of the NV 774 intersection, Oligocene and Miocene volcanics form the hills to the north. As the road starts upward through Lida Canyon, outcroppings

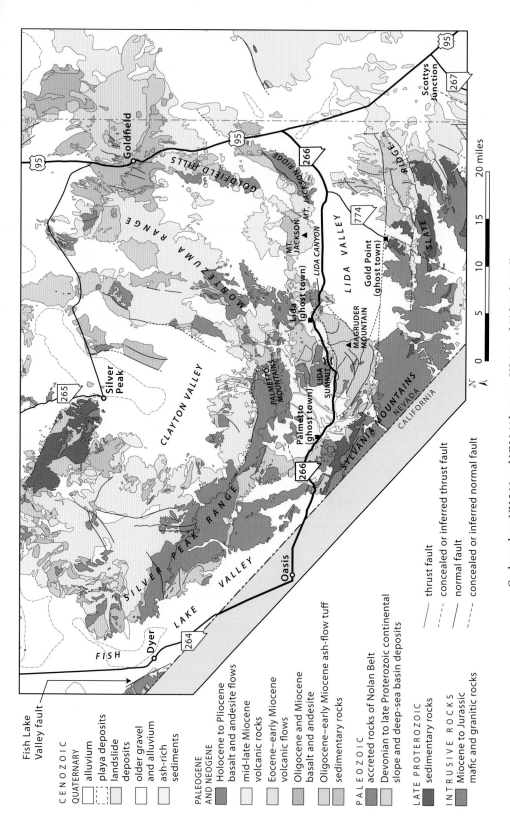

Fish Lake Valley fault

CENOZOIC

QUATERNARY
- alluvium
- playa deposits
- landslide deposits
- older gravel and alluvium
- ash-rich sediments

PALEOGENE AND NEOGENE
- Holocene to Pliocene basalt and andesite flows
- mid–late Miocene volcanic rocks
- Eocene–early Miocene volcanic flows
- Oligocene and Miocene basalt and andesite
- Oligocene–early Miocene ash-flow tuff
- sedimentary rocks

PALEOZOIC
- accreted rocks of Nolan Belt
- Devonian to late Proterozoic continental slope and deep-sea basin deposits

LATE PROTEROZOIC
- sedimentary rocks

INTRUSIVE ROCKS
- Miocene to Jurassic mafic and granitic rocks

— thrust fault
--- concealed or inferred thrust fault
— normal fault
--- concealed or inferred normal fault

Geology along NV 266 and NV 264 between US 95 and Fish Lake Valley.

0   5   10   15   20 miles

on both sides are dominated by Proterozoic and early Paleozoic rocks but younger rhyolitic tuffs occur immediately south of the road at Lida Summit.

Between Lida Summit and the ghost town of Palmetto, areas to the north, including the Palmetto Mountains, are characterized by Cambrian and Ordovician rock units stacked in a complex mosaic of multiple thrust sheets and folds tilted to a horizontal plane by the Antler Orogeny. The Ordovician Palmetto Formation, a deepwater sequence of chert, shale, limestone, and quartzite, contains abundant graptolite fossils, which are branched colonial organisms.

A rich vein of silver led to the founding of Palmetto in the 1860s, but it played out after only a couple of months and the town declined. Several businesses again sprang up in 1906 with another mining boom, but once again the town lasted only a few months. Some old travel articles claim that much of the town was erased in a flash flood and that store safes filled with money and receipts remain buried to this day in flood debris.

North of Palmetto, an extensive erosional surface sloping up to the Palmetto Mountains is developed on ash-rich sandstone and conglomerate, incised as much as 300 feet in places. The Sylvania Mountains to the south of Palmetto are composed of 155-million-year-old biotite quartz monzonite typified by large pink orthoclase crystals. These granitic intrusive rocks also form the westernmost row of hills along the east side of Fish Lake Valley and are exposed in the westernmost outcrop along the highway before entering the valley.

Fish Lake Valley Fault

At the Oasis junction, 4 miles west of the California border, you can continue north back to Nevada in Fish Lake Valley to see some of the most impressive fault scarps in the country. They reach heights of up to 280 feet where they cut alluvial fans and valley fill along the mountain front to the west. Begin watching for them at milepost 0 at the south end of NV 264 (at the California state line). In the afternoon, they cast long linear shadows. The scarps vary in height, sometimes split into parallel strands, and sometimes disappear completely, only to reappear on another fan to the north or south. The scarps define the trace of the Fish Lake Valley fault, the 50-mile-long, northernmost segment of the 155-mile-long Death Valley fault zone. In contrast, the alluvial fans on the east side of the valley are not faulted and present a long, smooth, unbroken surface from the apex of the fans to the valley bottom. At the north end of the valley the faulting steps over to the east side of the valley, as expressed by fault scarps along the Emigrant Peak fault, which in turn transfers slip from along the Fish Lake Valley fault to the faults of the Walker Lane as part of the Mina deflection (see the US 6 road guide). The Fish Lake Valley fault is the single most active earthquake fault in the western Basin and Range Province and accounts for approximately half of the current rate of regional extension across the Basin and Range.

Volcanic ash layers in Fish Lake Valley have been important in studying the fault because they can be radiometrically dated and correlated with specific calderas. Fish Lake Valley is only about 30 miles due east of the Long Valley caldera, whose eruption about 740,000 years ago was one of the most explosive

SCARP

The fault scarps along the base of the mountain front at Dyer are the highest in Fish Lake Valley. Probably not coincidentally, the highest point in the White Mountains, White Mountain Peak, is also directly west of Dyer.

and largest in Pleistocene time, producing about 120 cubic miles of volcanic ash. East of Fish Lake Valley is the Silver Peak caldera, which erupted between 6 and 5 million years ago.

Based on geomorphic relationships and age dates of volcanic ash layers, geologists have determined that faulting along the Fish Lake Valley fault began around 10 million years ago. The long-term rate of right-lateral slip along the fault is 5 millimeters per year, for a total of 25 to 30 miles of right-lateral displacement. Vertical movement has also occurred on the fault as part of the Basin and Range extension. The White Mountains rose to the west as Fish Lake Valley dropped down. We know the valley existed 3.4 million years ago because lakebeds with ash of that age are buried beneath the alluvium.

The White Mountains, with a high point in California of White Mountain Peak at 14,246 feet, rise more than 9,000 feet above the floor of Fish Lake Valley. Note the thick deposits of unconsolidated fill, now undergoing dissection, that occur along the western side of the valley, all material eroded off the mountains to the west. The White Mountains are mostly metamorphosed rock intruded by light gray- and tan-weathering, 93- to 83-million-year-old plutons and 175- to 160-million-year-old plutons.

NV 278
Carlin—Eureka
92 miles

South from its junction with I-80, NV 278 follows the Humboldt River. Steam can sometimes be seen rising from hot springs along the floor of the valley. The bold escarpment west of the Humboldt River, known as the Palisades, forces the river southwest until it turns west to pass through the rugged chasm of Palisade Canyon. The rocks exposed in the Palisades west of NV 278 are Miocene andesite and rhyolite flows totaling more than 500 feet in thickness. Farther west in Palisade Canyon, the Humboldt River slices through dark-colored Mesozoic volcanic rock. Immigrants along the California Trail in the 1800s found the narrow canyon impassable to wagons due to the boulder-choked riverbed, so they traveled well north of Palisade Canyon along the present route of I-80. Even today, only rail tracks and a few dirt tracks pass through Palisade Canyon.

After passing the small historic settlement of Palisade, NV 278 continues south along the eastern side of lower Pine Valley, an asymmetric half-graben formed by active downfaulting of its eastern side. The basin is filled with interbedded lake deposits, sand and gravel alluvium, and volcanic materials of Miocene to recent age, which accumulated while Pine Valley was a closed basin with no drainage to the Humboldt River system. Due to regional uplift during the past 500,000 years, Pine Creek lowered its bed some 500 feet, cutting a channel that now connects it to the Humboldt River.

Roadcut along NV 278 exposes Miocene to Pliocene sediments and volcanic ash deposits.

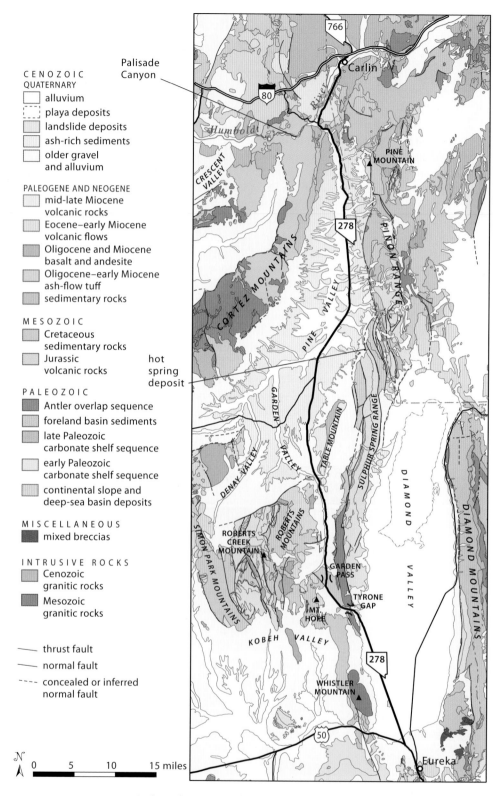

CENOZOIC
QUATERNARY
alluvium
playa deposits
landslide deposits
ash-rich sediments
older gravel
and alluvium

PALEOGENE AND NEOGENE
mid-late Miocene
volcanic rocks
Eocene–early Miocene
volcanic flows
Oligocene and Miocene
basalt and andesite
Oligocene–early Miocene
ash-flow tuff
sedimentary rocks

MESOZOIC
Cretaceous
sedimentary rocks
Jurassic
volcanic rocks

PALEOZOIC
Antler overlap sequence
foreland basin sediments
late Paleozoic
carbonate shelf sequence
early Paleozoic
carbonate shelf sequence
continental slope and
deep-sea basin deposits

MISCELLANEOUS
mixed breccias

INTRUSIVE ROCKS
Cenozoic
granitic rocks
Mesozoic
granitic rocks

— thrust fault
— normal fault
---- concealed or inferred
normal fault

Palisade
Canyon

hot
spring
deposit

N

0   5   10   15 miles

Geology along NV 278 between Carlin and Eureka.

Low, white bluffs east of NV 274 in Pine Valley consist of tuff, siltstone, clay, and sandstone deposited in the valley in Pliocene and Pleistocene time.

NV 278 parallels the western front of the Piñon Range. The lower, brownish slopes expose soft calcareous mudstones, shales, and fine sandstone of the Paleozoic Antler overlap sequence. The overlying volcanic and sedimentary sequence is generally lighter in color or is exposed as cliff-forming, dark-colored lava flows. From near the intersection of NV 278 and the Ferdelford Canyon road, you can see Pine Mountain, composed of Devonian limestone, part of a sheet of rock that was thrust to the east during the Antler Orogeny. Farther to the east in this area in the core of the Piñon Range, disseminated gold deposits were discovered in the 1980s in Mississippian siltstone and shale. The microscopic gold appears to have formed when magma intruded these sedimentary rocks about 39 million years ago, in the Eocene Epoch. These ores, known as the Rain deposits, were extensively mined between 1988 and the early 2000s, making this one of the major gold-producing areas in the southern Carlin trend.

Across Pine Valley to the west of NV 278, the northern end of the Cortez Mountains is Jurassic granitic and volcanic rocks intruded through a thick sequence of deformed Paleozoic sedimentary rock layers similar to those of the Piñon Range. Nevada's largest and longest continually operating gold mining area is located along the western slope of the southern Cortez Mountains and in Crescent Valley to the west. Disseminated gold occurs in Silurian and Devonian rocks, and mineralization appears to have involved igneous intrusions of both Jurassic and Miocene age. Mining for silver ores began in the southern Cortez Mountains in 1862 and has been active in varying intensity ever since.

In the mid-1900s, natural oil seeps in Pine Valley stimulated interest, and drilling led to the discovery of several small oil fields. The oil is trapped in porous Oligocene volcanic rocks and in small cavities in soluble Devonian limestone buried beneath the valley. The petroleum may have originated in other organic-rich Paleozoic sediments and migrated into the reservoir rocks after downfaulting formed the Pine Valley graben.

The brown cliffs along the west slope of the Sulphur Spring Range consist of thick layers of Pennsylvanian and Permian sandstone and conglomerate of the Antler overlap sequence.

About 30 miles south of Carlin, NV 278 traverses a broad alluvial plain where drainages from the surrounding highlands join upper Pine Creek. Most of the streams are ephemeral but have well-incised channels that indicate vigorous erosion when the streams are filled with snowmelt or runoff from summer thunderstorms. Large ranches utilize the groundwater, mostly pumped from unconsolidated alluvium aquifers, generally less than 50 feet below the surface of the broad basin.

South of the intersection with the gravel-surfaced Quartz Road, NV 278 leaves Pine Valley and continues due south through Garden Valley. The mountains east of the road are the Sulphur Spring Range and its lower foothill ridge known as Table Mountain. The rocks exposed along the western side of the Sulphur Springs Range are mostly Pennsylvanian and Permian limestone, sandstone, and conglomerate of the Antler overlap sequence.

South of Table Mountain, NV 278 passes through a narrow valley east of the Roberts Mountains, where the Roberts thrust fault, the most prominent fault associated with the Antler Orogeny, was first mapped and studied. It is difficult to see this major structure from the highway, but the low foothills on the east and northeast side of the Roberts Mountains consist of early Paleozoic deep-sea sediments moved eastward along the Roberts Mountains thrust fault over Paleozoic continental shelf deposits that make up the interior of the mountains. Prior to the uplift and erosion of the Roberts Mountains, the deep-sea deposits of chert and black shale entirely covered the limestone and dolomite of Ordovician to Devonian age. The interior of the Roberts Mountains is thus what geologists call a window, an opening eroded through a thrust sheet that exposes the underlying rocks.

In the vicinity of Garden Pass, NV 278 passes over smooth, sagebrush-covered hills of soft black shales and chert of the upper plate of the Roberts Mountains thrust. About 3 miles south of Garden Pass, you can see the Mt. Hope mining area west of the road. Molybdenum, zinc, lead, and silver mineralization at Mt. Hope is related to an igneous complex that intruded the Paleozoic rock layers 38 to 36 million years ago. Heat, hot gases, and hydrothermal fluids penetrated the older rocks as they were invaded by the magma. The igneous activity in the Roberts Mountains continued into the Miocene Epoch, when numerous northwest-trending dikes related to the southern end of the Northern Nevada Rift intruded into the older Paleozoic rocks.

At Tyrone Gap, NV 278 passes through a ridge of steeply east-dipping layers of well-cemented, 300-million-year-old conglomerate of early Permian age. The pebbles were rounded and transported by streams draining the Antler highland and deposited on the eroded surface of the Roberts Mountains thrust sheet as part of the Antler overlap sequence.

South from Tyrone Gap to its intersection with US 50, NV 278 travels along the western margin of Diamond Valley, a large graben separating the Diamond Mountains to the east from the Sulphur Spring Range to the west. Because the annual rainfall across the floor of Diamond Valley is only about 10 inches per year and there are no large permanent streams, irrigation water for crops comes primarily from groundwater aquifers in unconsolidated sand and gravel alluvium. Though this alluvium has a maximum thickness of 7,500 feet in the center of Diamond Valley, the majority of the water extracted by wells occurs

Steeply dipping layers of Permian conglomerate west of NV 278 near Tyrone Gap.

within a few hundred feet of the surface. As agricultural production increased from the 1960s to the early 2000s, the water table in the southern part of Diamond Valley fell by as much as 100 feet. Water conservation methods and improved irrigation techniques are currently helping to meet the challenge of the declining water table.

A major normal fault is largely responsible for the bold western escarpment of the Diamond Mountains, which are mostly sedimentary rocks deposited in the shallow seas that covered the continental shelf of Laurentia in Paleozoic time. Toward the southern end of the range, these Paleozoic rocks are intruded by Cretaceous plutonic rocks and younger Cenozoic volcanic materials. Interactions between the older Paleozoic carbonate rocks and the younger igneous materials resulted in widespread mineralization in the vicinity of Eureka. (See the US 50 road guide for more information about the Eureka mining district.)

Whistler Mountain forms the western border of southern Diamond Valley north of the intersection of NV 278 and US 50. This small mountain block consists mostly of Jurassic granitic rocks emplaced into Devonian and older limestone and dolomite layers. Sills and dikes extend from the main intrusive mass into the surrounding Paleozoic rocks in several places.

NV 305
Battle Mountain—Austin
89 miles

For its entire length from Battle Mountain to Austin, NV 305 follows the Reese River, a north-flowing tributary to the Humboldt River, through some of the most remote and sparsely populated land in the Great Basin. Battle Mountain is the prominent scarred mountain just south of the town of the same name. The area around Antler Peak, in the central part of Battle Mountain, is where geologists in the 1960s first discovered evidence for the Paleozoic mountain building event that is today known as the Antler Orogeny. As is obvious when driving past Battle Mountain with its many mining pits, prospects, and roads, this is also one of Nevada's most mineralized tracts. Battle Mountain lies at the north end of the Battle Mountain–Eureka trend, a linear zone that hosts several enormous mines.

Battle Mountain consists primarily of Ordovician and Cambrian sedimentary rocks deposited in a deep-sea basin, overlain by the Antler overlap sequence of Pennsylvanian to Permian age. These rocks are deformed by thrust faults and folds and intruded by bodies of Cretaceous and Paleogene plutonic rocks. The Caetano Tuff, a deposit of welded volcanic ash with quartz crystals and rock fragments, buried the older rocks in Oligocene time. The Caetano Tuff was the product of a violent volcanic blast 34 million years ago that left a 12-mile-wide caldera in the Shoshone Range to the east. As NV 305 swings east of Battle Mountain, you can see a prominent mesa, culminating in a hump known as Elephant Head, made of the Caetano Tuff.

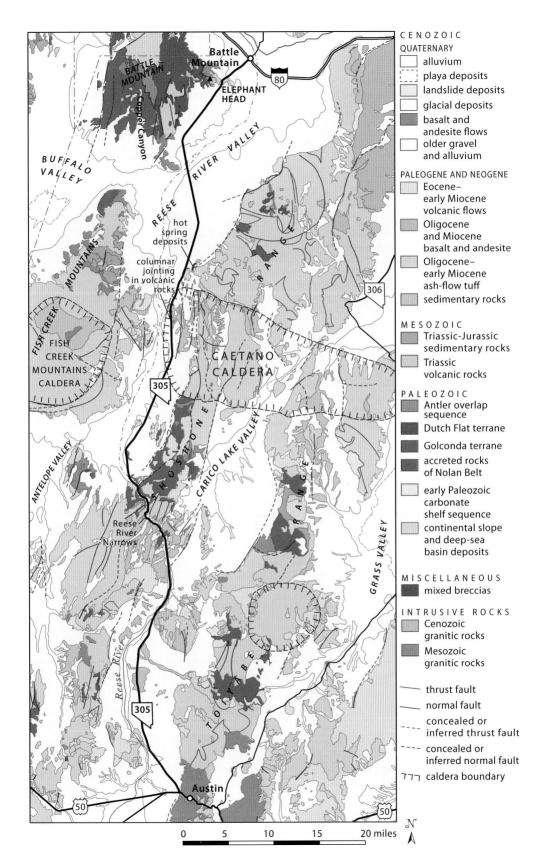

CENOZOIC

QUATERNARY

alluvium

playa deposits

landslide deposits

glacial deposits

basalt and
andesite flows

older gravel
and alluvium

PALEOGENE AND NEOGENE

Eocene–
early Miocene
volcanic flows

Oligocene
and Miocene
basalt and andesite

Oligocene–
early Miocene
ash-flow tuff

sedimentary rocks

MESOZOIC

Triassic-Jurassic
sedimentary rocks

Triassic
volcanic rocks

PALEOZOIC

Antler overlap
sequence

Dutch Flat terrane

Golconda terrane

accreted rocks
of Nolan Belt

early Paleozoic
carbonate
shelf sequence

continental slope
and deep-sea
basin deposits

MISCELLANEOUS

mixed breccias

INTRUSIVE ROCKS

Cenozoic
granitic rocks

Mesozoic
granitic rocks

—— thrust fault

—— normal fault

- - - concealed or
inferred thrust fault

- - - concealed or
inferred normal fault

⊤⊤⊤ caldera boundary

Battle
Mountain

BATTLE
MOUNTAIN

Copper Canyon

ELEPHANT
HEAD

80

BUFFALO
VALLEY

REESE RIVER VALLEY

hot
spring
deposits

columnar
jointing
in volcanic
rocks

FISH CREEK MOUNTAINS

FISH
CREEK
MOUNTAINS
CALDERA

306

CAETANO
CALDERA

R A N G E

305

ANTELOPE VALLEY

H O S H O N E

CARICO LAKE VALLEY

R A N G E

GRASS VALLEY

Reese
River
Narrows

Reese River

305

T O I Y A B E

Austin

50

305

50

0   5   10   15   20 miles

N

The Copper Basin mining complex is conspicuous on the eastern side of Battle Mountain. The high peak in the distance is Antler Peak. The dark mass of volcanic rock at the left is part of Elephant Head, a landform consisting of Caetano Tuff of Oligocene age.

In the vicinity of Elephant Head, the view west from NV 305 is dominated by the expansive tailings from the large open-pit mines in the Copper Basin area, where ores of copper, molybdenum, gold, and silver were mined beginning in the 1860s. A few miles south of the Copper Basin area on the east slope of Battle Mountain, the Copper Canyon road leads west from NV 305 toward a separate mining area on the southern flanks of the range. (See the in-depth discussion of Battle Mountain in the I-80 road guide.)

About where NV 305 bends to the south and crosses the usually dry bed of the Reese River, the view to the west is dominated by the Fish Creek Mountains, the wide southern portion of which is mostly an extensive sequence of volcanic rocks. The magma rose through older, deformed Paleozoic rocks, and about 25 million years ago, an enormous mass of lava exploded out of the subsurface, forming a major caldera in the Fish Creek Mountains. Ash from this violent eruption exceeded a depth of 3,000 feet near the caldera. Later, in Miocene time, volcanic activity resumed when basalt and rhyolite flows related to the Northern Nevada Rift were erupted over the older tuff. Most recently, from 6 to less than 1 million years ago, basalt flows erupted in the central and northwest Fish Creek Mountains. The intense Cenozoic igneous activity played an important role in forming the gold deposits mined from altered Mesozoic rocks in the north-central part of the mountains.

To the east of NV 305, the northern part of the Shoshone Range is essentially an east-tilted block bounded by normal faults along its western base. The rocks are dominantly Ordovician, Silurian, and Devonian shale, chert, and sandstone, originally deposited in a deep-sea basin and now arranged in a complex stack of thrust slices. The slivers of deformed rocks were transported from the west over limestone, dolomite, and sandstone of about the same age that were deposited in shallow water on edge of the continental shelf in Paleozoic time. The enormous caldera that erupted the Caetano Tuff once stretched nearly 30 miles from the central Shoshone Range to the southeast. More than 200 cubic miles of ash was blown from this caldera and settled out as a blanket of hot ash some 15,000 feet thick.

About 40 miles south of Battle Mountain, NV 305 passes close to the western escarpment of the Shoshone Range. Oligocene and Miocene volcanic rocks, mostly andesite and rhyolite flows and tuffs, dominate the exposures east of the road, where crude columnar jointing can be seen in places. NV 305 crosses the Shoshone Range through Reese River Narrows, a 5-mile-long gorge cut by the Reese River through a thick, layered pile of tuff and sedimentary rocks. The tuffs are welded to varying degrees and record at least four periods of ash accumulation between about 25 and 22 million years ago. The sedimentary rocks formed from silt, mud, and sand that was washed into ancient lakes, ponds, and river valleys during the volcanic rampage. Most of these sediments contain at least some ash and are weakly lithified. The volcanic rocks are relatively resistant to weathering and tend to form brown to tan cliffs and ledges through the Reese River Narrows, while the sedimentary rocks weather to form smooth, light-gray slopes and badlands exposures along the highway.

Columnar jointing has produced the crude vertical columns in the Miocene lava flows of the western Shoshone Range, seen to the east from NV 305 in the Reese River Valley.

South of the Reese River Narrows, the Toiyabe Range forms the eastern boundary of the valley. Pleistocene glacial sediments have been identified on the middle slope of Mt. Callaghan, the highest peak directly east of NV 305 at 10,187 feet.

West of the highway in the southern Shoshone Range are Paleozoic rocks thrust eastward on the Roberts Mountains thrust fault during the Antler Orogeny. Below the fault are Cambrian to Silurian sedimentary rocks that accumulated in shallow seawater on the outer edge of the continental shelf. Several mining districts were established in the early 1900s in the southern Shoshone Range from which small amounts of gold, silver, lead, and copper ores, along with barite, were produced.

As NV 305 approaches US 50 from the north, several low outcrops along the road expose Neogene sedimentary layers and tuff deposits. To the west, across the Reese River Valley, river terraces are well-developed along the modern floodplain. The nearly flat upper surface of the terraces represents the older floodplain of the river prior to the initiation of downcutting by vigorous stream flow in response to either regional uplift or a drop in base level, the lowest elevation to which a river can erode its channel. Both factors may be involved in the development of the river terraces here. The many earthquakes in this part of Nevada, some of them very powerful, indicate that uplift of the mountain blocks along normal faults continues and helps invigorate small rivers. The lower portion of the Reese River Valley was probably internally drained until geologically recent times. Once a connection was established between the Reese River and the Humboldt River to the north, the overall gradient of the river system increased, and the stream draining the formerly enclosed valley became energized. Though the modern flow of the Reese River is generally only a trickle, when it swells with spring snowmelt or cloudburst runoff, it actively erodes its earlier deposits.

NV 318
Hiko—Lund
107 miles

NV 318, one of the busier two-lane highways in southern Nevada, is the most direct route between Las Vegas and US 50 or I-80. On the third Sunday of May and September, this public highway is closed to traffic for the Silver State Classic Challenge's road races. Anyone wishing to drive 95 miles per hour or faster (and who passes safety tests and a high-performance driving course) can enter. Very experienced drivers with race-equipped cars have their own event where speeds are can exceed 150 miles per hour.

When the road is clear of racing cars, NV 318 serves up a variety of distinctive Paleozoic strata, classic Cenozoic units, and satisfying Quaternary views. For its entire distance the road follows the White River Valley, which drains into the Colorado River, but it has been a long time since a stream has flowed along the length of the White River Valley—probably at least since Pleistocene

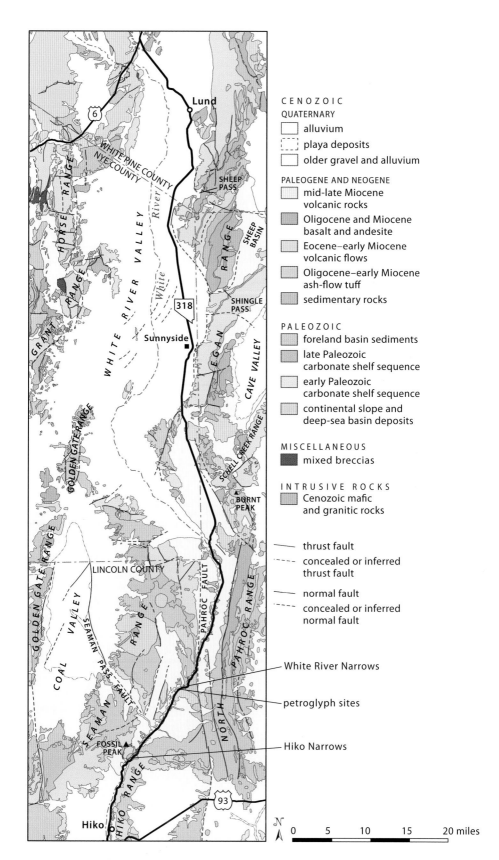

CENOZOIC

QUATERNARY
- alluvium
- playa deposits
- older gravel and alluvium

PALEOGENE AND NEOGENE
- mid-late Miocene volcanic rocks
- Oligocene and Miocene basalt and andesite
- Eocene–early Miocene volcanic flows
- Oligocene–early Miocene ash-flow tuff
- sedimentary rocks

PALEOZOIC
- foreland basin sediments
- late Paleozoic carbonate shelf sequence
- early Paleozoic carbonate shelf sequence
- continental slope and deep-sea basin deposits

MISCELLANEOUS
- mixed breccias

INTRUSIVE ROCKS
- Cenozoic mafic and granitic rocks

— thrust fault
- - - concealed or inferred thrust fault
— normal fault
- - - concealed or inferred normal fault

White River Narrows

petroglyph sites

Hiko Narrows

Lund

SHEEP PASS

SHEEP BASIN

SHINGLE PASS

Sunnyside

CAVE VALLEY

WHITE PINE COUNTY
NYE COUNTY

HORSE RANGE

GRANT RANGE

WHITE RIVER VALLEY

White River

EGAN RANGE

SCHELL CREEK RANGE

BURNT PEAK

GOLDEN GATE RANGE

GOLDEN GATE RANGE

COAL VALLEY

SEAMAN PASS FAULT

LINCOLN COUNTY

SEAMAN RANGE

PAHROC FAULT

PAHROC RANGE

NORTH PAHROC RANGE

FOSSIL PEAK

HIKO RANGE

Hiko

6

318

93

N

0   5   10   15   20 miles

time. Nevertheless, extensive incised stream terraces, canyons, and a wide valley bottom tease the imagination about how the White River must have looked at one time.

About 9 miles north of Hiko, the highway passes through the Hiko Narrows, the first of two narrows eroded through tuffs by the Pleistocene White River. The Hiko Tuff, which weathers to bulbous forms that look like granite, and the underlying Bauers Tuff of the Condor Canyon Formation are exposed for 2 miles through the Hiko Narrows. Paleozoic rock layers form the higher hills away from the road, including Fossil Peak to the northwest, formed mostly of the Ordovician Pogonip Group. Shales in the group contain fossils of calcareous algae known as sunflower corals.

The second narrows, the White River Narrows, exposes eighteen different volcanic layers erupted over a span of about 12 million years from three different caldera complexes: the Central Nevada caldera complex to the northwest, the Indian Peak complex to the northwest, and the Caliente complex to the southeast. The tuffs, which range in age from about 30 to 18 million years, overlap and interfinger. The most recognizable at highway speeds is probably the Leach Canyon Formation, with its cliff faces cut by large, columnar joints. It extends at road level north into the narrows from the southern end. At the south end of the narrows, you can take a dirt road to the east to see a number of petroglyphs etched into the tuffs.

Columnar jointing in tuff of the Leach Canyon Formation in the White River Narrows.

The highway crosses the Pahroc fault at the north end of the White River Narrows, where the tuff ends abruptly in a north-trending cliff line. The Seaman Range, to the west, has been uplifted along this fault, along with the tuff layers of the narrows. As movement on the fault incrementally lifted up the rocks, the ancient White River cut down, maintaining its meandering path.

About 15 miles north of the White River Narrows, near the Lincoln-Nye County Line, look east to see the reddish pyramid of Burnt Peak. This conical peak is the neck of a rhyolitic intrusion of Cenozoic age, emplaced into lava flows of approximately the same age. Surrounding the volcanic structure are Paleozoic sedimentary rocks that weather more rapidly to form smooth slopes and benches.

North of the Sunnyside pullout, east-dipping Paleozoic sedimentary rocks are visible in the Egan Range to the east. Prominent light-colored bands of quartzite and dolomite can be traced for miles along the mountain front. The Ordovician Eureka Quartzite and Ely Springs Dolomite can be seen near the base of the range. The Devonian Sevy Dolomite forms the prominent light-colored unit midway through the section, and the massive limestone cliffs at the top are the Devonian Guilmette Formation.

About 5 miles north of Sunnyside, Shingle Pass forms a break in the mountain front. The range to the north is downdropped 2.5 miles along a northeast-trending fault through the pass, relative to the range to the south. Preserved in the pass is a succession of seven regional tuff sheets deposited from about 31 to 23 million years ago, in Oligocene time.

The extremely flat area around Lund was the bottom of a lake in Pliocene time that persisted for thousands of years. Boreholes have penetrated more than 1,300 feet of lake sediments in the northern end valley and 900 feet at another location.

Burnt Peak, the neck of a Cenozoic rhyolitic intrusion.

Multiple faults have broken the Paleozoic rock layers in the Egan Range. The Guilmette Formation makes up the highest peak, at left center. The Sevy Dolomite forms the prominent white cliff band. View east of NV 318 about 8 miles south of Lund.

NV 338
Smith Valley—California Border
30 miles

Flat fields of the Smith Valley, irrigated by water from the West Walker River, border NV 338 along the first few miles south of NV 208. Tertiary sedimentary and lake deposits are visible in bluffs along the river, attesting to the presence of Lake Wellington, which occupied the area in Pleistocene time.

The Wellington Hills, composed of Miocene-age volcanic rocks, were lifted up by active faults that line the east base of the hills west of NV 338. An andesitic breccia forms the gray craggy cliffs in the vicinity of milepost 29. A ridgeline of Mesozoic metamorphosed rocks of the Pine Nut assemblage is preserved as flatirons along the linear front of the hills north of Desert Creek Road, which intersects NV 338 from the southwest near milepost 26. To the east, across the flat lakebed of Lake Wellington, is Valley Point, a cliff face of Cretaceous or Jurassic granite. South of it, Mesozoic metasedimentary rocks form the more rugged outcrops.

Abundant roadcuts in the 8-mile-long Dalzell Canyon offer a handy study of Miocene volcanic breccias and interbedded sedimentary rocks and ash-falls. However, the exposure on the east side of the highway between milepost 19 and milepost 18 is granite, similar to that of Valley Point to the north. The granite was buried by the products of the volcanic eruptions in Miocene time.

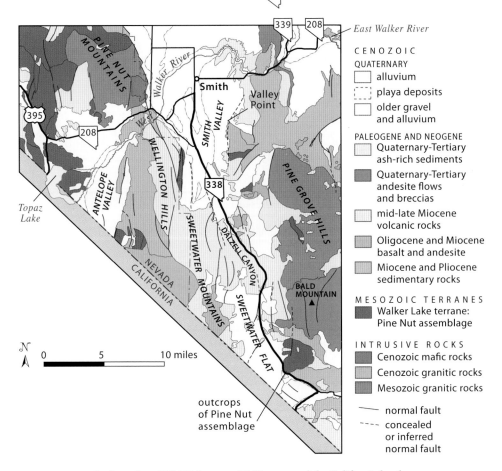

Geology along NV 338 between Wellington and the California border.

Some of the volcanic breccias bordering the roadside contain boulders up to 8 feet in diameter. In contrast, a white ash-fall deposit between milepost 17 and milepost 16 contains pumice and rock fragments about 1 inch in diameter, and fine-grained stream deposits are exposed in the roadcut at about milepost 14.

From about milepost 12 to the California state line, broad sagebrush flats lead up to the 10,000- to 11,000-foot peaks of the Sweetwater Mountains to the west. The grayish East and Middle Sisters are Cretaceous granite, but the east face of South Sister is metavolcanic and metasedimentary rocks capped by andesitic lahar and flow rocks of middle to late Miocene age. The colorful mass to the south of South Sister in California is also Miocene volcanic rock, primarily rhyolite tuff breccia that has been hydrothermally altered, and rhyolitic flows and domes.

Sweetwater Summit, a slightly elevated section of the highway near milepost 10, is a good viewpoint for Sweetwater Flat. Miocene volcanics form the low hills to the east, and the higher barren ridge descending from Bald Mountain,

Ash-fall deposits overlain by a coarse andesitic debris flow near milepost 17.

Air-fall deposits interbedded with stream sands and gravels at milepost 14.

Metavolcanic rock of the Pine Nut assemblage at milepost 6 on NV 338.

farther east, is Pliocene to Quaternary andesite and basalt flows, the youngest volcanic units here. At milepost 6, about a half mile south of the Sweetwater Ranch, the highway funnels between two outcrops of metavolcanics, the Triassic to Jurassic Pine Nut assemblage of the Walker Lake terrane, the oldest rocks in the area. Most of these rocks formed in a marine island arc that became attached to the western part of Nevada in Mesozoic time.

Another white ash-fall, overlain by a coarse volcanic breccia, is exposed at milepost 3. Near milepost 2, the hills to the west are gravel of Pliocene to Pleistocene age. At the California state line, a dark, welded quartz latite ash-flow with conspicuous pumice fragments forms low vertical cliffs. This flow erupted about 9.3 million years ago from the Little Walker volcanic center in California and traveled eastward, constrained in a valley that is, at this location, coincident with the modern-day East Walker River.

NV 341 and NV 342
Virginia City Loop
21 miles

From its intersection with US 395 south of Reno, NV 341 heads south, climbing the steep Geiger Grade into the Virginia Range before descending to the mining areas of Virginia City, Gold Hill, and Silver City. A prominent normal fault on the steep western side of the Virginia Range has elevated the mountains several thousand feet relative to Truckee Meadows, the downdropped block to the west. Though this fault probably originated in the early Miocene Epoch, much of the displacement is relatively young, having occurred over the past 3 million

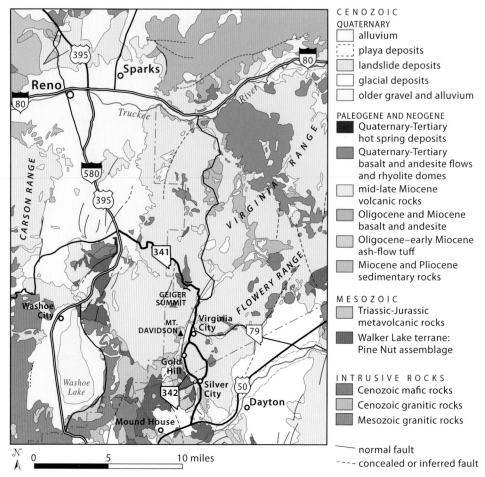

CENOZOIC
QUATERNARY
- alluvium
- playa deposits
- landslide deposits
- glacial deposits
- older gravel and alluvium

PALEOGENE AND NEOGENE
- Quaternary-Tertiary hot spring deposits
- Quaternary-Tertiary basalt and andesite flows and rhyolite domes
- mid-late Miocene volcanic rocks
- Oligocene and Miocene basalt and andesite
- Oligocene–early Miocene ash-flow tuff
- Miocene and Pliocene sedimentary rocks

MESOZOIC
- Triassic-Jurassic metavolcanic rocks
- Walker Lake terrane: Pine Nut assemblage

INTRUSIVE ROCKS
- Cenozoic mafic rocks
- Cenozoic granitic rocks
- Mesozoic granitic rocks

— normal fault
---- concealed or inferred fault

Geology of the Virginia City area.

years. The north side of the Virginia Range is bounded by the Olinghouse fault, a northeast-trending left-lateral strike-slip fault that runs along the Truckee River canyon. Another northeast-trending left-lateral strike-slip fault terminates the south side of the mountains along the valley of the Carson River.

The Virginia Range is composed of mostly of Oligocene to Miocene volcanic rocks that were erupted over Mesozoic metamorphic rocks and granite. Volcanic activity was especially intense from about 18 to 8 million years ago. Flows of dacite and andesite lavas repeatedly buried the older surface, cooling into thick sequences of solid lava in some places and building piles of volcanic rubble (breccias) in others. Volcanic mudflow deposits known as lahars are also fairly common. Some of the magma fueling this period of volcanism was emplaced underground where it slowly cooled to become the Davidson Diorite, which is well exposed in the vicinity the Mt. Davidson, the highest peak in the Virginia Range. After the most intense volcanic rampage, eruptions continued until about 1 million years ago.

As NV 341 begins to climb up the Geiger Grade, roadside outcrops are almost entirely Cenozoic volcanic rocks, although a small outcrop of the Cretaceous granitic rocks is visible north of the road about 1.5 miles from the US 395 junction. The volcanic rocks are commonly stained orange, brown, red, or yellow, the result of alteration of the original minerals by hot acidic water and steam generated by the rising magma. Black silicate minerals like biotite and hornblende were transformed into vividly colored iron oxides, including red hematite and orange-brown goethite. Much of the feldspar in the volcanic rocks was hydrothermally altered into clay minerals, creating the white, bleached appearance of many of the hills. About 3 miles from its junction with US 395, NV 341 winds through a series of strikingly deep red outcrops surrounded by white bleached zones. Called ferricrete, the red exposures are chunks of dacite or andesite of a volcanic breccia cemented by iron oxides and other minerals deposited by hydrothermal solutions.

About halfway between the US 395 intersection and Geiger Summit, NV 341 passes a scenic overlook along the west side of the road that affords excellent views to the west. (See discussions in the road guides for I-80, US 395, and NV 431 for the geology of the area visible from this overlook.)

For several miles southeast of the overlook, roadcuts reveal colorful exposures of hydrothermally altered volcanic rocks. In some of the roadcuts, you may notice that the alteration zones appear arranged as bands or streaks that cut though the less altered and darker-colored andesite. The linear zones are

Ferricrete develops when hydrothermal fluids cement volcanic breccias with iron oxides.

As NV 341 climbs toward Geiger Summit from the west, you can tell how altered the rock is by what is growing there. Low-growing piñon pines prefer darker, less acidic soils derived from the weathering of unaltered volcanic rocks, and tall ponderosa pines prefer light-colored, barren, acidic soils formed on hydrothermally altered rock.

Close-up view of relatively unaltered andesite with black hornblende and white feldspar crystals in a tan-gray matrix. Quarter for scale.

faults in which the crushed rock served as a conduit for the rapid migration of the hydrothermal fluids. About a half mile northwest of Geiger Summit, a large roadcut on the west side of the road affords an opportunity to view masses of unaltered andesite and highly altered andesite in close proximity to each other.

Virginia City marks the heart of the Comstock Lode. Mining peaked between 1860 and 1880, during which time as many as 25,000 people lived in the city, with another 10,000 people inhabiting Gold Hill to the south. The importance of the Comstock mining in the history of Nevada is impossible to overstate. Mines of the Virginia City earned for Nevada the nickname of the Silver State, accelerated the admission of the state into the Union, and strongly influenced the outcome of the Civil War.

The mines of the Comstock district were chiefly lode mines, where masses of mineralized rock formed along a fracture or fault plane in bedrock, usually by fluids migrating along the zone of shattered rock. Valuable metals were deposited in mineralized veins about 14 million years ago. Among these minerals were acanthite and argentite, both consisting of silver sulfide, but with different crystal forms. These two minerals were primary targets of the silver mining that made Virginia City famous. The mineralized rock of the Comstock Lode also contained galena (lead sulfide), chalcopyrite (copper iron sulfide), pyrite (iron sulfide), and gold.

The Comstock Lode was discovered in the Gold Hill area in 1859 and was originally referred to as the Old Red Ledge because it consisted mostly of reddish-brown quartz. The ledge was a mass of rock composed of numerous veins formed along a fault plane that dipped down to the east at an angle of about 45 degrees. Where it reached the surface, this sheet of rock was exposed in a north-trending zone from Gold Hill to the north end of Virginia City between what are now A and C Streets (C is the main street). This exposure has now been mined out and replaced by city streets and buildings, but on the slopes above town to the west you can still see a few knobby outcrops of the lesser mineralized rock.

Because the Comstock Lode dipped to the east at an angle greater than the slope of the land, the ore bodies were farther below the surface to the east of Virginia City, and the mines had to be deeper in that direction to reach the

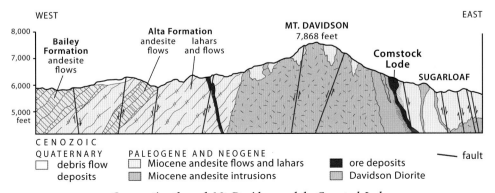

Cross section through Mt. Davidson and the Comstock Lode.

valuable rock. The heaps of tailings marking the locations of the historic mines generally become larger downslope (to the east). The deepest mines were about 3,200 feet below the surface, where the air temperature was well in excess of 100°F, and rock was as hot as 167°F. Steaming acidic water poured through the mines, rotted the support timbers, and caused the clay minerals to swell into masses of slippery mud. Roof collapses and cave-ins were common in the Comstock mines, and miners also suffered from breathing the hot, humid air and rock dust created by underground drilling.

The need for drainage and ventilation in the Comstock mines inspired Adolph Sutro, a German immigrant who arrived in Virginia City in 1863, to design a tunnel through the hills of the Flowery Range east of Virginia City that would intersect the deeper levels of the mines. Sutro began work on the tunnel in 1869 and the excavation finally reached the Savage Shaft in Virginia City in 1878. The 4-mile-long tunnel was designed to carry water from the mines to a discharge point near the present town of Dayton, not far from the Carson River. However, by the time the tunnel reached the underground shafts, many of them were already as much as 1,500 feet below the level of the drain, and the mining boom days were over. Despite its failure to serve its intended purpose, some Comstock Lode mines were successfully drained by the Sutro Tunnel and water still flows through it. It is no longer passable due to accumulated mud and sediment, but the Sutro Tunnel Company still exists in case deep underground mining returns to Virginia City in the future.

South from Virginia City, NV 341 splits to the east, while the main road continues south (as NV 342) toward Gold Hill and Silver City. The discussion that follows pertains to NV 342. As NV 342 heads south from Virginia City, the view to the east reveals an isolated cone in Sixmile Canyon known as Sugarloaf. This small peak is a 12-million-year old plug of andesite that intruded through slightly older volcanic rocks at the time that the Comstock deposits were forming. There was probably a much larger volcanic structure built where Sugarloaf now stands, but much of it has since been eroded.

South from Virginia City, NV 342 winds through the rugged and scenic Gold Canyon toward Gold Hill, the original discovery site of the Comstock Lode in 1859. Gold particles had been discovered nine years earlier in deposits of sand and gravel far downstream where Gold Canyon meets the Carson River near Dayton. Such placer deposits always accumulate downstream from the location of the gold vein, so after their initial discovery miners began tracing the gold particles upstream. Small gold-bearing veins were located near the site of Silver City, but some miners continued to explore farther upstream, eventually discovering the Old Red Ledge. It contained small amounts of gold but was especially rich in silver sulfide minerals such as acanthite. The mining frenzy began to fade in 1880s but never really died completely in Gold Hill. Low-grade ore from the original ledge was the target of mining operations in the 1970s that left the conspicuous elongated pit along the mountain slope to the west as the road passes through town. This pit follows the south end of the Comstock Lode and is located about where the original Old Red Ledge was discovered on the surface.

View east from Virginia City down Sixmile Canyon. The prominent peak in the middle is Sugarloaf, a Miocene volcanic plug.

Devils Gate, near Silver City on NV 342, is a gap through Miocene volcanic rock crushed along a northeast-trending set of faults and later silicified into a hard mass.

As the highway continues south through Gold Hill, you can see old head frames and related structures that were used to lower equipment and miners into the subsurface veins and to hoist workers and ore back to the surface. Just north of Silver City, NV 342 passes through a narrow notch in Miocene andesite known as Devils Gate. The andesite at Devils Gate had been crushed by faults and later hardened when fluids migrating through the pulverized rock deposited quartz in spaces between the fragments.

The mineralization at Silver City occurs along the Silver City fault zone, a set of fractures along which silver-bearing quartz veins formed. Just south of Silver City, American Ravine enters from the west, and the rocks exposed in this area are metavolcanic materials of Mesozoic age, much older than the volcanic materials to the north.

NV 361
Middlegate (US 50)—Luning (US 95)
63 miles

Middlegate was a station on the Pony Express Trail in 1860–1861 and later supported mining camps near Fairview Peak, the loftiest point on the horizon to the southwest. South from the Middlegate junction, NV 361 gently climbs though hilly terrain of Miocene and early Pliocene volcanic rocks and sediments. The ash-rich sediments accumulated in lakes and along stream valleys situated between volcanoes and calderas formed by violent eruptions some 15 to 5 million years ago. Plant fossils collected from the lakebeds indicate a lush, semitropical environment prevailed during the volcanic interludes. Stubby lava flows and welded tuffs form resistant brown ledges in the smooth slopes developed on the softer sediments.

About 12 miles south of Middlegate, NV 361 winds through undulating hills along the western margin of the Broken Hills, mainly of Miocene volcanic rocks, including welded rhyolitic tuff, andesite flows, and fragmental volcanic breccias. In 1905, mineralized veins containing silver, lead, and zinc ores were discovered in these volcanic rocks, but only small quantities were ever produced, mainly between 1913 and 1920.

South of the Broken Hills area, NV 361 follows Gabbs Wash, normally a dry gravelly streambed on the west side of the highway. The channel is incised into alluvial sediments, forming terraces some 15 to 40 feet high on either side of the wash. Such terraces result from the downcutting that occurs during flash floods. Entrenched washes and associated stream terraces also provide evidence of recent and ongoing uplift, because rising land increases the erosive power of the streams.

On the east side of the road, the low hills of mostly light-colored rock are the Lodi Hills, the northern end of which is light-colored sandstone and volcanic rock of the Quartz Mountain terrane. These faulted and disrupted rocks are probably Jurassic in age but may be older. Farther south, Triassic and Jurassic carbonate and metasedimentary rocks of the Walker Lake terrane

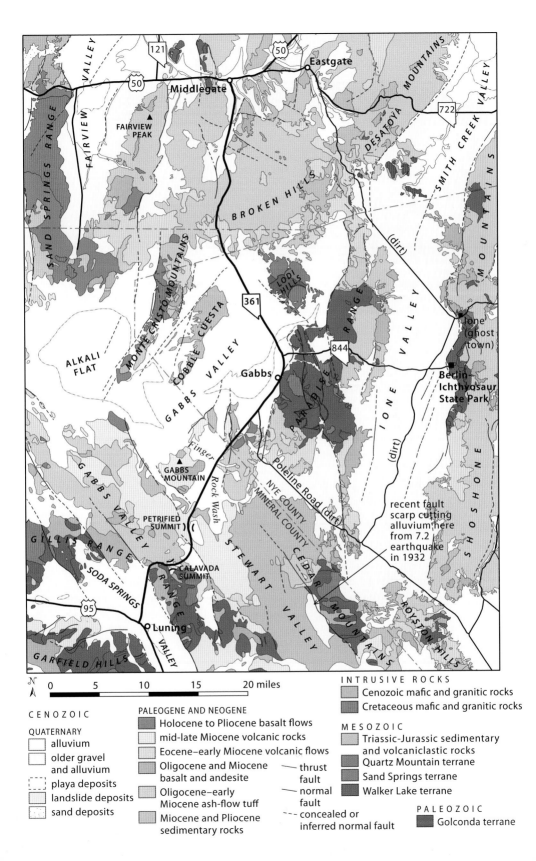

N
0   5   10   15   20 miles

CENOZOIC

QUATERNARY
☐ alluvium
☐ older gravel and alluvium
▨ playa deposits
▨ landslide deposits
▨ sand deposits

PALEOGENE AND NEOGENE
■ Holocene to Pliocene basalt flows
▨ mid-late Miocene volcanic rocks
▨ Eocene–early Miocene volcanic flows
▨ Oligocene and Miocene basalt and andesite
▨ Oligocene–early Miocene ash-flow tuff
▨ Miocene and Pliocene sedimentary rocks

— thrust fault
— normal fault
--- concealed or inferred normal fault

INTRUSIVE ROCKS
▨ Cenozoic mafic and granitic rocks
▨ Cretaceous mafic and granitic rocks

MESOZOIC
☐ Triassic-Jurassic sedimentary and volcaniclastic rocks
▨ Quartz Mountain terrane
▨ Sand Springs terrane
■ Walker Lake terrane

PALEOZOIC
■ Golconda terrane

Ledge of welded rhyolitic tuff exposed east of NV 361 on the western flank of the Broken Hills.

(Pamlico-Lodi assemblage) are in fault contact with the Quartz Mountain strata. Several thrust faults slice and shuffle the older Triassic strata into a complex stack, all intruded by granitic plutons of Cretaceous age. Finally, on the southern end of the Lodi Hills, Miocene to Oligocene volcanic rocks form the craggy brown exposures seen from the highway. Silver, lead, zinc, tungsten, and talc have all been mined, at one time or another, in the Lodi Hills.

The low, jagged skyline west of NV 361 is the northern Monte Cristo Mountains, a block of tilted layers of 25-million-year-old tuff, possibly from an ancient caldera-forming eruption centered in the Gabbs Valley area to the south. The caldera margin was presumably downfaulted later in Cenozoic time and is now buried under thousands of feet of valley-filling alluvium. The tuff overlies older Jurassic and Triassic oceanic volcanic and sedimentary rocks of the Sand Springs terrane, along with a body of Cretaceous plutonic rock.

As NV 361 approaches Gabbs from the northwest, the high Paradise Range dominates the scenery to the east. The bedrock in this part of the range is composed mainly of two components of the Triassic and early Jurassic Walker Lake terrane: the Pamlico-Lodi assemblage along the western mountain front and the Luning-Berlin assemblage farthest east in the higher parts of the range. Shallow marine carbonate rocks, such as dolomite and limestone of Triassic age, are common in both assemblages. However, the Pamlico-Lodi strata are interbedded with volcanic rocks, while the Luning-Berlin limestone layers are associated with mudstone, sandstone, and conglomerate derived from a continental source to the east.

About 2 miles south of the NV 844 intersection, NV 361 passes a conspicuous magnesite mine to the east and continues through the small mining town of Gabbs, named for the illustrious geologist and paleontologist William More Gabb. A world traveler, he studied the rocks and fossils of western Nevada in 1867. The magnesite mine, reputed to be the longest continuously active mine

BERLIN-ICHTHYOSAUR STATE PARK

About 2 miles north of Gabbs, take NV 844 east 18 miles to Berlin-Ichthyosaur State Park, where you can see fossils of large sea creatures near the historic mining town of Berlin. Two miles east of NV 361, NV 844 passes outcrops and roadcuts of gray Triassic dolomite of the Luning Formation, the same formation that contains the fossils at Berlin. Just east of these roadcuts, the highway crosses an overturned thrust fault that separates the gray Triassic limestone from the brown and tan-gray marble, hornfels, and sandstones of early Jurassic age. These rocks are all part of the Walker Lake terrane.

As NV 844 ascends toward Green Springs Summit, it passes into a thick sequence of Miocene to Oligocene volcanic rocks that cap the older terrane rocks. Among these volcanic rocks is the unwelded tuff exposed in the roadcuts at the summit, as well as the 24- to 21-million-year-old welded tuff of Sherman Peak, northeast of the road, which displays crude columnar jointing that formed when the hot ash cooled.

East from Green Springs Summit, NV 844 winds its way down toward Ione Valley, beyond which stand the southern Shoshone Mountains, mostly composed of a 10,000-foot-thick section of volcanics that includes ash and lava erupted from multiple sources over a span of some 10 to 15 million years. The thick volcanic pile overlies Triassic sedimentary rocks, and NV 844 heads directly to the area of Triassic exposures in the vicinity of Berlin-Ichthyosaur State Park.

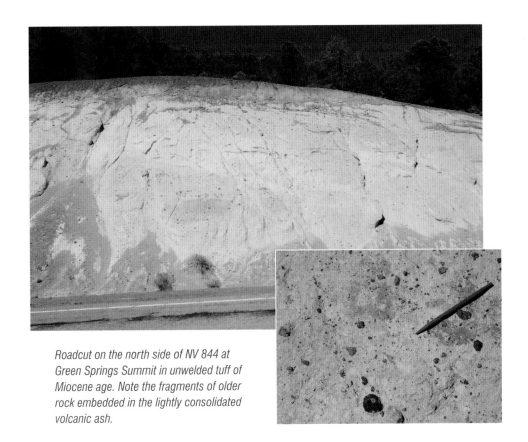

Roadcut on the north side of NV 844 at Green Springs Summit in unwelded tuff of Miocene age. Note the fragments of older rock embedded in the lightly consolidated volcanic ash.

Near the park boundary, you can explore preserved and restored buildings of the historic mining town of Berlin. At the height of mining activity in the early 1900s, about 250 people lived in Berlin. The gold deposits at Berlin were veins in dark-colored Permian greenstone, basically metamorphosed andesite or diorite, that underlies the Triassic strata exposed in the higher slopes above the town.

The road continues through the old town site and turns east into West Union Canyon, passing a steeply dipping ledge of resistant Triassic conglomerate at the canyon entrance. Continuing up West Union Canyon, the road passes outcrops of silty limestone of the late Triassic Luning Formation, the same rock that contains the ichthyosaur fossils protected by the building erected over the quarry about 2 miles from the town site.

Ichthyosaurs were fascinating residents of the shallow tropical seas that covered this part of Nevada in late Triassic time, about 217 million years ago. These large predatory reptiles were as long as 65 feet or more, weighed as much as 40 or 50 tons, and occupied the top tier in the marine food chain. Powerful tail fins propelled their long, streamlined bodies through the water at high speeds, and they used their paddle-like appendages to maneuver as they pursued prey. Ichthyosaurs had large eyes and excellent vision and could hunt prey in murky or deeper water. These reptiles also gave birth to live offspring that could survive on their own, another factor behind their remarkable success. The remains of ichthyosaurs have been found in Triassic strata of every continent except Antarctica, demonstrating their unparalleled success in the world's ancient oceans.

Ichthyosaur fossils were first noticed in West Union Canyon by miners from Berlin in the 1890s, though there is no evidence that the miners understood what the curious disk-

A portion of the bone bed within the silty limestone of the late Triassic Luning Formation at Berlin-Ichthyosaur State Park. Piles of long ichthyosaur ribs are visible in the center of the photo, while the circular objects in the lower part are end-on views of the main part of the vertebrae making up the backbone of these large reptiles.

A sketch of the complete skeleton of the ichthyosaur Shonisaurus popularis. *Scale bar equals 10 feet.*

shaped stones were. In 1928, Siemon Muller of Stanford University identified the fossils as ichthyosaurs, but the amazing concentration of fossils in West Union Canyon would not become apparent until after 1954, when Charles Camp and his colleague Samuel Welles of the University of California–Berkeley, began large-scale excavations at the site. The remains of about thirty-seven different ichthyosaur individuals are preserved in a thin interval of shaly limestone in the lower Luning Formation. Camp named the new species *Shonisaurus populari*s, in reference to the Shoshone Mountains, where the remains were excavated and the number of individuals found huddled together at the site. The protected bone bed contains the remains of nine large ichthyosaurs that have been left in situ. In 1977 *Shonisaurus populari*s was designated the official state fossil of Nevada.

The nature and origin of the bone bed is perhaps the most intriguing and mysterious aspect of the Berlin site. The bone bed preserves nearly complete skeletons in which most of the bony elements are in proper position. Such articulated remains suggest minimal post-mortem decomposition and transport. The remains of the nine large specimens left in place and several others that were removed during the excavations are aligned in roughly the same direction. The shale limestone matrix containing the fossils is clearly lithified carbonate mud that accumulated in shallow, warm seas when this part of North America was situated near the equator. Fossils of other swimming and floating animals, such as ammonites and conodonts (small, eel-like animals) accompany the ichthyosaur remains, but bottom-dwelling invertebrate remains, such as shells of clams and crustaceans, are rare. How did so many ichthyosaurs die and accumulate in a relatively small area on the shallow Triassic seafloor?

Some paleontologists have suggested that the large reptiles might have died in a shallow bay after a sudden low tide stranded them and prevented their escape to the open sea. Other scientists have concluded that the ichthyosaurs died one at a time in a shallow bay that was repeatedly visited for mating or birthing of young. Another hypothesis suggests that the bone bed originated beneath deeper water farther offshore when stagnant, poorly oxygenated bottom conditions developed seasonally. Perhaps, as was recently proposed, a harmful algal bloom, similar to the red tide caused by dinoflagellates in modern seas, triggered the death of the great swimming reptiles. These are all valid hypotheses, but none of them can be conclusively substantiated by the geological evidence. However, one other recent and well-publicized idea lacks any scientific evidence whatsoever: that a giant squid-like monster killed the ichthyosaurs and placed them on the seafloor for later consumption. Not only is this idea absurdly fanciful and untestable, but paleontologists have no evidence at all that such sea monsters existed.

in Nevada, has been producing the minerals brucite (magnesium hydroxide) and magnesite (magnesium carbonate) from Triassic dolomite since 1935. Magnesium is a valuable light metal used in the aircraft, automotive, and metallurgical industries. The concentration of these magnesium ores in irregular masses near a granitic pluton results from contact metamorphism and hydrothermal alteration of dolomite, a magnesium calcium carbonate mineral.

The lowlands west of the highway are part of Gabbs Valley, the west side of which is delineated by several low ridges and cuestas. About 12 miles west of the highway, Gabbs Valley merges with an extensive playa where the Don A. Campbell geothermal power plant went online in late 2013. The plant utilizes 260°F groundwater pumped from depths between 1,500 and 1,800 feet. The geothermal area on the west side of Gabbs Valley is located along the eastern edge of the Walker Lane, a zone of prominent northwest-trending strike-slip faults.

The low, north-trending 10-mile-long ridge west of Gabbs and NV 361 is Cobble Cuesta, the lower slopes of which are 13- to 9-million-year-old, ash-rich, lake-deposited sediments, ash layers, and stream-deposited sandstones. Conglomerate of Pliocene age caps the ridge, and cobbles weathered from this deposit are the basis for the unusual name. In 1954, a powerful earthquake to the northwest resulted in surface faulting along the northwest side of Cobble Cuesta. Cobble Cuesta appears to be a new fault-block mountain range beginning to rise from the low terrain in Gabbs Valley.

Exposure of a lahar (volcanic mudflow) deposit of Miocene age east of NV 361 near the Nye-Mineral county line. Note the large rocks that were carried by the flowing mud.

Near the Mineral-Nye county line about 8 miles southwest of Gabbs, tilted layers of white, gray, and reddish-brown volcanic rocks are exposed on the western slope of the southern Paradise Range. These rocks are mostly early Miocene ash-flow tuffs and associated lavas situated above the gray Triassic strata. The dark-colored rounded hills in the distance southeast of the highway are also Triassic rocks. On the west side of the road, the communications tower stands on a ridge of Miocene andesitic lava flows and tuffs that parallels the highway for several miles. Just south of the county line, a volcanic mudflow (lahar) deposit within the thick succession of Oligocene to Miocene volcanic rocks is exposed east of the road.

About 2 miles southwest of the Nye-Mineral county line, NV 361 crosses Finger Rock Wash, which drains Stewart Valley, to the southeast. Miocene volcanic and sedimentary rocks are well exposed in Stewart Valley, including lake- and stream-deposited sandstone and shale containing abundant fossils first noticed by paleontologists in 1959. Subsequent collecting expeditions to Stewart Valley revealed one of the most complete records of Miocene life in the world, leading the Bureau of Land Management to protect nearly 16,000 acres of the valley from unauthorized collecting.

The fossils from Stewart Valley are concentrated in two different horizons within a sequence of ash-rich lake deposits from 16 to 15 million years old. To the southwest, an active volcanic center in what is now the southern Gabbs Valley Range produced clouds of ash that fell into the lake basin along with silt, clay, and sand washed in by local streams. The lake waters were generally calm and may have occasionally been slightly acidic and saturated with silica from the ash. These conditions allowed organic remains entering the lake to sometimes escape normal decomposition and become preserved in the bottom sediments as fossils with exquisite detail. Even delicate bird feathers have been preserved as fossils.

Paleontologists have identified more than eighty-five different species of plants (including standing tree stumps); thirty-five species of clams and snails; no fewer than ninety-eight different types of fish, reptiles, birds, and mammals; and fossil insects, plankton, pollen, and spores. The ancient lake was surrounded by a heavily forested shore that hummed with insects, supported dense flocks of birds, and nurtured an astonishing array of wildlife. Even though the first fossils were discovered more than fifty years ago, paleontologists today continue to collect and study fossils from Stewart Valley. No one can predict what new aspects of Miocene life will be revealed in the future, and that it is why it is important to protect this area.

In 1932, near the south end of Finger Rock Wash, one of the largest earthquakes in Nevada history rattled residents in Carson City and Reno. The Cedar Mountain earthquake, estimated magnitude 7.2, ripped open no fewer than sixty fissures and scarps in the ground from Stewart Valley south into Monte Cristo Valley, a distance of more than 20 miles. Such a powerful earthquake in this part of western Nevada is not surprising in view of the proximity to the Walker Lane, only about 15 miles to the west of NV 361. This zone of intense strike-slip faulting is thought by many geologists to be a nascent plate boundary that will continue to evolve into a system similar to the San Andreas transform fault.

This fossil fly is an example of the spectacular detail of the fossils preserved in the mid-Miocene sediments of Stewart Valley. —Courtesy of Marwa El-Faramawi, University of California Museum of Paleontology

Southwest from Finger Rock Wash, NV 361 passes east of Gabbs Mountain, a small knob of Miocene andesite flows 22 to 15 million years old. NV 361 climbs over two passes as it makes its way westward across the Gabbs Valley Range. The northern pass, Petrified Summit, is through hills and outcrops of Oligocene and Miocene tuff as the highway follows close to the trace of the northwest-trending Petrified Springs fault. This right-lateral strike-slip fault is part of the Walker Lane and exhibits several miles of displacement.

The bedrock in the Gabbs Valley Range includes extensive sheets of ash-flow tuff mingled together with andesite and rhyolite flows formed from eruptions that occurred 27 to 22 million years ago. Beneath these volcanic rocks, Triassic and Jurassic sedimentary rocks of the Walker Lake terrane are arranged in thrust slices and fault-bounded blocks of deformed strata. In the southern Gabbs Valley Range, one block of relatively undeformed and only slightly metamorphosed Mesozoic strata contains one of the best records in the world of the transition in marine life at the boundary between the Triassic and Jurassic Periods, about 200 million years ago. The rocks include abundant fossils of ammonites, distant relatives of the modern nautilus. This locality was considered for designation as the global reference section defining the base of the Jurassic Period until an alternate site in Austria was selected in 2010.

North of NV 361 at Calavada Summit, the picturesque crags result from the erosion of layers of 28- to 25-million-year-old tuff that have varying degrees of welding. Oxidation of iron-bearing minerals in the tuff is responsible for the brown, tan, and reddish hues of the jagged pillars. To the south of the highway and faulted against the tuff are folded layers of gray Triassic limestone. The

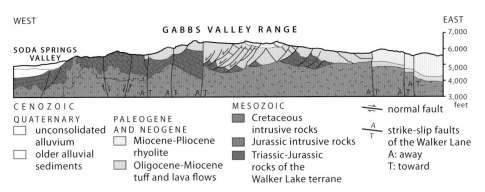

WEST

GABBS VALLEY RANGE

SODA SPRINGS VALLEY

EAST
- 7,000
- 6,000
- 5,000
- 4,000
- 3,000 feet

CENOZOIC

QUATERNARY
- ☐ unconsolidated alluvium
- ☐ older alluvial sediments

PALEOGENE AND NEOGENE
- ☐ Miocene-Pliocene rhyolite
- ☐ Oligocene-Miocene tuff and lava flows

MESOZOIC
- ☐ Cretaceous intrusive rocks
- ☐ Jurassic intrusive rocks
- ☐ Triassic-Jurassic rocks of the Walker Lake terrane

⇌ normal fault

A/T strike-slip faults of the Walker Lane
A: away
T: toward

The Gabbs Valley Range is cut into narrow slivers of rock by right-lateral strike-slip faults of the Walker Lane.

North of NV 361 at Calavada Summit, late Oligocene tuff layers are eroded in ragged pinnacles and knobs.

large, abandoned open-pit mine between the highway and the folded Triassic limestone is part of the historic Santa Fe mining district. Gold and silver ores were mined from the contact zone between the limestone and a subsurface body of Cretaceous intrusive rock as recently as the mid-1990s.

West from Calavada Summit, NV 361 winds though outcrops and road-cuts of rusty-colored metamorphosed Triassic sandstone, shale, dolomite, and andesite before descending the alluvial slopes to the valley floor. Soda Springs Valley is so named because many of the fault-controlled springs in the valley are naturally carbonated. A prominent normal fault lies along the western base of the mountain range and is responsible for the nearly 4,000 feet of relief. Look for 10- to 15-foot-high scarps in the Quaternary alluvium to the south of NV 361 at the base of the mountains.

NV 375
The Extraterrestrial Highway
Hiko (US 93)—Warm Springs (US 6)
98 miles

NV 375, another lonely Nevada highway, was officially titled the Extraterrestrial Highway in 1996 in response to reports of UFO sightings and other strange activities, and to promote tourism. The highway skirts the northeastern edge of the Nevada Test and Training Range, providing the closest access to the restricted areas of Area 51 and Groom Lake, the existence of which was officially acknowledged by the US Central Intelligence Agency in July 2013. The traveler must decide whether to be on the road during the time of new moon, so the skies will be the blackest and the UFOs more readily seen, or to drive the route in full daylight and enjoy the geology.

One of the highway's geologic claims to fame is that it passes through the area most impacted by a meteor that exploded above the shallow sea of the continental shelf about 382 million years ago, in Devonian time. The Alamo Breccia, rock shattered by the explosion, was first observed by petroleum geologists studying the Devonian rocks in southern Nevada. The breccia is most intensely developed northwest of the town of Alamo (south of Hiko on US 93), and decreases in thickness and disruption in a radial pattern away from that location. The actual impact site has not been found, but it likely lies below alluvium in the Sand Spring Valley to the west. The timing of the impact is pinpointed by the graptolite fossil record in the Devonian rock layers.

Paleozoic sedimentary strata and overlying Tertiary volcanic rocks form a mosaic at the eastern end of NV 375 in the Pahranagat Valley. Devonian limestones form the Hiko Range to the east, and you can see the bulbous weathering form of the Hiko Tuff along US 93. As NV 375 climbs westward up an alluvial

The Alien Research Center in Crystal Springs, with layers of Miocene tuff in the Mt. Irish Range in distance.

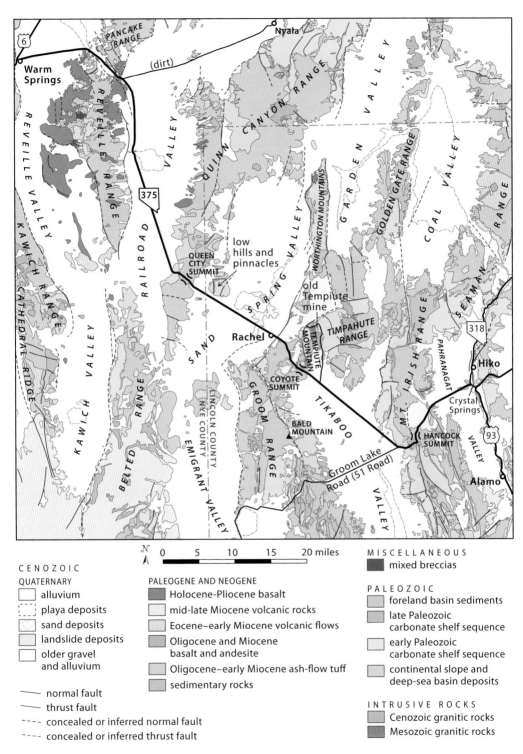

CENOZOIC

QUATERNARY

- alluvium
- playa deposits
- sand deposits
- landslide deposits
- older gravel and alluvium

- normal fault
- thrust fault
- concealed or inferred normal fault
- concealed or inferred thrust fault

PALEOGENE AND NEOGENE

- Holocene-Pliocene basalt
- mid-late Miocene volcanic rocks
- Eocene–early Miocene volcanic flows
- Oligocene and Miocene basalt and andesite
- Oligocene–early Miocene ash-flow tuff
- sedimentary rocks

MISCELLANEOUS

- mixed breccias

PALEOZOIC

- foreland basin sediments
- late Paleozoic carbonate shelf sequence
- early Paleozoic carbonate shelf sequence
- continental slope and deep-sea basin deposits

INTRUSIVE ROCKS

- Cenozoic granitic rocks
- Mesozoic granitic rocks

Geology along NV 375 between Hiko and Warm Springs.

fan, you can see eastward-tilted ash-flow tuffs covering Paleozoic rocks in the hills bordering the western side of the valley. The tuffs were erupted in Miocene time from calderas to the southeast.

Near Hancock Summit, ridges of vertical to overturned beds of Devonian through Mississippian limestones crop out on both sides of the road, overlain by Cenozoic volcanics. The eastern roadcut near the summit exposes faulted and tilted ash-rich sediments and air-fall tuff, whereas the western roadcut reveals contorted and vertical beds of Paleozoic limestones and shales.

Black vitrophyre, a glassy volcanic rock containing large crystals, can be found Hancock Summit. It forms when magma containing already-formed crystals erupts at the surface and cools instantly.

View north of highway from the west side of Pahranagat Valley. Devonian through Mississippian limestones dip westward in foreground, with gently east-dipping layers of Miocene rhyolitic tuff behind, and Paleozoic rocks peeking out on the distant skyline (far right and far left).

An impressive escarpment of Ordovician through Mississippian rock layers of the Mt. Irish Range borders the northeastern side of the Tikaboo Valley. In the central part of the escarpment, the Eureka Quartzite of Ordovician age forms a prominent white band near the base, with its accompanying thin dark band of the overlying Ely Springs Dolomite. The preponderance of the cliffs is tan-colored Devonian dolomites. The type section for the Alamo Breccia occurs in Devonian rocks near the base of the western grade of Hancock Summit.

Oligocene to Miocene siliceous ash-flow tuffs at the northern end of the Tikaboo Valley form colorful low hills, whereas the volcanics in the Groom Range to the west are more gray. The Paleozoic basement of the Groom Range consists of a 20,000-foot-thick section of eastward-tilted Cambrian rock, overlain by a thin section of Ordovician sedimentary rocks, which are exposed along the western flank, and across the southern part of the range north of the Groom Lake Road. Oligocene to Miocene age volcanics currently bury the eastern part of the range, although a significant portion of the volcanic cover has been removed by erosion following uplift of the range in the last 10 million years. Bald Mountain, the barren peak in the northern portion of the range, is the erosional remnant of material that filled the 6-mile-wide Bald Mountain caldera. Following the eruption, the central part of the caldera filled with ash-flow tuffs and slide blocks from the surrounding Paleozoic rocks. The outer caldera walls have worn down to elevations lower than the in-filled material, an example of inverted topography. Tuff erupted from the caldera between 26 and 17 million years ago is crossed by NV 375 in the vicinity of and to the west of Coyote Summit.

In the Timpahute Range, on the north side of Tikaboo Valley, the eastward-dipping Paleozoic section ranges from Ordovician at the base to Pennsylvanian at the top and includes one and possibly two thrust sheets. Mines in the Timpahute Range have produced tungsten along the margins of two small intrusions of 92-million-year-old granite.

The Worthington Mountains, the isolated, thin, north-trending range to the northwest of the Timpahute Range, consist of Ordovician through Silurian strata, complicated with thrust sheets and normal faults. A mining district centered on small Cretaceous intrusions at the north end of the mountains has produced small amounts of gold, silver, lead, zinc, and tungsten. The carbonates contain caves and sinkholes, the largest of which is Leviathan Cave.

Volcanic ash-flow tuffs along the road for about 3 miles west of Coyote Summit were erupted from the Bald Mountain caldera, to the south in the Groom Range. Near milepost 11, west of Rachel, the highway crosses a dissected, north-trending, west-facing Quaternary fault scarp that cuts the alluvial fan surface. Farther west, sand dunes skirt the playa north of the highway.

The rocks visible from NV 375 in Railroad Valley are entirely Cenozoic volcanics, with the exception of a small outcropping of Cambrian dolomite and limestone on the west side of Queen City Summit. In the vicinity of the summit, small quantities of mercury have been produced from breccias and jasperoid in faults and fractures that cut both the Paleozoic rock and the overlying volcanics. The volcanic rocks have several sources. Older tuffs erupted in Oligocene to early Miocene time from calderas in the Central Nevada caldera complex. Quaternary-age basalt erupted from the Lunar Crater volcanic field, centered north of NV 375 in the Pancake Range. The basalt magma oozed to the surface along northeast-trending fissures that extend through the Reveille Range. (The volcanic field, along with hot springs fueled by magma at depth, are discussed in the US 6 road guide.)

East-facing fault scarps offset Quaternary alluvial fans on the west side of the highway north of the whitish playa deposits in the center of Railroad Valley. At milepost 19, the south end of the Pancake Range is due north, living up to its name with stacked, flat layers of Oligocene to Miocene tuff. Black basalt flows of Quaternary age are on both sides of the road near the turnoff to Nyala and at the summit. Colorful ash-flow tuffs line the highway to the north as the road crosses into the Hot Springs Valley near the Twin Springs Ranch Road.

East-facing fault scarps offset Quaternary-age alluvium near milepost 26, with the volcanics of the Reveille Range in the distance.

The Pancake Range, named for its consistently flat, stacked volcanic layers, extends northward from Echo Canyon Reservoir in Hot Creek Valley.

NV 376
US 50 near Austin—US 6 near Tonopah
102 miles

NV 376 runs through Big Smoky Valley, a classic north-trending graben separating two of central Nevada's most magnificent fault-block mountains: the Toiyabe Range to the west and the Toquima Range to the east. A zone of numerous east-dipping normal faults runs along the base of the Toiyabe Range. Although the active faults are commonly buried under alluvial fans that emerge from the mouths of canyons, there are many indications of the youth and magnitude of faulting in this area. Ridges sloping from the Toiyabe Range toward the valley floor terminate in triangular facets, forming truncated spurs of varying sizes. As the mountain block rises along the east-dipping normal faults, the exposed bedrock ridge forms facets. In time, erosion causes such facets to recede toward the mountain crest, but many of those along the eastern face of the Toiyabe Range are still located near the range front fault zone. Another indication of recent uplift is the narrow wineglass canyons. Streams draining toward the valley experience a significant increase in energy when the mountain block is elevated by faulting. The intense downcutting that follows creates a nearly vertical slot canyon at the canyon mouth. Upstream, the canyon is wider and V-shaped. Thus, when seen in cross section, the canyons have a profile similar to a wineglass.

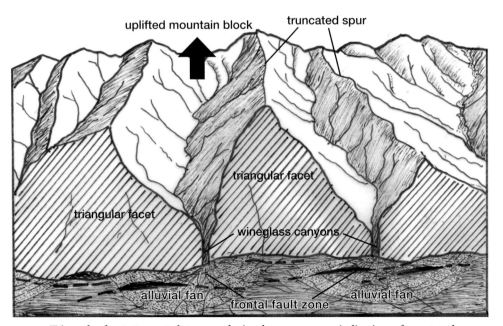

Triangular facets, truncated spurs, and wineglass canyons are indications of recent and rapid uplift of the mountains west of the Toiyabe Range fault zone.

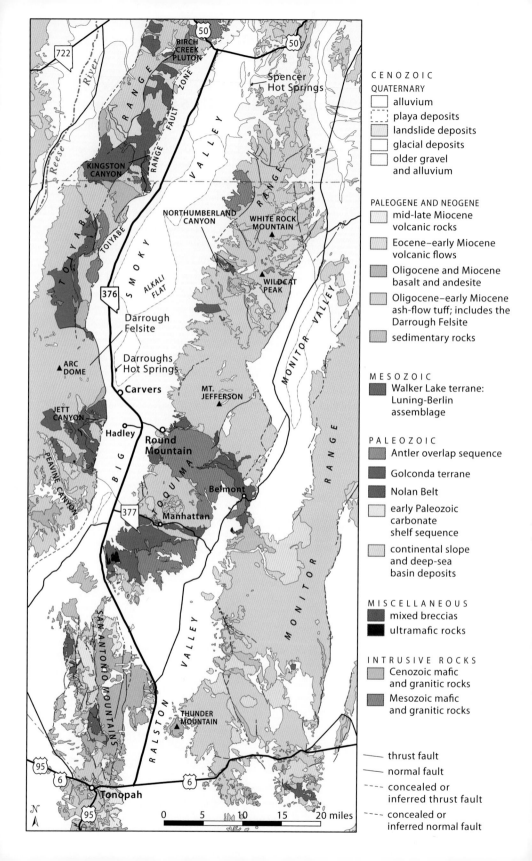

CENOZOIC

QUATERNARY

- alluvium
- playa deposits
- landslide deposits
- glacial deposits
- older gravel and alluvium

PALEOGENE AND NEOGENE

- mid-late Miocene volcanic rocks
- Eocene–early Miocene volcanic flows
- Oligocene and Miocene basalt and andesite
- Oligocene–early Miocene ash-flow tuff; includes the Darrough Felsite
- sedimentary rocks

MESOZOIC

- Walker Lake terrane: Luning-Berlin assemblage

PALEOZOIC

- Antler overlap sequence
- Golconda terrane
- Nolan Belt
- early Paleozoic carbonate shelf sequence
- continental slope and deep-sea basin deposits

MISCELLANEOUS

- mixed breccias
- ultramafic rocks

INTRUSIVE ROCKS

- Cenozoic mafic and granitic rocks
- Mesozoic mafic and granitic rocks

— thrust fault
— normal fault
--- concealed or inferred thrust fault
--- concealed or inferred normal fault

Map labels: 722, Reese River, 50, BIRCH CREEK PLUTON, Spencer Hot Springs, 50, KINGSTON CANYON, RANGE, TOIYABE RANGE, RANGE FAULT ZONE, SMOKY VALLEY, NORTHUMBERLAND CANYON, WHITE ROCK MOUNTAIN, RANGE, 376, ALKALI FLAT, Darrough Felsite, WILDCAT PEAK, MONITOR VALLEY, ARC DOME, Darroughs Hot Springs, Carvers, MT. JEFFERSON, JETT CANYON, Hadley, Round Mountain, TOQUIMA, Belmont, PEAVINE CANYON, BIG SMOKY VALLEY, 377, Manhattan, RANGE, SAN ANTONIO MOUNTAINS, MONITOR RANGE, RALSTON VALLEY, THUNDER MOUNTAIN, 95, 6, 6, Tonopah, 95, N, 0 5 10 15 20 miles

Recent studies of the Toiyabe Range fault zone have identified a few places where very young alluvial fan deposits are cut and displaced by as much as 15 feet. In addition, about 2 miles south of the Birch Creek Ranch (3 miles south of US 50) near Tar Creek, trenches across the frontal fault zone have revealed evidence for at least two earthquakes powerful enough to have ruptured the surface in the recent geological past.

The bedrock in the northern Toiyabe Range is dominated by mostly Cambrian to Devonian sandstone, shale, and limestone, metamorphosed to quartzite and phyllite. These strata, exceeding 30,000 feet in aggregate thickness, are folded and intensely faulted into a jumble of tilted blocks. Granitic plutons of Cretaceous age (the Birch Creek pluton) and Jurassic age (the Austin pluton) are intruded into the older Paleozoic rock. Near the contacts with igneous bodies, minerals bearing gold, tungsten, uranium, silver, lead, copper, molybdenum, beryllium, and arsenic are present. Silver ores were discovered at the mouth of Birch Creek in 1863, and the Birch Creek mining district produced small but significant quantities of gold, silver, and uranium until about 1969.

The Big Smoky Valley, an expansive lowland, stretches east to the alluvial apron at the base of the Toquima Range. The valley surface is composed of sandy and gravelly alluvium, windblown sand and silt, and very fine-grained lake sediments. The depth of these unconsolidated valley-filling sediments ranges from as little as a few hundred feet near the mountains to more than 8,000 feet in the central part of the basin. The valley has no permanent streams flowing through it, but runoff (when present) migrates south about 30 miles to collect in a salt and clay playa known as Alkali Flat. Groundwater rises to the subsurface and discharges salty water around the fringe of the playa, forming salt marshes. During the mining days of the late 1800s, salt for smelting and refining of the ores was harvested from these salt marshes and the crusty surface of Alkali Flat. In Pleistocene time, Big Smoky Valley was occupied by Lake Toiyabe, a contemporary of the Lake Lahontan system to the north. At its maximum stage of development, Lake Toiyabe was more than 40 miles long and submerged the Alkali Flat area to a depth of nearly 200 feet.

Active and inactive hot springs are common along the margins of Big Smoky Valley, including Spencer Hot Springs, the white travertine terraces of which are visible east of NV 376 near the foothills of the northern Toquima Range. Farther south, McLeod Ranch and Darroughs Hot Springs are situated much closer to the highway at the foot of the Toiyabe Range. In several other places, patches of altered rock and sediment associated with hydrothermal spring deposits provide evidence of older hot springs that have become inactive. In the 1970s the Nevada Bureau of Mines and Geology found subsurface temperatures as high as 264°F, hot enough for a variety of geothermal energy applications. However, no large-scale commercial energy is currently being produced, likely the consequence of the remote location and minimal population.

East of NV 376, the northern Toquima Range is composed mostly of gently tilted layers of Oligocene and Miocene ash-flow tuffs that form the tablelands capping the range crest. The tuffs lie on older Jurassic granitic rock that has intruded the deformed and thrust-faulted early to middle Paleozoic strata. Wildcat Peak, the most prominent pinnacle along the Toquima Range skyline, is composed of Pennsylvanian limestone and conglomerate resting on Ordovician chert and shale. To the north of this peak along the Toquima Range crest, the aptly named White Rock Mountain and the surrounding upland are composed of light-colored tuff about 30 million years old.

About 20 miles south of Kingston Canyon, NV 376 passes the junction with Northumberland Mine Road, which leads east across the Big Smoky Valley to Northumberland Canyon, in which rich silver ores were discovered in 1866. Disseminated gold deposits, turquoise, and barite were later discovered, leading to several large open-pit operations along with many small excavations. The host rock of the gold and silver deposits is predominantly early Ordovician through Devonian limestone and dolomite that are folded, faulted, and

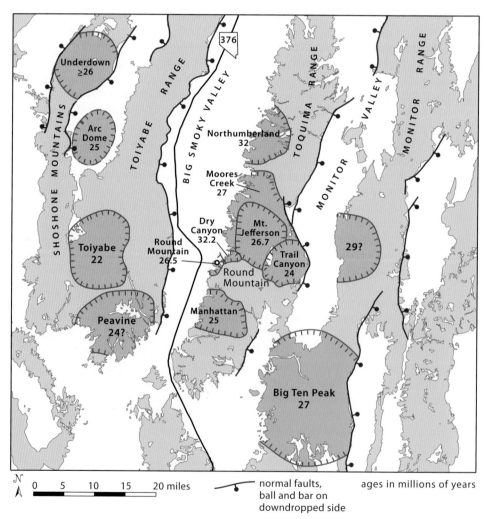

Numerous calderas formed in the vicinity of the Toquima and Toiyabe Ranges in Oligocene and Miocene time.

arranged in multiple thrust sheets. The thick succession of deformed Paleozoic strata was intruded by magma 154 to 151 million years ago during the Jurassic Period and again in Cretaceous time, when multiple dikes of diorite and granite were injected into the older rock. After a lull in geologic activity, an enormous surge of magma moved up through the rock in the Oligocene and Miocene Epochs, manifesting in several cataclysmic caldera-forming eruptions. The Northumberland caldera, centered just south of the canyon, formed 32 million years ago, was about 20 miles in diameter, and is filled with 2,000 feet of tuffs and landslide deposits. Most of the gold and silver deposits in the Northumberland district likely formed during this great volcanic outburst.

South of the Northumberland Road junction, most of the rock exposed in the eastern escarpment of the Toiyabe Range is early to middle Paleozoic sedimentary rocks overlain by thrust sheets of the Golconda terrane. About where the Toquima Road joins NV 376 from the east, the state highway passes an internal fault in the Toiyabe Range that terminates the Paleozoic strata. To the south of the fault is a massive sequence of Miocene volcanic rocks, the most widespread of which is the Darrough Felsite, a mass of welded ash-flow tuff and rhyolite flows more than 10,000 feet thick. This sequence of volcanic rocks was erupted between 27 and 22 million years ago, within a huge collapsed caldera. These rocks are heavily silicified, probably as a consequence of continuing volcanic activity and hydrothermal activity in the later Miocene Epoch. The silicification hardened the relatively soft volcanic rocks, making them more resistant to erosion and resulting in the rugged and craggy peaks.

The resistant silicified rhyolite of the Darrough Felsite creates the rugged escarpment of the central Toiyabe Range.

Two miles north of the small town of Carvers, NV 376 passes just west of a marshy area that marks Darroughs Hot Springs. The hot springs have been well-known since the 1800s from the expedition of John C. Frémont in 1845, to the stagecoach roads establish here in 1863, to the twentieth-century mining booms. The hot springs form a warm marshy area extending nearly 2 miles east of NV 376.

The high peaks of the Toquima and Toiyabe Ranges were glaciated multiple times during the Pleistocene ice ages. John Muir first noticed glacial landforms in the Toquima Range in 1878, when he hiked the high area now within the Alta Toquima Wilderness Area surrounding Mt. Jefferson, the loftiest peak in the Toquima Range. Muir recognized relatively short U-shaped valleys ascending from an elevation of about 9,200 feet that culminated in well-formed cirques, with which Muir was familiar from his experience in the California's Sierra Nevada. The glaciers in the Toquima Range were relatively small and only covered approximately 17 square miles of the highest part of the range. In the higher and broader Toiyabe Range to the west, hundreds of square miles of the alpine ramparts exhibit glacial feature such as cirques, rock striations and polish, and moraine deposits. The bedrock in both of these glaciated areas is Oligocene and Miocene rhyolitic welded tuffs and lavas erupted from numerous calderas.

Southeast of Carvers, NV 376 trends directly toward the massive tailings and leach pads of the Round Mountain Mine, one of the largest gold producers in Nevada. Prior to the discovery of gold, Round Mountain was an isolated, rounded hill consisting mostly of late Oligocene ash-flow tuffs erupted from the Round Mountain caldera about 26 million years ago. So much rock has been removed with modern open-pit mining methods that Round Mountain has almost disappeared.

Gold was discovered in alluvium around the Round Mountain area in 1906. The alluvial placer deposits were worked until about 1962, when rich gold deposits were discovered in the volcanic rock of Round Mountain, concentrated in veins and disseminated through the rhyolitic ash-flows in association with sulfide and oxide minerals. This mineralization was the result of hydrothermal alteration of the volcanic rock after the caldera in which it formed had

Panoramic view of the tailings and leach piles of the Round Mountain Mine, west of NV 376 in Big Smoky Valley.

collapsed. The mineralizing event occurred in less than 50,000 years, almost instantaneous, at least by geological standards.

About 12 miles south of the Round Mountain turnoff, NV 377 leads east from the highway toward the mining area of Manhattan in the southern Toquima Range. The side road follows an east-trending fault into Manhattan Gulch, which generally separates the deformed Paleozoic strata on the south from the Cenozoic volcanic rocks on the north. The volcanic rocks at Manhattan Gulch erupted from and then filled the Manhattan caldera about 25 million years ago. Silver ores were discovered in 1867, but gold produced the majority of the mineral wealth of the district. The gold deposits are concentrated along a ring fracture system in Manhattan Gulch that represents the margin of the filled caldera. Gold-bearing veins in Cambrian limestone and shale were very rich and probably formed during the intense wave of Oligocene and Miocene volcanic activity.

About 3 miles south of the intersection with NV 377, Peavine Canyon Road leads west from NV 376 into the southern Toiyabe Range. Thick accumulations of ash-flow tuffs and rhyolite flows erupted from the Peavine caldera, an early Miocene volcanic depression formed 24 to 23 million years ago. Mineralization similar to but somewhat less extensive than that in the Round Mountain and Manhattan areas of the Toquima Range also occurred along the edge of the Peavine caldera. The Jett mining district, established for the copper and silver ores discovered in 1875, is scattered between Peavine Canyon on the south to Jett Canyon on the north near Hadley. Small amounts of antimony, mercury, lead, and zinc were also mined from the Jett district.

NV 376 swings southeast through a broad alluvial gap between the Toquima Range and the San Antonio Mountains to the south. The gap is related to northwest-trending strike-slip faults associated with the Walker Lane. Several mining areas that produced gold and silver from quartz veins are aligned along the strike-slip faulting, including the old Midway Mine, the Thunder Mountain region (Hannapah mining district), and the Ellendale mining district south of US 6. At the north end of the San Antonio Mountains, molybdenum, gold, silver, and copper have been mined since the mid-1800s. The deposits include a large but relatively low-grade porphyry molybdenum deposit almost 1 mile wide.

In the vicinity of the intersection with a road leading east to Belmont and Monitor Valley, you can see the south end of the Monitor Range to the east across Ralston Valley. The gently dipping layers along the skyline are sheets of welded tuff and breccia that mark the Big Ten Peak caldera, yet another late Oligocene structure.

Thunder Mountain, the large brown hill rising to the east, is composed of 16-million-year-old andesite flows capping older Oligocene ash-flow tuff. The volcanic rocks in this area rest on Ordovician shale and slate, which makes up the hills along the highway. About 11 miles north of US 6, NV 376 passes the Rye Patch Pumping Station on the east. Water wells were drilled here in 1904 to provide a water supply to the boomtown of Tonopah. Today, groundwater pumped over the San Antonio Mountains still is the primary source of water for the modern town. Rocks in the vicinity of the pumping station are mostly Miocene welded tuffs and ash-flow tuffs.

NV 431
Mt. Rose Highway
Reno—Lake Tahoe
24 miles

Southwest of its intersection with US 395/I-580, NV 431 climbs the gentle slope of the Mt. Rose alluvial fan as it begins its ascent over the Carson Range en route to Lake Tahoe. You can see the Steamboat Hills and the geothermal power installations (discussed more fully in the US 395 road guide) to the southeast. Not all of the hot springs in the Steamboat Hills have been captured for heat, and it is common to see steam rising on cold days. Much of the colorful rock used for landscaping and erosion control along NV 431 was quarried from the Steamboat Hills, where hydrothermal alteration of volcanic rock added iron oxides and other metallic compounds.

Uplift of the Carson Range, which rises about 6,000 feet above the floor of the Truckee Meadows, occurred within the past 5 to 3 million years, and many of the normal faults along its eastern escarpment are considered still active. The highest peak in the Carson Range is saddle-shaped Mt. Rose, rising to an elevation of 10,776 feet. Mt. Rose is capped by dark-colored Miocene andesite flows and associated rocks that cover the lighter-colored Cretaceous granodiorite, part of the Sierra Nevada batholith. The capping andesite was once part of a much more extensive sequence of volcanic rocks related to the Ancestral

View north from the Mt. Rose Summit area on NV 431. The peak with the brown cap of andesite is Mt. Rose, while the lighter peak to the right is composed of granodiorite.

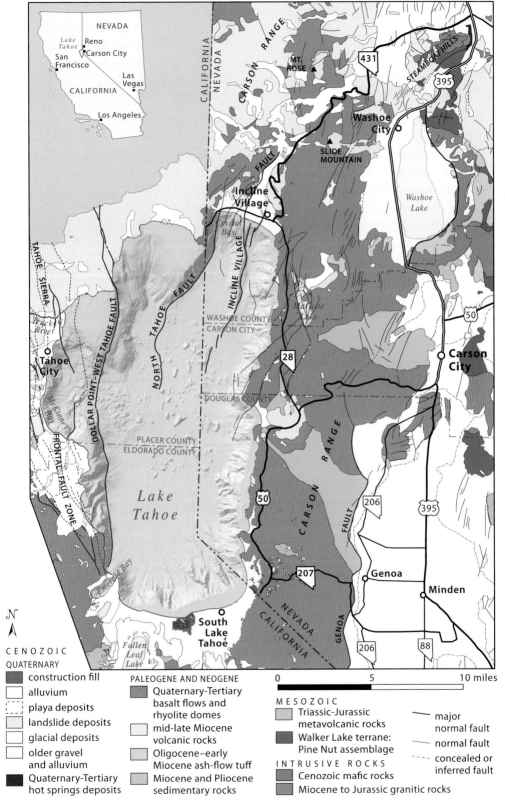

Geological map of the Lake Tahoe region. —Based on maps from US Geological Survey and Nevada Bureau of Mines and Geology

CENOZOIC
QUATERNARY

- construction fill
- alluvium
- playa deposits
- landslide deposits
- glacial deposits
- older gravel and alluvium
- Quaternary-Tertiary hot springs deposits

PALEOGENE AND NEOGENE

- Quaternary-Tertiary basalt flows and rhyolite domes
- mid-late Miocene volcanic rocks
- Oligocene–early Miocene ash-flow tuff
- Miocene and Pliocene sedimentary rocks

MESOZOIC

- Triassic-Jurassic metavolcanic rocks
- Walker Lake terrane: Pine Nut assemblage

INTRUSIVE ROCKS

- Cenozoic mafic rocks
- Miocene to Jurassic granitic rocks

— major normal fault
— normal fault
--- concealed or inferred fault

0   5   10 miles

N
↑

Cascades. Following the uplift of the Carson Range, erosion removed much of the cover of younger volcanic rocks and exposed the granitic bedrock to the scouring effects of Pleistocene glaciers. The prominent peak scarred with ski runs and topped by broadcast antenna towers is Slide Mountain. The volcanic rocks have been completely eroded from its summit, exposing light-colored granodiorite.

Much of the rock rubble seen on the surface of the Mt. Rose alluvial fan along NV 431 consists of granodiorite and andesite boulders transported from the higher parts of the Carson Range during Pleistocene time. At least three periods of late Pleistocene glaciation, approximately 20,000, 65,000, and 150,000 years ago, affected the Carson Range. Each time the climate cooled, lobes of ice formed in the higher parts of the range and flowed down the canyons, carving U-shaped valleys in the process. The most severe and persistent cold intervals appear to have been the older ones, both of which are associated with a glacial period known as the Tahoe glaciation in the Sierra Nevada. The Tahoe glaciers descended eastward nearly to the valley floor, then receded during a brief warming interval after about 65,000 years ago. The glaciers returned during the Tioga glaciation, which peaked at about 20,000 years ago, but were smaller and less persistent that those of the earlier Tahoe glaciation. On the east slopes of Mt. Rose, erosional features and sediment associated with the late Pleistocene glaciers are particularly prominent in the valleys of Galena Creek and Browns Creek, both of which are traversed by NV 431.

Just west of the junction with Callahan Ranch Road, NV 431 crosses a series of small normal faults with displacements that are hard to see on the surface. The Galena fire station, north of the road, lies astride one of these minor faults, part of the active fault zone along the base of the Carson Range. Small earthquakes are not uncommon in this area. For the next few miles, roadcuts along NV 431 expose glacial outwash sediments consisting of poorly sorted accumulations of sand, gravel, and large light-colored boulders of granitic rocks carried from the high slopes by Pleistocene glaciers and redeposited over the surface of the Mt. Rose fan by local streams. About 7 miles southwest from its junction with US 395, the highway crosses onto the Cretaceous granitic rocks of the Carson Range and continues to pass over these rocks as it climbs higher into the mountains.

Just southwest from the Galena Creek Regional Park visitor center, NV 431 begins a series of tight turns as the road steepens. Several roadcuts expose lahars (volcanic mudflows) and andesite flows, easy to spot on the basis of the large boulders of volcanic rocks embedded in a matrix of solidified volcanic ash and sandy material. Other roadcuts expose the light-colored, weathered granodiorite beneath the volcanic materials or glacial outwash deposits consisting of boulders, gravel, and sand transported by meltwater streams during the Pleistocene ice ages.

As NV 431 approaches Mt. Rose Summit from the northeast, it winds through an open area that is part of a large cirque, a bowl-shaped depression carved into the granodiorite bedrock by Pleistocene glaciers. To the north, you can see the dark-colored andesite at the top of Mt. Rose covering the light-colored granodiorite beneath it. South of the pass, in the vicinity of ski runs,

Glacial moraine deposits exposed in a roadcut along NV 431 in the vicinity of Sky Tavern contain large white boulders of granodiorite.

This strongly jointed granodiorite of Cretaceous age in the Mt. Rose Summit area has at least two sets of joints that intersect, one close to vertical and one subhorizontal in this view. The granodiorite is mostly light-colored feldspar minerals, accompanied by black crystals of hornblende and biotite. Inset is 4 inches across.

the steep escarpment on the north side of Slide Mountain is the headwall of the cirque. Numerous sets of joints, which are fractures without displacement, cut through the granodiorite exposures. The visitor center at the summit is a good place to closely examine exposures of the granodiorite, with its light-gray to white crystals of feldspars, sprinkled with small rectangular crystals of black hornblende and tiny flakes of black biotite mica.

For several miles southwest of the summit, NV 431 weaves along the North Tahoe–Incline Village fault zone, composed of several northeast-trending normal faults that cut across the Carson Range. About 5 miles southwest from Mt. Rose Summit, the highway makes a sharp bend above Incline Village. On the west side of the road, a scenic viewpoint provides the best view of Lake Tahoe from the road and is a good place to become acquainted with the Lake Tahoe Basin. Downhill from the overlook, NV 431 passes outcrops of granodiorite and the overlying brownish-green andesitic flows.

Incline Village received its name in the early 1880s from a 4,000-foot-long tramway (incline) that lifted lumber up the steep west face of the Carson Range immediately east of the town. This lumber was harvested from the forests surrounding Lake Tahoe, cut at sawmills in Incline Village, and transported to the Comstock silver mines in the Virginia Range to the east. Flumes were used to carry the wood downhill to the Carson Valley. Timber harvesting was so intense in the Lake Tahoe Basin in the 1880s that most of mountain slopes surrounding the lake were completely deforested. By 1900, however, the mines of the Comstock Lode were inactive, and the demand for timber and fuelwood all but disappeared. The flumes, along with the inclined winch at Incline Village, were abandoned, and today only faint traces of them remain in the second-growth forests of the Carson Range.

Lake Tahoe Basin

Lake Tahoe is a natural lake, although a small dam on its west side raises the water level by 10 feet. The lake reaches a maximum depth of 1,636 feet, making it one of the deepest lakes in the world. Sixty-three streams drain into Lake Tahoe, the most important being the Upper Truckee River, which flows into the lake from the south. At Tahoe City, on the northwest shore of the lake, water is released at the dam into the lower Truckee River canyon, from which point it flows more than 100 miles into Pyramid Lake, northeast of Reno. Thus, Lake Tahoe is a Great Basin lake and none of its crystal-blue water ever enters the ocean.

The Lake Tahoe Basin is a complex half-graben, a depression formed by numerous normal faults, mostly on its western side, that became active in this region 3 to 2 million years ago. Prior to the migration of normal faulting into this area from the east, the Carson Range was part of the main mass of the Sierra Nevada. Ancient channels and valleys draining west from the modern crest of the Sierra Nevada can be traced into the Carson Range, across the Lake Tahoe Basin. The young faults that form the basin generally trend north-south, paralleling the longest dimension of the lake. The displacement on these faults is normally up to the west, with rocks west of the lake displaced upward more than 4,400 feet.

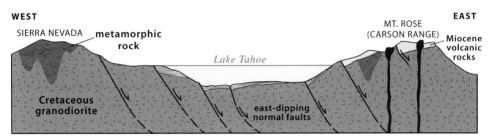

Generalized cross sections of the Lake Tahoe Basin. The south-to-north section (top) shows that volcanics impounded the lake at its north end. The west-to-east section (bottom) shows the normal faulting that formed the basin.

As the normal faults began to form the Lake Tahoe Basin, two other events that shaped the landscape commenced as well: the climate oscillations of the Pleistocene ice ages and volcanic activity at the north end of the collapsing graben. The high ramparts on the north and northwest side of the lake consist of young volcanic rocks, most of which were erupted during the past 4 to 3 million years from the Tahoe-Truckee volcanic field. The natural dam formed by the volcanic materials blocked the northward flow of the ancestral Truckee River, submerging the basin upstream to create the earliest predecessor of today's lake. Several cycles of glaciation brought water and ice into the basin, feeding a lake that was sometimes larger and sometimes smaller than modern Lake Tahoe. When the ancient lake rose above the lowest point on the basin rim near Tahoe City, along the northwestern shore, the water spilled over and carved the impressive gorge of the lower Truckee River.

The largest Pleistocene glaciers entered the Lake Tahoe Basin from the high Sierra Nevada to the west, repeatedly descending down broad U-shaped canyons to the edge of the lake. The glaciers in the Carson Range to the east were much smaller and did not extend into the lower parts of the lake basin. The high peaks of the Sierra Nevada created a rain shadow, capturing most of the snow from passing Pleistocene storms before it reached the Carson Range. Even today, this effect persists: each year about 90 inches of precipitation falls in the mountains west of Lake Tahoe, while only about 40 inches of water arrives in the higher parts of the Carson Range.

On the deep floor of Lake Tahoe in the northern part of the basin, a remarkable field of rock debris was discovered in the late 1990s when geologists compiled the first high-resolution images of the lake bottom. Gigantic boulders and blocks of material were spread out across an area of more than 75 square miles directly east of McKinney Bay, a large embayment along the west shore of the lake. The debris is from a large landslide that simultaneously created the large recess in which the bay is now situated. This event is thought to have been triggered by an earthquake of magnitude 7 or greater that occurred in late Pleistocene time between 21,000 and 12,000 years ago. The massive slide generated a series of tsunamis, some as high as 100 feet, that sloshed ashore around the basin. The lake bottom images also show fault scarps, including the prominent escarpment, some 30 feet high, of the West Tahoe–Dollar Point fault.

If you head south on NV 28 along the east shore of Lake Tahoe, you'll see rounded masses of granodiorite partly buried by loose granular material released from the crumbling rock. When plutonic igneous rock such as this is exposed at the surface, intersecting joints develop that break the rock into large, mostly rectangular blocks. As water penetrates into the joints, chemical weathering softens the minerals in the granodiorite, weakening the rock and accelerating its disintegration. Over time, the joints widen and the sharp angular edges of the blocks of rock between the joints become smooth and rounded. Geologists refer to this as spheroidal weathering.

Some of the granitic rock appears to be broken into thin sheets or curving flakes, a process known as exfoliation. As the Carson Range was uplifted, erosion removed several kilometers of rock above the granitic mass that was formerly buried deep underground. As granitic masses are unroofed by erosion, the weight of the overlying rock (and the confining pressure it produces) are reduced, allowing the rock to expand. This expansion can form sets of curving joints that cause the plutonic rock to shed plates or flakes of rock, somewhat like layers of an onion.

Roadside outcrop of spheroidal weathering in granodiorite along NV 28 south of Incline Village.

NV 445
Pyramid Lake Highway
Sparks—Pyramid Lake
30 miles

NV 445 leads north from I-80 at Sparks through Spanish Springs Valley en route to Pyramid Lake, a remnant of the Pleistocene-age Lake Lahontan. About 2 miles north of Sparks, NV 445 winds through low hills of Miocene volcanics. The brownish knobs of hard silicified volcanic rocks protrude from the softer, clay-rich products of the hydrothermal alteration of andesite. This alteration also produced small concentrations of ore minerals, such as argentite, galena, and sphalerite, that became the targets of mining activities in the late 1800s. The peak activity produced small amounts of mostly silver ores in the early 1900s, following a large investment by John Sparks, former governor of Nevada. In 1903, hot water made acidic from the oxidation of sulfide ores seeped into the mines and ultimately caused their failure. Today, a maze of shafts and tunnels still exists underground, and occasionally buildings are damaged from ground subsidence into unknown cavities.

At Spanish Springs, a bustling suburb of Reno and Sparks, spring-fed mead-ows formerly occupied the low areas east of the highway but mostly disap-peared following overuse of groundwater. Small remnants are maintained by water diverted from the Truckee River. Spanish Springs Valley is a half-graben, tilted to the west by the active faulting along Hungry Ridge, to the west. Uncon-solidated sediment washed into the valley is thickest beneath the western por-tion of the valley, where more than 1,000 feet of sand, silt, and gravel have accumulated during Quaternary time. In June of 2002, heavy rains triggered a flood and mudslide down the steep face of the southern extension of Hungry Ridge that significantly damaged Spanish Springs High School. To the east, the less abrupt slopes of the Pah Rah Range are composed mostly of dark-colored basalt flows of late Miocene age.

In the northern part of Spanish Springs Valley, a large quarry along the base of the Hungry Ridge escarpment is visible from the road for several miles. This quarry extracts sand, gravel, and crushed rock from weathered exposures of Cretaceous granodiorite, a light-colored igneous rock similar to granite. The normal fault at the base of Hungry Ridge has precrushed the rock, accelerating its weathering and disintegration and simplifying the quarrying process. Just east of the road in this same general area is Sugarloaf Peak, the lower slopes consisting of weathered Cretaceous granodiorite and the upper portion of darker Miocene basalt flows.

As NV 447 passes through the north end of Spanish Springs Valley, you can see dark-colored Oligocene ash-flow tuffs west of the road capping the lighter-colored granodiorite of Hungry Ridge. Geologists studying the variations in thickness and patterns of dispersal in these 30- to 25-million-year-old ash-flow tuffs have concluded that the ash reached this location by traveling down ancient river channels. The ash is thickest in the old river valleys and much thinner on the flanks or over intervening divides between adjacent riverbeds.

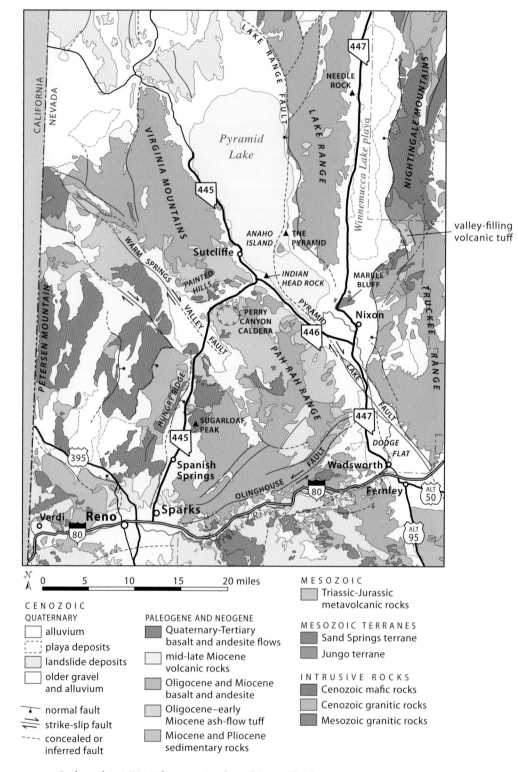

Geology along NV 445 between Sparks and Pyramid Lake. —Faults adapted from Tingley and others, 2005

The upper half Sugarloaf Peak, viewed east from NV 445, is dark-colored basalt flows, which cap Cretaceous granodiorite of the lighter, lower half.

The channels extend to the east and southeast, indicating that the volcanoes discharging the ash were located in that direction.

About 21 miles north of Sparks, NV 445 passes the Bureau of Land Management Wild Horse and Burro adoption facility as it enters the northwest-trending Warm Springs Valley (also known as Palomino Valley). The valley is filled with Pliocene and Pleistocene sediments to a maximum depth of more than 3,000 feet. Warm Springs Valley is so named because hot groundwater naturally surfaces along faults along its southwest margin. With a maximum temperature of about 150°F, this water is not hot enough to be used for the generation of electricity. The valley is part of the Walker Lane, a major fault zone consisting of several prominent northwest-trending, right-lateral strike-slip faults. The Warm Springs Valley fault continues more than 50 miles to the northwest into California. Trenching studies along the fault indicate it has produced several major earthquakes over the past 20,000 years and has the potential to cause earthquakes of magnitude 7 or greater in the future.

As NV 445 bends to the northeast through Mullen Pass, which separates the Pah Rah Range to the southeast from the Virginia Mountains on the northwest, rocks exposed on both sides of the highway are parts of a thick sequence of early Miocene tuffs, lava flows, and volcanic domes related to the Perry Canyon caldera at the northern end of the Pah Rah Range. Volcanic ash and rubble that blasted from the caldera 23 million years ago accumulated in thicknesses exceeding 2,000 feet. The volcanic rocks are sometimes interbedded with diatomite, a sedimentary rock consisting mostly of the remains of microscope algae

View northeast along NV 445 where it turns northeast toward Mullen Pass. The colorful rocks to the left (northwest) of the road are Miocene tuffs, lava flows, and domes.

mixed with silt and clay. These sediments accumulated in an ancient lake nestled between volcanic centers about 16 to 15 million years ago. Recent studies suggest that the region near Mullen Pass may have been 10,000 feet above sea level in Miocene time, about twice as high as the modern valley floors and much cooler and wetter, with conifers and hardwood trees.

In the northern Pah Rah Range, the volcanic rocks of the Perry Canyon caldera are cut by numerous veins of sulfide minerals containing valuable ores of silver, gold, and copper, first discovered in 1863. By 1876, the Pyramid mining district was organized, but activities were small and intermittent compared to other Nevada mining areas, with total production of less than $100,000 worth of metals. In 1954, small amounts of uranium were discovered in the Pyramid mining district, and several surges of mining exploration for copper, molybdenum, and gold followed in the 1980s and 1990s. The ore-bearing veins consist of metal-rich sulfide minerals such as pyrite, enargite, sphalerite, and galena, which oxidize into the vivid red, brown, and ochre colors that can be seen in the volcanic rocks in the Mullen Pass area. The Painted Hills and Incandescent Rocks, at the southern end of the Virginia Mountain, feature vividly colored volcanic layers, the pink, red, and white produced by iron-bearing minerals and clay.

Pyramid Lake

NV 445 joins NV 446 near a viewpoint and state historical marker overlooking Pyramid Lake. From the overlook, you can see on the far (eastern) side of the lake the triangular, 600-foot-high tufa mound that inspired John C. Frémont to give this lake its name when he explored this region in 1844. Southwest of the Pyramid is Anaho Island, a rocky prominence that is an important nesting area for waterfowl. Pyramid Lake is the terminus of the Truckee River, which enters the lake from the south after flowing more than 100 miles from the Lake Tahoe region. The lake is more than 350 feet deep, but the lake level, and hence the depth, fluctuate over time depending on climate cycles and upstream diversions of water from the Truckee River. The historic low occurred in 1967, when the lake fell to a surface elevation of 3,784 feet, substantially lower than the 3,860 feet witnessed by Frémont in 1844. Due to the high rates of evaporation and limited inflow from the Truckee River, Pyramid Lake is very slightly saline, with a dissolved mineral content of approximately 0.6 percent, about one-sixth the salinity of seawater. Freshwater fish and other organisms can survive in the lake, and fishermen come to catch the large Lahontan cutthroat trout. Pyramid Lake is also the only body of water in the world where a black sucker fish known as cui-ui *(Chasmistes cujus)* is found. This endemic endangered species was an important source of food for the Paiute people who have inhabited the Pyramid Lake region for many centuries.

The low basin in which Pyramid Lake rests is a downfaulted half-graben that tilts gently eastward toward the Lake Range on its east side. The Lake Range, composed mostly of a thick sequence of Miocene lava flows, is uplifted and tilted east along the Lake Range fault, a prominent normal fault that runs near the base of the western escarpment and has at least 15,000 feet of displacement.

Pyramid Lake is the largest remnant of Pleistocene Lake Lahontan, an enormous body of interconnected waterways that covered some 8,500 square miles of northwest Nevada at its most recent maximum stage of development, between 15,000 and 13,000 years ago. At that time, the water of Lake Lahontan was about 900 feet deep in the Pyramid Lake basin. From the overlook near the junction of NV 445 and NV 446, wave-cut benches and horizontal terraces are visible on the slopes south of the road, marking the prehistoric levels of Lake Lahontan.

The Pyramid, a 600-foot-high tufa mound, can be seen on the far side of Pyramid Lake from the overlook near the junction between NV 445 and NV 446.

The Pyramid is composed of tufa, a calcium carbonate deposit formed when calcium-rich groundwater issuing from springs on a lake bottom mixes with alkaline lake water. The precipitation of the mineral calcite near the mouth of the submerged springs gradually builds a mound of tufa on the lake bottom. The exposed height of the Pyramid is several hundred feet above the current lake level, indicating that the tufa formed tens of thousands of years ago, when this area was part of the much deeper Lake Lahontan. Other tufa mounds in the vicinity of the Pyramid suggest that some of the lake bottom springs were aligned along the Lake Range fault.

Calcite also can be precipitated from lake water in the absence of springs whenever the water becomes saturated with calcium carbonate. Tufa forms coatings, layers, mounds, and sheets along the former floor and shorelines of Lake Lahontan where no springs exist. Some of the tufa crusts near Pyramid Lake exceed 10 feet in thickness and commonly form bulbous or knoblike

Close-up view of the spongy, banded layers of tufa deposited from lake water at Indian Head Rock.

Indian Head Rock, a large tufa mound east of NV 446 along the southwest shore of Pyramid Lake.

masses of brown, spongy-textured calcite covering boulders, gravel, and bedrock. Calcite in tufa that formed in relatively cool water slowly recrystallizes into a crystalline form known as thinolite, characterized by irregular pillars and columns up to several inches long.

You can explore the southern tip of Pyramid Lake by taking NV 446 south as it skirts the northeast edge of the Pah Rah Range. For a few miles southeast of the junction, you can see several tufa mounds east of NV 446. One of the largest of these mounds is known as Indian Head Rock, at which there is a pullout and picnic tables. The tufa formed when the lake level stood several hundred feet higher than the modern surface of Pyramid Lake. Sand and gravel along the ancient shoreline has been cemented with tufa deposits, forming slabs of cemented sediment known as beach rock.

Large tufa-covered boulders just west of the highway are known as Popcorn Rock. Several mounds of tufa are aligned in a northwest trend, suggesting that springs on the floor of the prehistoric lake may have been controlled by faults running parallel to the Pah Rah Range. As the highways passes Popcorn Rock, look east to see sediments deposited by the Truckee River as it enters Pyramid Lake. When the lake was lower, the Truckee River cut downward through both modern and ancient lake deposits and extended farther out into the lake basin than it now does.

NV 447
Wadsworth—Gerlach—California Border
142 miles

See map on page 346 for Wadsworth to Nixon.

Between Wadsworth and Nixon, NV 447 follows a northwest-trending valley aligned along the Pyramid fault zone, a prominent structure within the Walker Lane of strike-slip faults. The right-lateral displacement along the Pyramid fault zone, which began between 9 and 3 million years ago, is approximately 5 miles. Geologists have documented at least four major earthquakes over the past 10,000 years along the fault zone. The Pyramid Lake fault, the most prominent of several faults in the Pyramid fault zone, appears to merge with the Lake Range fault to the northwest, where the lateral displacement along the fault shifts to more vertical displacement.

North of Wadsworth, the valley of the Truckee River widens into the broad greasewood expanse known as Dodge Flat, west of which the rocks of the southern Pah Rah Range consist mostly of felsic ash-flow tuffs of Miocene age, cut by several intrusive bodies and domes of rhyolite. Hydrothermal alteration of these volcanic rocks has bleached them a bright white in some places, while depositing metal-rich minerals in others. Oxidation of the metal-rich rocks produces the colorful bands and patches of rusty reddish-brown, pale-green, and lavender to the west of NV 447. The altered rocks also contained significant amounts of gold, mostly concentrated in veins that formed some 10 million years ago along faults.

Between Dodge Flat and Nixon, the Truckee River flows northward in a valley east of the road. Prior to the late nineteenth century, the Truckee River flowed toward Pyramid Lake in a highly meandering channel that split into several sloughs as it approached the southern end of the lake. Since the late 1880s, diversion and consumption of water upstream from Pyramid Lake reduced the flows of the Truckee River considerably, and the lake level fell from about 3,878 feet in 1868 to its historic low of 3,784 feet in 1967, a decline of more than 90 feet. The lowering of Pyramid Lake steepened the overall gradient of the lower Truckee River, accelerating the water flow. As a result, the Truckee River began to incise a gorge and straighten its channel through its own floodplain sediments for about 10 miles south of Nixon. Below the river gravels and floodplain sediments, the horizontal layers of light-colored Lake Lahontan lakebeds can be seen in the walls of the river gorge. The Truckee Range, east of the river, is composed mostly of a thick sequence of dark-colored Miocene basalt flows erupted from one or more volcanic vents about 10 million years ago. On the higher slopes of the Truckee Range, well above the incised Truckee River gorge, you can see several horizontal terraces of Lake Lahontan.

Nixon, the headquarters of the Pyramid Lake Indian Reservation, was the site of a small Paiute village when John Frémont passed through this area in 1844. As NV 447 continues north from Nixon, it passes across the Mud Lake

The lower Truckee River has incised its channel into light-colored silts and clay deposited in Lake Lahontan. View southeast from NV 447.

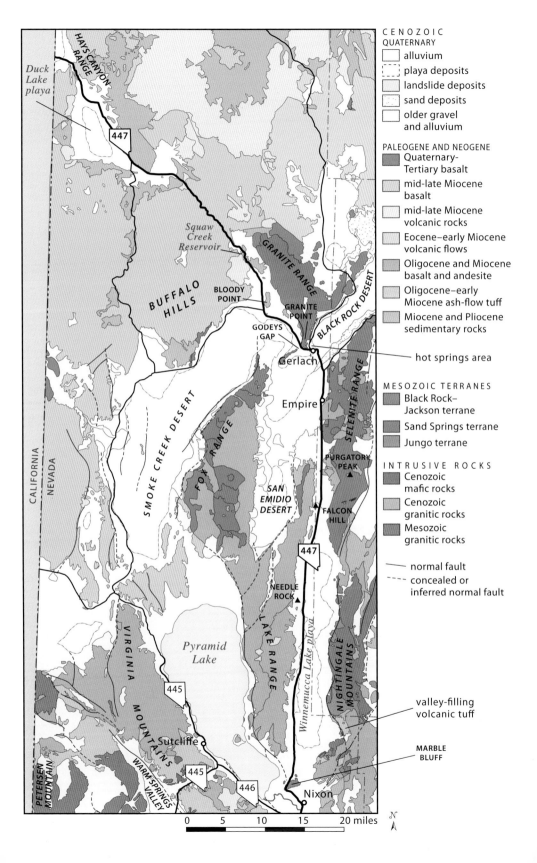

CENOZOIC
QUATERNARY
alluvium
playa deposits
landslide deposits
sand deposits
older gravel
and alluvium

PALEOGENE AND NEOGENE
Quaternary-
Tertiary basalt
mid-late Miocene
basalt
mid-late Miocene
volcanic rocks
Eocene–early Miocene
volcanic flows
Oligocene and Miocene
basalt and andesite
Oligocene–early
Miocene ash-flow tuff
Miocene and Pliocene
sedimentary rocks

○— hot springs area

MESOZOIC TERRANES
Black Rock–
Jackson terrane
Sand Springs terrane
Jungo terrane

INTRUSIVE ROCKS
Cenozoic
mafic rocks
Cenozoic
granitic rocks
Mesozoic
granitic rocks

—— normal fault
----- concealed or
inferred normal fault

valley-filling
volcanic tuff

Duck
Lake
playa

HAYS CANYON RANGE

447

Squaw
Creek
Reservoir

BUFFALO
HILLS

BLOODY
POINT

GRANITE RANGE

GRANITE
POINT

BLACK ROCK DESERT

GODEYS
GAP

Gerlach

Empire

SELENITE RANGE

PURGATORY
PEAK ▲

FALCON
HILL ▲

SMOKE CREEK DESERT

FOX RANGE

SAN
EMIDIO
DESERT

447

NEEDLE
ROCK ▲

CALIFORNIA
NEVADA

VIRGINIA MOUNTAINS

Pyramid
Lake

445

LAKE RANGE

Winnemucca Lake playa

NIGHTINGALE MOUNTAINS

MARBLE
BLUFF

PETERSEN MOUNTAIN

Sutcliffe

445

WARM SPRINGS VALLEY

446

Nixon

0   5   10   15   20 miles

N

Slough. During the Pleistocene Epoch, this low area was submerged, forming a narrow passageway linking the Pyramid Lake arm of Lake Lahontan to the Winnemucca Lake arm to the northeast. The connection between the basins persisted into the early 1900s, when Winnemucca Lake was perennial and as deep as 80 feet, though its level fluctuated seasonally. Subsequent erosion along the lower Truckee River severed the connection. The Winnemucca Lake basin has been dry since 1939, except for brief periods following heavy rains when a few inches of water might accumulate on the exposed floor of the formerly large lake.

About 3 miles north of Nixon, the road ascends Marble Bluff, passing through a prominent roadcut that reveals light-gray marble formed when limestone and dolomite of Mesozoic age were subjected to the heat and chemical activity associated with igneous intrusions in the nearby ranges. The carbonate sedimentary rocks from which this mass of dolomite formed were transported to North America as part of the Sand Springs terrane, a block of rock accreted to the western edge of the continent during the Mesozoic Era when subduction was active in western Nevada. On the lower slopes of Marble Bluff, several prominent shorelines of Lake Lahontan are visible, dating to about 14,000 years ago. The ancient shorelines are encrusted with brown, bulbous masses of tufa. (See the in-depth discussion of tufa in the NV 445 road guide.)

About 4 miles north from Marble Bluff, NV 447 passes into the Winnemucca Lake basin, an extensive valley dropped down along a west-dipping normal fault along the base of the Nightingale Mountains to the east. Along the margins of the currently dry lakebed, you can see fine-grained lake sediments of

NV 447 roadcut at the west end of Marble Bluff. The gray rock in the cut is dolomite of Mesozoic age. The dark rock above it is draped with tufa, indicating the former depth of Pleistocene Lake Lahontan.

View north from NV 447 of the Winnemucca Lake playa. The brown knobs on the basin floor are tufa mounds. The Nightingale Mountains, east of the playa is visible to the right. Red and brown layers of Oligocene tuff in the southern Nightingale Mountains at the far right of th photo flowed down and filled an ancient valley eroded into dark-colored Triassic and Jurassic metamorphic rocks to the left (north).

Pleistocene age and numerous knoblike exposures of tufa that formed on the bottom of the Winnemucca arm of Lake Lahontan. Artifacts found in caves in the Nightingale Range to the east and carvings in the tufa deposited around the Winnemucca Lake basin suggest that primitive humans inhabited the shores of this lake. The rock carvings have been dated to an interval between 14,000 years and 10,500 years ago, the precise time when the Winnemucca Lake arm would have last reached its maximum stage of development.

The Nightingale Mountains consist mostly of Cretaceous granitic rocks between about 105 and 90 million years old, emplaced into older Jurassic and Triassic oceanic sediments such as limestone, mudstone, and shale. The dark-colored sedimentary rocks, most of deep-ocean origin and part of the Jungo terrane, were thrust from the west during late Jurassic time and have been metamorphosed into slate, phyllite, and marble, which is composed of calcite, epidote, and garnet. The tungsten-bearing mineral scheelite occurs in marble near the contact zones with the younger plutonic rocks. The mineralization was first discovered in 1917. In addition to tungsten minerals, minor uranium, gold, silver, molybdenum, and copper deposits were also discovered in the contact zones. The principal mining activity in the Nightingale district took place in World War II and the Korean War, but the most of the mines have since become inactive.

NV 447 continues north, following the flanks of the Lake Range to the west, an east-tilted fault block. The dominant rock formation in the Lake Range is the Pyramid sequence, a 3,000-foot-thick series of basaltic lava flows interposed with minor lava flows of felsic composition, ash-flow tuffs, and stream-deposited sediment. The volcanic rocks erupted between about 16 and 13 million years ago.

Near the northern end of the Winnemucca Lake playa, you can see thick accumulations of Lake Lahontan sediments east of NV 447 along the lower

View east from NV 447 across the Winnemucca Lake basin toward gullied tablelands of Lake Lahontan sediments at the base of the northern Nightingale Mountains. These fine-grained sediments are overlapped by coarse alluvial fan deposits at the mouths of canyons.

Needle Rock, west of NV 447 near milepost 43, is a tower of tufa that precipitated where calcium-rich springwater reacted with the alkaline water of Pleistocene Lake Lahontan.

slopes of the northern Nightingale Mountains. The nearly flat upper surface of the sediments is a good approximation of the level to which the basin was filled by water during the ice ages. NV 447 is built on a similar surface of lake sediments. The bedrock of this part of the Nightingale Mountains is mostly light-colored granitic rocks of Cretaceous age.

On the west side of the road near milepost 43, the highway passes Needle Rock, an impressive tufa tower deposited on the bottom of Lake Lahontan, probably at the site of a submerged spring. Calcium-bearing springwater mixed with the alkaline lake water containing bicarbonate, forming a tall, towerlike pipe of calcium carbonate.

North of the Winnemucca Lake playa, NV 447 passes just east of Falcon Hill, a brown knob of Miocene dacite, a felsic volcanic rock similar to rhyolite. The dacite is part of the Pyramid sequence and was erupted about 14 million years ago. Two faint Lake Lahontan shorelines, marked by subtle terraces draped with tufa, can be discerned on the lower slopes of Falcon Hill. North of Falcon Hill, more of the Pyramid sequence, including some dark-colored basalt flows, is exposed along the eastern flank of the northern Lake Range west of the road. Across the valley to the east, the prominent peaks of the Selenite Range are a large body of 92-million-year-old granodiorite.

Gerlach, Black Rock Desert, and the Granite Range

About 10 miles south of Gerlach, the barren southern end of the Black Rock Desert borders the highway on the west, while the Selenite Range forms the eastern skyline. The Selenite Range takes its name from the silky or clear form of gypsum, the principal component of plaster, occurring in Triassic metasedimentary rocks of the Sand Springs terrane. The gypsum was mined at varying levels of intensity from the 1920s to 2011, and you can see the gypsum mines to the east in the foothills.

The vast expanse of the Black Rock Desert playa, one of the flattest surfaces on Earth, extends northeast of Gerlach. About 900 square miles of playa varies only a few feet from the average elevation 3,905 feet above sea level. This flat playa was the floor of a large arm of Lake Lahontan during late Pleistocene time, and its surface is composed mostly of clay and silt deposited under hundreds of feet of water. The Black Rock playa is isolated from the Smoke Creek Desert basin to the southwest by a low ridge called Godeys Rock, west of Gerlach. During the Pleistocene high stands of Lake Lahontan, the lakes in these two basins were connected by a narrow passageway at Godeys Gap.

Gerlach was established in 1906 as a station along the Western Pacific Railroad. At the height of its population, when the gypsum mines in the Selenite Range were most active, more than one thousand people lived in this isolated community. Today, about one hundred residents live here, but thousands of people visit the region to participate in amateur rocketry or attend the famous Burning Man Festival each September.

Just north of Gerlach, at the base of the Granite Range, lies an area of geothermal activity known as the Great Boiling Spring. Mud Springs, southwest of the town, is another area where hot water flows to the surface. Normal faults along the eastern base of the Granite Range serve as conduits along which deeply circulating groundwater moving though the hot rock of the thin Great Basin crust rises to the surface. The water flowing from the Great Boiling Spring has a maximum temperature of about 200°F, close to boiling! Extensive drilling and exploration of the geothermal resources has occurred in recent years, and power production is already underway 15 miles to the south in the San Emidio Desert. The bedrock of the southern Granite Range consists of highly fractured granodiorite of Cretaceous age. In the vicinity of the hot springs, the granitic rock has been hydrothermally altered into clay and oxide minerals, sometimes cemented by silica deposited from the hot water.

View north from NV 447 of Granite Peak, the highest point in the Granite Range. Bloody Point, composed of Miocene sedimentary and volcanic rocks, extends to the center of photo from the right. Horizontal terraces in the center foreground are ancient Lake Lahontan shorelines.

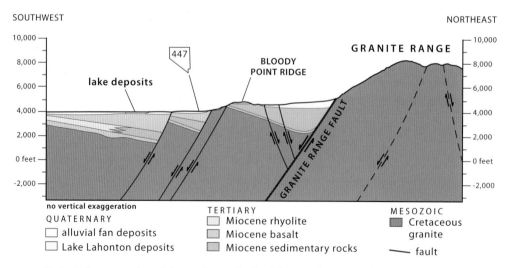

Geological cross section of the southwest flank of the Granite Range along NV 447, showing subsurface normal faults and Bloody Point. —Modified from Faulds and Ramelli, 2005

North of Gerlach, NV 447 passes through Godeys Gap, south of Granite Point, to continue along the southwest margin of the Granite Range, following the northwest-striking normal fault zone along the base of the mountain block. You can see the Smoke Creek Desert playa to the southwest. Nine miles northwest of Gerlach, NV 447 curves to the north around Bloody Point, a mound of Miocene sedimentary and volcanic rocks capped by dark-brown basalt flows. Bloody Point and the ridge it stands on are a sliver of rock faulted down relative the main block of the Granite Range. On the lower slopes of the ridge immediately northwest of the road, well-developed shoreline terraces mark the level of the Smoke Creek Desert arm of Lake Lahontan about 14,000 years ago.

West of the Granite Range are the Buffalo Hills, composed mostly of thick Miocene basalt flows that form a large, undulating lava plain. The lava flows are interbedded with layered, weakly lithified sediments that accumulated in stream channels, floodplains, and lakes in the volcanic highlands.

View south from NV 447 toward the Buffalo Hills over Squaw Creek Valley. The Buffalo Hills are composed of a thick sequence of Miocene basalt flows and associated volcanic and sedimentary rocks.

Glossary

accreted. Something that has been added on, such as an accreted terrane that has been added to the North American continent through plate motions.

air-fall. An accumulation of material that fell onto the ground from the atmosphere, such as volcanic ash or pumice.

alluvial fan. A gently sloping, fan-shaped accumulation of sediments deposited by a stream where it flows out of a narrow valley onto a wider, flatter area.

alluvium. An accumulation of water-transported sediments.

andesite. A volcanic rock that cools from lava containing about 60 percent silica. Andesite may be tan, brown, reddish, or pale gray and sometimes contains small, isolated crystals of the minerals hornblende or feldspar.

Antler Orogeny. A mountain-building event in which thrust faults transported folded rock sequences eastward over the edge of the Paleozoic continental shelf. The Antler event began in late Devonian time and continued at least until the end of the Paleozoic Era, about 250 million years ago, and may have continued into the Mesozoic Era in some Nevada localities.

argillite. A very fine-grained sedimentary rock consisting of microscopic clay-sized mineral grains. Argillite is similar to shale but does not split easily and generally lacks obvious laminations.

ash-fall. An accumulation of volcanic ash particles that have fallen out of the atmosphere.

ash-flow tuff. Rock formed from the consolidation and compaction of an ash-flow, a mixture of volcanic gases and ash that travels across the ground surface.

asthenosphere. A soft, partially molten, zone in the upper mantle over which the rigid lithospheric plates move. The asthenosphere extends from an average depth of about 60 miles below the surface to about 400 miles underground.

basalt. A dark-colored volcanic rock that contains less than 52 percent silica.

basement. The deepest crustal rocks of a given area. They are typically igneous or metamorphic rock.

bedding. Layering as seen in a sedimentary rock. A single layer is called a **bed**. When different rock types are interlayered with each other, they are described as **interbedded**.

bedrock. Rock that remains in its place of origin and has not been moved by erosional processes.

breccia. A sedimentary rock composed of angular rock fragments greater than 2 millimeters in size. Breccia deposits are generally associated with limited transport of rock fragments as in landslides, rock avalanches, or slumping events.

caldera. A steep-walled, subcircular depression in a volcano, at least 1 mile across, that formed by collapse into an emptied or partially emptied magma chamber below.

caliche. A hard horizon composed of calcium carbonate in soil.

carbonates. Rocks, such as limestone or dolomite, that are formed by the combination of atoms of calcium or magnesium with carbon and oxygen.

chert. A hard, dull sedimentary rock composed of microcrystalline quartz.

clast. A grain or fragment of a rock. **Clastic rock** is sedimentary rock composed of broken fragments, such as sand grains, derived from preexisting rocks.

coarse-grained. A term used to describe a rock with large particles or crystals, typically visible to the naked eye, about 1 millimeter in diameter or larger.

columnar jointing. The fracturing in a lava flow upon cooling that causes the rock to break into columns.

conglomerate. A sedimentary rock consisting of lithified gravel, sand, and boulders generally deposited by swift rivers or mudflow events. Particles of rock in conglomerate are well-rounded by abrasion during transport.

continental shelf. The gently inclined part of the continental landmass lying between the shoreline and the more steeply inclined continental slope.

continental slope. The most steeply sloped part of the continental margin, lying between the shelf and the rise.

cuesta. A geomorphic term describing an asymmetric hill or ridge with one steep side and an opposing gentle slope. Essentially, a tilted tableland. Cuestas commonly develop through the differential weathering of tilted strata of rock with varying hardness.

dacite. A felsic volcanic igneous extrusive rock, intermediate in composition between andesite and rhyolite. Dacite in Nevada is particularly common in the Neogene volcanic fields in the western part of the state.

detachment (fault). A low angle (nearly horizontal) normal fault into which several higher-angle faults merge below the surface. Detachments form under extreme tensional stresses and may be exposed at the surface by later uplift and erosion.

diatomite. A sedimentary rock that consists mostly of diatoms, single-celled freshwater or marine algae that consist of silica.

dike. A tabular intrusive body that cuts across layering in the host rock.

diorite. An intrusive igneous rock that is between gabbro and granite in silica content. It is the intrusive equivalent of andesite.

dolomite. A chemical sedimentary rock composed dominantly of the mineral dolomite (a calcium magnesium carbonate). Dolomite forms most readily in shallow, warm seas, and layers of this rock are commonly associated with limestone strata. Much of the dolomite in Nevada is thought to have formed from limestone after it was deposited on the seafloor through a geochemical replacement process.

ductile. A term that describes deformation of a body of rock by bending, flowing, or folding rather than by fracturing. Folded sequences of rock layers are the result of ductile deformation under compression.

escarpment/scarp. A sudden steep rise in the landscape formed by faulting, erosion, or gravitational movements such as slumps and landslides.

evaporite. A term that describes several chemical sedimentary rocks that form when water becomes saline through evaporation. Evaporites are dominated by soluble minerals such as halite (rock salt; sodium chloride), gypsum (calcium sulfate), and calcite (calcium carbonate).

fanglomerate. A term that describes a coarse-grained sedimentary rock or deposit (conglomerate) that originated as gravel in an alluvial fan.

fault. A fracture or zone of fractures in Earth's crust along which blocks of rock on either side have shifted. A **normal fault** forms under extensional stresses, and one side drops relative to the other side. A **detachment fault** is a low-angle normal fault. A **reverse fault** forms under compressional stresses, and one side is pushed up and over the other side. A **thrust fault** is a low-angle reverse fault. In a **strike-slip fault**, rock on one side moves sideways relative to rock on the other side.

fault scarp. An abrupt cliff or steep section in an otherwise even landscape because of offset along a fault.

felsic. A compositional term that describes igneous rocks rich in alkali feldspars and quartz. Felsic igneous rocks contain about 70 percent silicon and oxygen and include such common types as granite and rhyolite.

fine-grained. A term used to describe a rock with small particles or crystals, typically not visible to the naked eye, less than about 1 millimeter in diameter.

foliation. A directional property of many metamorphic rocks in which mineral grains are aligned in a preferred direction to produce banding, elongated steaks, or fissile splitting.

foreland basin. A sedimentary basin that subsided in response to loading of the crust from thrusting in an adjacent orogenic highland.

formation. A body of sedimentary, igneous, or metamorphic rock that can be recognized over a large area. It is the basic stratigraphic unit in geologic mapping. A formation may be part of a larger group and may be broken into members.

fossils. Remains, imprints, or traces or impressions of plants or animals preserved in rock.

gabbro. Dark-colored intrusive igneous rock that consists of less than 52 percent silica. It has the same chemical composition as basalt.

gneiss. A coarse-grained, high-grade metamorphic rock characterized by alternating bands or streaks of light- and dark-colored minerals.

graben. A block of rock that has been faulted downward along two parallel normal faults.

granite. A light-colored plutonic igneous rock consisting of large (visible to the unaided human eye) intergrown crystals of quartz, mica, and feldspar minerals. Granite is a plutonic igneous rock that forms from the slow underground cooling of magma.

granodiorite. A felsic plutonic igneous rock similar in appearance and origin to granite, but with less quartz and more plagioclase feldspar.

greenstone. Volcanic rocks, typically basalt, that have been metamorphosed and have grown green metamorphic minerals.

gypsum. A soft white or colorless mineral composed of hydrated calcium sulfate. Gypsum is commonly used as a primary ingredient in plaster products, including wallboard, soil conditioners, and statuary plaster.

half-graben. An asymmetrical depression formed by normal faulting that displaces bedrock on one side of the basin more than on the opposing side. The floor of a half-graben typically tilts downward toward the more active normal fault.

horst. An elongated block of elevated rock bounded on either side by normal faults.

hydrothermal alteration. Chemical and physical modification of rock under the influence of hot fluids associated with young volcanic rocks or magma in the subsurface. Hydrothermal fluids commonly contain highly reactive chemicals such as acids and gases in solution, and may cause the deposition of metal-rich minerals.

igneous rock. Rock that solidified from the cooling of molten magma.

ignimbrite. An igneous rock composed of particles of volcanic ash that are thoroughly welded together, reflecting the high temperatures of the originally incandescent ash. The classical language roots for this term mean "fire cloud rock," an apt description of the manner in which ignimbrite forms.

intrusive igneous rocks. Rocks that cool from magma beneath the surface of Earth. The body of rock is called an **intrusion**.

island arc. An offshore volcanic arc or linear chain of volcanoes formed along a convergent plate margin.

jasperoid. A purplish-brown, hard and brittle rock that typically forms along shear zones and thrust faults through the silicification of sedimentary rocks such as dolomite, limestone, and shale. Jasperoid in Nevada is mostly of middle to late Paleozoic age and is mineralized by fluids migrating along shear zones or thrust faults.

lahar. An Indonesian term for a volcanic mudflow. Lahars deposits typically consist of large boulders of volcanic rock such as andesite mixed with cobble and pebbles and cemented in a matrix of volcanic ash, sand, and silt. Lahars can travel great distances from their source before they come to rest, so many of the lahar deposits in Nevada's volcanic rock sequences cannot be precisely associated with specific eruptive centers.

latite. A fine-grained felsic igneous rock of volcanic origin that contains less than 5 percent quartz and equal amounts of the minerals alkali feldspar and plagioclase feldspar. Latite in Nevada is mostly of Cenozoic age and may be light tan to rusty brown.

lava. Molten rock erupted on the surface of Earth.

limestone. A sedimentary rock composed of calcium carbonate formed by precipitation in warm water, usually aided by biological activity.

lineament. An extensive linear feature on the surface of Earth.

listric (normal) fault. A curving tensional fault that flattens from a high angle near the surface to a nearly horizontal plane with depth.

lithification. Compaction and cementation of sediment into sedimentary rock.

lithosphere. The outer rigid shell of Earth that is broken into plates. It ranges from 60 to 100 miles thick.

mafic. A term used to describe igneous rocks rich in iron- and magnesium-bearing silicate minerals. Mafic igneous rocks are generally dark-colored, such as basalt and gabbro, two of the most common types.

magma. Essentially, molten rock. An underground liquid consisting of silicon, oxygen, and a variety of less abundant components including iron, magnesium, calcium, sodium, potassium, and aluminum. Magma may also contain dissolved gases and small crystals.

marble. A crystalline metamorphic rock composed of carbonate minerals (calcite and dolomite) that forms from the alteration of limestone or dolomite.

marl. A calcareous clay deposit.

magmatic arc. A zone of magma production that stretches in an arc-like fashion above and parallel to a subduction zone.

metamorphic rock. Rock derived from preexisting rock that has changed mineralogically, texturally, or both in response to changes in temperature and/or pressure, usually deep within Earth.

metamorphism. Recrystallization of an existing rock. Metamorphism typically occurs at high temperatures and often high pressures.

moraine. A mound or ridge of an unsorted mixture of silt, sand, and gravel left by a melting glacier.

mylonite. A fine-grained, sheared metamorphic rock with a banded or streaky appearance produced along faults and shear zones at extremely high temperatures.

normal fault. A high-angle fault that forms under tension. The block above the fault plane (hanging wall) moves down with respect to the opposing foot wall.

obsidian. A glassy-textured volcanic rock that results from the instantaneous cooling of lava on Earth's surface or underwater. Obsidian is generally black, red, or brown and may be associated with pumice.

ore. A mass of rock or other material in which a valuable mineral commodity is sufficiently concentrated to permit profitable mining, processing, and extraction.

orogeny. A tectonic event that forms a mountain range.

phyllite. A foliated metamorphic rock, intermediate in grade between slate and schist, characterized by a shiny, satinlike sheen of light reflected from foliation surfaces

plagioclase. A feldspar mineral rich in sodium and calcium. One of the most common rock-forming minerals in igneous and metamorphic rocks.

plate tectonics. The theory that Earth's lithosphere is broken into large fragments or plates that move slowly over a somewhat malleable asthenosphere, with intense geological activity at plate boundaries.

playa. A flat surface in desert basins that results from fine sediments and salts accumulating after shallow floodwater evaporates. Playa sediments are generally white to light tan or gray and consist primarily of fine silt and clay mixed with halite, gypsum, and other minerals precipitated from solution.

Pleistocene. The last 2 million years of geologic time, during which periods of extensive continental glaciation alternated with warmer interglacial periods of glacial retreat.

pluton. A body of intrusive igneous rock.

porphyry. An igneous rock of any composition that contains conspicuous crystals in a fine-grained groundmass.

pumice. A low-density, light-colored volcanic rock possessing numerous small cavities formed by gases separating from molten lava prior to its cooling. Pumice has a distinctive bubbly or frothy appearance that makes it unique among igneous rocks.

pyrite. A brass- or gold-colored mineral composed of iron sulfide.

pyroclastic. Pertaining to a clastic rock formed of volcanic particles fragmented during explosive eruptions.

quartz. A hard and durable common silicate mineral with the composition SiO_2. Quartz may be colorless, white, yellowish, pink, purple, banded, or black depending on trace impurities and/or crystal lattice defects.

quartzite. A metamorphic rock composed mostly of small quartz grains welded together through the application of heat and pressure to sandstone. Quartzite is a hard and durable rock that commonly forms ledges, cliffs, and crags when weathered at the surface. In addition to its metamorphic definition, the term *quartzite* is also sometimes applied to a very well-cemented and well-sorted quartz sandstone.

quartz monzonite. A quartz-bearing granitic rock with equal amounts of alkali feldspar and plagioclase. A rock with more plagioclase is granodiorite.

rhyolite. A light-colored, fine-grained volcanic rock consisting of minerals similar to those found as larger crystals in granite. Rhyolite is generally light-colored but may be brown, gray, tan, greenish, or even purple in color.

scarp. A cliff or embankment formed at the surface by faulting, erosion, or gravitational movements such as slumps and landslides.

schist. A well-foliated metamorphic rock that is characterized by a flaky appearance resulting from the parallel alignment of mica minerals, either silvery flakes of muscovite or black sheets of biotite. Schist is a medium- to high-grade metamorphic rock.

sedimentary rock. A rock formed from the compaction and cementation of sediment.

shale. A fine-grained, laminated or thinly-bedded sedimentary rock containing clay and silt particles. Shale forms from mud and ooze that accumulates on the floor of deep oceans and lakes.

silica. The compound **silicon dioxide**. The most common mineral made entirely of silica is quartz.

sill. An igneous intrusion that parallels the planar structure or bedding of the host rock.

slate. A well-foliated, fine-grained metamorphic rock that tends to split into thin, even layers due to the parallel alignment of microscopic mineral grains. Slate represents the relatively modest metamorphism of clay-rich shale or siltstone.

strike-slip fault. A fault across which the displacement of adjacent blocks has been dominantly horizontal, rather than vertical. Strike-slip faults are the result of shear stresses and may be right-lateral (opposite side shifted to the right) or left-lateral (opposite side shifted to the left).

subduction. The process of one lithospheric plate sliding downward beneath another. Generally, subducting plates carry thin, dense oceanic crust and descend beneath overriding plates with thicker or less dense crust.

supercontinent. A clustering of all or most of Earth's continental masses into one major landmass. This has occurred at least three times in geologic history.

terrace. An erosional remnant of a former floodplain, standing above the present river.

terrane. A mass of exotic rock sutured to the leading edge of a tectonic plate above a subduction zone. Terranes are packages of rock, sometimes quite complex and highly deformed, generally bounded by faults, and dissimilar in age and/or lithology to surrounding rocks.

thrust fault. A low-angle fault (less than 45 degrees) formed by compression that drives the block of rock above the fault plane over the block of rock beneath it.

tilted fault block. A mountain or mountain range that is uplifted along one side by a normal fault and shows a consistent tilt in its bedding away from the fault.

tufa. A hard rock composed of calcium carbonate that is precipitated underwater in an alkaline lake. It often has a spongy or porous appearance.

tuff. A volcanic rock consisting mostly of small particles of volcanic ash fused and consolidated into a coherent rock. Tuff may be soft and crumbly, or durable and hard, depending on the degree of welding of the ash particles. Tuff is widespread in Nevada, sometimes exhibits flow-banding and glassy zones, and may contain larger mineral crystals and rock fragments in a matrix of fine-grained ash.

unconformity. A depositional contact across which the rock record is missing. The rocks beneath the unconformity are typically significantly older than the ones above it.

vein. A deposit of minerals that fills a fracture in rock.

vent. A place where volcanic materials erupt.

vitrophyre. A glassy volcanic rock with visible crystals scattered throughout.

weathering. The physical disintegration and chemical decomposition of rock at Earth's surface.

REFERENCES

NONTECHNICAL READING

DeCourten, F. L. 2003. *The Broken Land: Adventures in Great Basin Geology.* University of Utah Press.

Fiero, B. 2009. *Geology of Nevada.* University of Nevada Press.

Tingley, J. V., K. A. Pizarro, C. Ross, et al. 2005. *Geology and Natural History Tours in the Reno Area.* Nevada Bureau of Mines and Geology Special Publication 19.

Tingley, J. V., K. A. Pizarro, C. Ross, et al. 2010. *A Geologic and Natural History Tour through Nevada and Arizona along US Highway 93.* Nevada Bureau of Mines and Geology Special Publication 35.

Tingley, J. V., B. W. Purkey, E. M. Duebendorfer, et al. 2001. *Geologic Tours in the Las Vegas Area.* Nevada Bureau of Mines and Geology Special Publication 16.

Tingley, J. V., and S. L. Tingley. 2000. *Exploring East of the Summit: A Field Trip Guide to Steamboat Springs, Lake Tahoe, and the Comstock Area.* Nevada Bureau of Mines and Geology Educational Series E-38.

Trimble, S. 1999. *The Sagebrush Ocean: A Natural History of the Great Basin.* University of Nevada Press.

TECTONICS AND GEOLOGY OF NEVADA AND THE BASIN AND RANGE PROVINCE

Adams, K. D., S. G. Wesnousky, and B. G. Bills. 1999. Isostatic rebound, active faulting, and potential geomorphic effects in the Lake Lahontan basin, Nevada and California. *Geological Society of America Bulletin* 111 (12): 1739–56.

Bennett, R. A., B. P. Wernicke, N. A. Niemi, et al. 2003. Contemporary strain rates in the northern Basin and Range Province from GPS data. *Tectonics* 22 (2): 1–31.

Benson, L. V., E. M. Hattori, and B. A. Southon. 2013. Dating North America's oldest petroglyphs, Winnemucca Lake sub-basin, Nevada. *Journal of Archaeological Science* 40 (12): 4466–76.

Best, M. G., D. L. Barr, E. H. Christensen, et al. 2009. The Great Basin altiplano during the middle Cenozoic ignimbrite flare-up: Insights from volcanic rocks. *International Geology Review* 51: 589–633.

Best, M. G., E. H. Christensen, and S. Gromme. 2013. The 36–18 ma southern Great Basin, USA, ignimbrite province and flareup: Swarms of subduction-related supervolcanoes. *Geosphere* 9 (2): 260–74.

Burke, D. B., and E. H. McKee. 1979. Mid-Cenozoic volcano-tectonic troughs in central Nevada. *Geological Society of America Bulletin* 90 (2): 1181–84.

Busby, C. J. 2013. Birth of a plate boundary at ca. 12 ma in the Ancestral Cascades arc, Walker Lane belt of California and Nevada. *Geosphere* 9 (5): 1147–60.

Busby, C. J., G. D. M. Andrews, A. K. Koerner, et al. 2016. Progressive derangement of ancient (Mesozoic) east-west Nevadaplano paleochannels into modern (Miocene-Holocene) north-northwest trends in the Walker Lane. *Geosphere* 12 (1): 1–40.

Busby, C. J., J. C. Hagan, K. Putirka, et al. 2008. The Ancestral Cascades arc: Cenozoic evolution of the central Sierra Nevada (California) and the birth of the new plate boundary. In *Ophiolites, Arcs, and Batholiths*, eds. J. E. Wright and J. W. Shervais, p. 1–47. Geological Society of America Special Paper 438.

Camp, V. E., K. L. Pierce, and L. A. Morgan. 2015. Yellowstone plume triger for Basin and Range extension, and coeval emplacement of the Nevada–Columbia Basin magmatic belt. *Geosphere* 11 (2): 203–25.

Cashman, P. H., J. H. Trexler, Jr., T. W. Muntean, et al. 2009. Neogene tectonic evolution of the Sierra Nevada: Basin and Range transition zone at the latitude of Carson City, Nevada. In *Late Cenozoic Structure and Evolution of the Great Basin–Sierra Nevada Transition*, eds. J. S. Oldow and P. H. Cashman, p. 171–88. Geological Society of America Special Paper 447.

Christiansen, R. L., and R. S. Yeats. 1993. Post-Laramide geology of the US Cordilleran region. In *The Cordilleran Orogen: Conterminous US*, eds. B. C. Burchfiel, P. W. Lipman, and M. L. Zoback, p. 261–406. Geological Society of America.

Coats, R. R. 1987. *Geology of Elko County, Nevada*. Nevada Bureau of Mines and Geology Bulletin 101.

Colgan, J. P., T. A. Dumitru, and E. L. Miller. 2004. Diachroneity of Basin and Range extension and Yellowstone hot spot volcanism in northwest Nevada. *Geology* 32 (2): 121–24.

Colgan, J. P., and C. D. Henry. 2009. Rapid middle Miocene collapse of the Sevier orogenic plateau in north-central Nevada. *International Geology Review* 51: 920–61.

Coney, P. J., and T. A. Harms. 1984. Cordilleran metamorphic core complexes: Cenozoic extensional relics of Mesozoic compression. *Geology* 12 (9): 550–54.

Cousens B., J. Prytulak, C. Henry, et al. 2008. Geology, geochronology, and geochemistry of the Miocene-Pliocene Ancestral Cascades arc, northern Sierra Nevada, California and Nevada: The roles of the upper mantle, subducting slab, and the Sierra Nevada lithosphere. *Geosphere* 4 (5): 829–53.

Crafford, A. E. J. 2007. *Geologic Map of Nevada*. US Geological Survey Data Series 249.

Crafford, A. E. J. 2008. Paleozoic tectonic domains of Nevada: An interpretive discussion to accompany the geologic map of Nevada. *Geosphere* 4 (1): 260–91.

Crowe, B. M., and W. J. Carr. 1980. *Preliminary Assessment of the Risk of Volcanism at a Proposed Nuclear Waste Repository in the Southern Great Basin*. US Geological Survey Open-File Report 80-375.

DeCelles, P. G. 2004. Late Jurassic to Eocene evolution of the Cordilleran thrust belt and foreland basin system, western USA. *American Journal of Science* 304: 105–68.

DeCelles, P. G., and J. C. Coogan. 2006. Regional structure and kinematic history of the Sevier fold-and-thrust belt, central Utah. *Geological Society of America Bulletin* 118 (7–8): 841–64.

DePolo, D. M., and C. M. dePolo. 1999. *Earthquakes in Nevada: 1852–1998*. Nevada Bureau of Mines and Geology Map 119, scale 1:1,000,000.

Dickinson, W. R. 2002. The Basin and Range as a composite extensional domain. *International Geology Review* 22: 1–38.

Dickinson, W. R. 2006. Geotectonic evolution of the Great Basin. *Geosphere* 2 (7): 353–68.

Dingler, J., G. Kent, N. Driscoll, et al. 2009. A high-resolution seismic CHIRP investigation of active normal faulting across the Lake Tahoe Basin, California-Nevada. *Geological Society of America Bulletin* 121 (7–8): 1089–1107.

Dixon, T. H., S. Robaudo, J. Lee, et al. 1995. Constraints on present-day Basin and Range deformation from space geodesy. *Tectonics* 14 (4): 755–72.

Dong, S., G. Ucarkus, S. G. Wesnousky, et al. 2014. Strike-slip faulting along the Wassuk Range of the northern Walker Lane, Nevada. *Geosphere* 10 (1): 40–48.

Eisses, A. K., A. Kell, G. M. Kent, et al. 2015. New constraints on fault architecture, slip rates, and strain portioning beneath Pyramid Lake, Nevada. *Geosphere* 11 (3): 683–704.

Evans, J. G., and T. G. Theodore. 1978. *Deformation of the Roberts Mountains Allochthon in North-Central Nevada.* US Geological Survey Professional Paper 1060.

Faulds, J. E., and C. D. Henry. 2008. Tectonic influences on the spatial and temporal evolution of the Walker Lane: An incipient transform fault along the evolving Pacific–North American plate boundary. *Arizona Geological Society Digest* 22: 437–70.

Faulds, J. E., C. D. Henry, M. F. Coolbaugh, et al. 2005. Late Cenozoic strain field and tectonic setting of the northwestern Great Basin, western USA: Implications for geothermal activity and mineralization. In *Window to the World*, eds. H. N. Rhoden, R. C. Steininger, and P. G. Vikre, p. 1091–1104. Geological Society of Nevada Symposium Proceedings.

Faulds, J. E., C. D. Henry, N. H. Hinz, et al. 2005. Transect across the northern Walker Lane, northwest Nevada and northeast California: An incipient transform fault along the Pacific–North American plate boundary. In *Interior Western United States*, eds. J. Peterson and C. M. Dehler, p. 129–50. Geological Society of America Field Guide 6.

Finney, S. C., B. D. Perry, P. Emsbo, et al. 1993. Stratigraphy of the Roberts Mountains allochthon, Roberts Mountains and Shoshone Range, Nevada. In *Crustal Evolution of the Great Basin and the Sierra Nevada*, eds. M. M. Lahren, J. H. Trexler, Jr., and C. Spinosa, p. 197–230. University of Nevada.

Glen, J. M. G., E. H. McKee, S. Ludington, et al. 2004. *Geophysical Terranes of the Great Basin and Parts of Surrounding Provinces.* US Geological Survey Open-File Report 2004-1008.

Glen, J. M. G., and D. A. Ponce. 2002. Large-scale fractures related to inception of the Yellowstone hotspot. *Geology* 30 (7): 647–50.

Grauch, V. J. S. 1986. Regional aeromagnetic and gravity data of northern Nevada: Relation to tectonics and disseminated gold deposits. *Terra Cognita* 6 (3): 496–97.

Greene, R. C. 1976. *Volcanic Rocks of the McDermitt Caldera, Nevada-Oregon.* US Geological Survey Open-File Report 76-753.

Hammond, W. C., and W. Thatcher. 2004. Contemporary tectonic deformation of the Basin and Range Province, western United States: 10 years of observation with the Global Positioning System. *Journal of Geophysical Research* 109: 1–21.

Henry, C. D. 2008. Ash-flow tuffs and paleovalleys in northeastern Nevada: Implications for Eocene paleogeography and extension in the Sevier hinterland, northern Great Basin. *Geosphere* 4 (1): 1–35.

Henry, C. D., J. E. Faulds, and C. M. dePolo. 2007. Geometry and timing of strike-slip and normal faults in the northern Walker Lane, northwestern Nevada and northeastern California: Strain partitioning or sequential extensional and strike-slip deformation?

In *Exhumation Associated with Continental Strike-Slip Fault Systems*, eds. A. B. Till, S. M. Roeske, J. C. Sample, et al., p. 59–79. Geological Society of America Special Paper 434.

Henry, C. D., N. H. Hinz, J. E. Faulds, et al. 2012. Eocene–early Miocene paleotopography of the Sierra Nevada–Great Basin Nevadaplano based on widespread ash-flow tuffs and paleovalleys. *Geosphere* 8 (1): 1–27.

Henry, C. D., and D. A. John. 2013. Magmatism, ash-flow tuffs, and calderas of the ignimbrite flareup in the western Nevada volcanic field, Great Basin, USA. *Geosphere* 9 (3): 951–1008.

Hildenbrand, T. G., and R. P. Kucks. 1988. *Total Intensity Magnetic Anomaly Map of Nevada*. Nevada Bureau of Mines and Geology Map 93A, scale 1:750,000.

Horton, T. W., D. J. Sjostrom, M. J. Abruzzese, et al. 2004. Spatial and temporal variation of Cenozoic surface elevations in the Great Basin and Sierra Nevada. *American Journal of Science* 304: 862–88.

Humphreys, E. D. 1995. Post-Laramide removal of the Farallon slab, western United States. *Geology* 23 (11): 987–90.

John, D. A., A. R. Wallace, D. A. Ponce, et al. 2000. New perspectives on the geology and origin of the Northern Nevada Rift. In *Geology and Ore Deposits 2000: The Great Basin and Beyond*, eds. J. K. Cluer, J. G. Price, E. M. Struhsacker, et al., p. 127–54. Geological Society of Nevada Symposium Proceedings.

Kent, G. M., J. M. Babcock, N. W. Driscoll, et al. 2005. 60 k.y. record of extension across the western boundary of the Basin and Range Province: Estimate of slip rates from offset shoreline terraces and a catastrophic slide beneath Lake Tahoe. *Geology* 33 (5): 365–68.

Ketner, K. B. 2008. *The Inskip Formation, the Harmony Formation, and the Havallah Sequence of Northwestern Nevada: An Interrelated Paleozoic Assemblage in the Home of the Sonoma Orogeny*. US Geological Survey Professional Paper 1757.

Ketner, K. B. 2012. *An Alternative Hypothesis for the Mid-Paleozoic Antler Orogeny in Nevada*. US Geological Survey Professional Paper 1790.

Ketner, K. B., and A. G. Alpha. 1992. *Mesozoic and Tertiary Rocks near Elko, Nevada: Evidence for Jurassic to Eocene Folding and Low-Angle Faulting*. US Geological Survey Bulletin 1988-C.

Ketner, K. B., W. C. Day, M. Elrick, et al. 1998. *An Outline of Tectonic, Igneous, and Metamorphic Events in the Goshute-Toano Range between Silver Zone Pass and White Horse Pass, Elko County, Nevada: A History of Superposed Contractional and Extensional Deformation*. US Geological Survey Professional Paper 1593.

Ludington, S., D. P. Cox, K. W. Leonard, et al. 1996. *Cenozoic Volcanic Geology of Nevada*. Nevada Bureau of Mines and Geology Open-File Report, chapter 5.

Macdonald, J. R. 1966. The Barstovian Camp Creek fauna from Elko County, Nevada. *Los Angeles County Museum Contributions in Science* 92: 1–18.

McQuarrie, N., and B. P. Wernicke. 2005. An animated tectonic reconstruction of southwestern North America since 36 ma. *Geosphere* 1 (3): 147–72.

Meert, J. G., and T. H. Torsvik. 2003. The making and unmaking of a supercontinent: Rodinia revisited. *Tectonophysics* 375: 261–88.

Miller, D. M., and T. D. Hoisch. 1995. Jurassic tectonics of northeastern Nevada and northwestern Utah from the perspective of barometric studies. In *Jurassic Magmatism and*

Tectonics of the North American Cordillera, eds. D. M. Miller and C. Busby, p. 267–94. Geological Society of America Special Paper 299.

Mix, H. T., A. Mulch, M. L. Kent-Corson, et al. 2011. Cenozoic migration of topography in the North American Cordillera. *Geology* 39 (1): 87–90.

Morrow, J. R., and C. A. Sandberg. 2008. Evolution of Devonian carbonate-shelf margin, Nevada. *Geosphere* 4 (2): 445–58.

Oldow, J. S. 1984. Evolution of a late Mesozoic back-arc fold and thrust belt, western Great Basin, USA. *Tectonophysics* 102: 245–74.

Parsons, T., G. A. Thompson, and N. H. Sleep. 1994. Mantle plume influence on the Neogene uplift and extension of the US western cordillera? *Geology* 22 (1): 83–86.

Pinto, J. A., and J. E. Warme. 2007. Alamo event, Nevada: Crater stratigraphy and impact breccia realms. In *The Sedimentary Record of Meteorite Impacts*, eds. K. R. Evans, J. W. Horton, Jr., D. T. King, Jr., et al., p. 99–137. Geological Society of America Special Paper 437.

Poole, F. G., and C. A. Sandberg. 2015. Alamo impact olistoliths in Antler orogenic foreland, Warm Springs–Milk Spring area, Hot Creek Range, central Nevada. In *Unusual Central Nevada Terranes Produced by Late Devonian Antler Orogeny and Alamo Impact*, eds. F. G. Poole and C. A. Sandberg, p. 39–104. Geological Society of America Special Paper 517.

Poole, F. G., and C. A. Sandberg. 2015. Olistostrome shed eastward from the Antler orogenic forebulge, Bisoni-McKay area, Fish Creek Range, central Nevada. In *Unusual Central Nevada Terranes Produced by Late Devonian Antler Orogeny and Alamo Impact*, eds. F. G. Poole and C. A. Sandberg, p. 1–38. Geological Society of America Special Paper 517.

Premo, W., P. Casteneiros, and J. L. Wooden. 2008. SHRIMP-RG U-Pb isotopic systematics of zircon from the Angel Lake orthogneiss, East Humboldt Range, Nevada: Is this really Archean crust? *Geosphere* 4 (6): 963–75.

Putirka, K. D., and C. J. Busby. 2012. Introduction: Origin and evolution of the Sierra Nevada and the Walker Lane. *Geosphere* 7 (6): 1269–72.

Rodriguez, B. D., and J. A. Sampson. 2012. *Constraining the Location of the Archean-Proterozoic Suture in the Great Basin Based on Magnetotelluric Soundings.* US Geological Survey Open-File Report 2012-1117.

Rodriguez, B. D., and J. M. Williams. 2008. Tracking the Archean-Proterozoic suture in the northeastern Great Basin, Nevada and Utah. *Geosphere* 4 (2): 315–28.

Saltus, R. W. 1988. *Regional, Residual, and Derivative Gravity Maps of Nevada.* Prepared by the US Geological Survey in cooperation with the Nevada Bureau of Mines and Geology, Mackay School of Mines, University of Nevada, Reno.

Silberling, N. J., D. L. Jones, M. C. Blake, Jr., et al. 1987. *Lithotectonic Terrane Map of the Western Conterminous United States.* US Geological Survey Miscellaneous Field Studies Map MF-1874-C, scale 1:2,500,000.

Silberling, N. J., K. M. Nichols, J. H. Trexler, Jr., et al. 1997. Overview of Mississippian depositional and paleotectonic history of the Antler foreland, eastern Nevada and western Utah. In *Proterozoic to Recent Stratigraphy, Tectonics, and Volcanology, Utah, Nevada, Southern Idaho, and Central Mexico*, eds. P. K. Link and B. J. Kowallis, p. 161–97. Geological Society of America Field Trip Guide Book, 1997 Annual Meeting, Salt Lake City. Brigham Young University Geology Studies 42.

Smith, J. G., E. H. McKee, D. B. Tatlock, et al. 1971. Mesozoic granitic rocks in northwestern Nevada: A link between the Sierra Nevada and Idaho batholiths. *Geological Society of America Bulletin* 82 (10): 2935–44.

Smith, M. E., A. R. Carroll, B. R. Jicha, et al. 2014. Paleogeographic record of Eocene slab rollback beneath western North America. *Geology* 42 (12): 1039–41.

Snell, K. E., P. L. Koch, P. Druschke, et al. 2014. High elevation of the "Nevadaplano" during the late Cretaceous. *Earth and Planetary Science Letters* 386: 52–63.

Sonder, L. J., and C. H. Jones. 1999. Western United States extension: How the West was widened. *Annual Review of Earth and Planetary Sciences* 27: 417–462.

Sorgehan, M. J., and G. E. Gehrels, eds. 2000. *Paleozoic and Triassic Paleogeography and Tectonics of Western Nevada and Northern California.* Geological Society of America Special Paper 347.

Stewart, J. H. 1972. Initial deposits of the Cordilleran geosyncline: Evidence of a late Precambrian (850 m.y.) continental separation. *Geological Society of America Bulletin* 83 (5): 1345–60.

Stewart, J. H. 1980. *Geology of Nevada.* Nevada Bureau of Mines and Geology Special Publication 4.

Stewart, J. H., and E. H. McKee. 1977. *Geology and Mineral Resources of Lander County, Nevada: Part I. Geology.* Nevada Bureau of Mines and Geology Bulletin 88.

Taylor, M. E., ed. 1997. *Early Paleozoic Biochronology of the Great Basin, Western United States.* US Geological Survey Professional Paper 1579.

Taylor, W. J., and D. D. Switzer. 2001. Temporal changes in fault strike (to 90°) and extension directions during multiple episodes of extension: An example from eastern Nevada. *Geological Society of America Bulletin* 113 (6): 743–59.

Thatcher, W., G. R. Foulger, B. R. Julian, et al. 1999. Present-day deformation across the Basin and Range Province, western United States. *Science* 283: 1714–18.

Thorman, C. H., W. E. Brooks, K. B. Ketner, et al. 1991. Late Mesozoic–Cenozoic tectonics in northeastern Nevada. In *Geology and Ore Deposits of the Great Basin*, eds. G. L. Raines, R. E. Lisle, R. W. Schafer, et al., p. 25–45. Geological Society of Nevada Symposium Proceedings.

Trexler, J., P. H. Cashman, W. S. Snyder, et al. 1991. Mississippian through Permian orogenesis in eastern Nevada: Post-Antler, pre-Sonoma tectonics of the western cordillera. In *Paleozoic Paleogeography of the Western United States II, Pacific Section, Society of Economic Paleontologists and Mineralogists*, eds. J. C. Cooper and C. H. Stevens, p. 317–29.

Trexler, J., P. H. Cashman, W. S. Snyder, et al. 2004. Late Paleozoic tectonism in Nevada: Timing, kinematics, and tectonic significance. *Geological Society of America Bulletin* 116 (5–6): 525–38.

Velasco, M. S., R. A. Bennett, R. A. Johnson, et al. 2010. Subsurface fault geometries and crustal extension in the eastern Basin and Range Province, western US. *Tectonophysics* 488: 131–42.

Wallace, A. R., M. E. Perkins, and R. J. Fleck. 2008. Late Cenozoic paleogeographic evolution of northeastern Nevada: Evidence from the sedimentary basins. *Geosphere* 4 (1): 36–74.

Warme, J. E., and C. A. Sandberg. 1996. Alamo megabreccia: Record of late Devonian impact in southern Nevada. *GSA Today* 6: 1–7.

Wesnousky, S. G., A. D. Barron, R. W. Briggs, et al. 2005. Paleoseismic transect across the northern Great Basin. *Journal of Geophysical Research* 110, B05408.

Wolfe, J. A., H. E. Schorn, C. E. Forest, et al. 1997. Paleobotanical evidence for high altitudes in Nevada during the Miocene. *Science* 276: 1672–74.

Wyld, S. J. 2002. Structural evolution of a Mesozoic backarc fold-and-thrust belt in the US cordillera: New evidence from northern Nevada. *Geological Society of America Bulletin* 114 (11):1452–68.

Zoback, M. L., E. H. McKee, R. J. Blakely, et al. 1994. The Northern Nevada Rift: Regional tectonomagmatic relations and middle Miocene stress direction. *Geological Society of America Bulletin* 106 (3): 371–82.

ICE AGE NEVADA

Adams, K. D., and S. G. Wesnousky. 1999. The Lake Lahontan highstand: Age, surficial characteristics, soil development, and regional shoreline correlation. *Geomorphology* 30: 357–92.

Benson, L. V. 1978. Fluctuation in the level of pluvial Lake Lahontan during the last 40,000 years. *Quaternary Research* 9 (3): 300–18.

Benson, L. V., D. Currey, Y. Lao, et al. 1992. Lake-size variations in the Lahontan and Bonneville basins between 13,000 and 9,000 ^{14}C yr B.P. *Palaeogeography, Palaeoclimatology, Palaeoecology* 95: 19–32.

Briggs, R. W., S. G. Wesnousky, and K. D. Adams. 2005. Late Pleistocene and late Holocene lake high stands in the Pyramid Lake subbasin of Lake Lahontan, Nevada, USA. *Quaternary Research* 64 (2): 257–63.

Chadwick, O. A., and J. O. Davis. 1990. Soil-forming intervals caused by eolian sediment pulses in the Lahontan basin, northwestern Nevada. *Geology* 18 (3): 243–46.

Davis, J. O. 1978. *Quaternary Tephrochronology of the Lake Lahontan Area, Nevada and California.* Nevada Archaeological Survey Research Paper 7.

Laabs, B. J. C., J. S. Munroe, L. C. Best, et al. 2013. Timing of the last glaciation and subsequent deglaciation in the Ruby Mountains, Great Basin, USA. *Earth and Planetary Science Letters* 361: 16–25.

Morrison, R. B. 1964. *Lake Lahontan: Geology of the Southern Carson Desert, Nevada.* US Geological Survey Professional Paper 401.

Morrison, R. B. 1991. Quaternary stratigraphic, hydrologic, and climatic history of the Great Basin, with emphasis on Lakes Lahontan, Bonneville, and Tecopa. In *Quaternary Nonglacial Geology: Conterminous US,* ed. R. B. Morrison, p. 283–320. Geology of North America, vol. K-2. Geological Society of America.

Morrison, R. B., and J. C. Frye. 1965. *Correlation of the Middle and Late Quaternary Successions of the Lake Lahontan, Lake Bonneville, Rocky Mountain (Wasatch Range), Southern Great Plains, and Eastern Midwest Areas.* Nevada Bureau of Mines Report 9.

Munroe, J. S., and B. J. C. Laabs. 2011. New investigations of Pleistocene glacial and pluvial records in northeastern Nevada. In *Geologic Field Trips to the Basin and Range, Rocky Mountains, Snake River Plain, and Terranes of the US Cordillera,* eds. J. Lee and J. P. Evan, p. 1–25. Geological Society of America Field Guide 21.

Munroe, J. S., and B. J. C. Laabs. 2013. Latest Pleistocene history of Lake Franklin, northeast Nevada, USA. *Geological Society of America Bulletin* 125 (3–4): 322–42.

Reheis, M. C. 1999. *Extent of Pleistocene Lakes in the Western Great Basin.* US Geological Survey Miscellaneous Field Studies Map MF-2323.

Reheis, M. C., and R. Morrison. 1997. High old pluvial lakes of western Nevada. In *Proterozoic to Recent Stratigraphy, Tectonics, and Volcanology, Utah, Nevada, Southern Idaho, and Central Mexico,* eds. P. K. Link and B. J. Kowallis, p. 459–92. Geological Society of America Field Trip Guide Book, 1997 Annual Meeting, Salt Lake City. Brigham Young University Geology Studies 42.

Reheis, M. C., R. L. Reynolds, W. A. M. Sarna-Wojcicki, et al. 1997. Ages of pre–late Pleistocene deep-lake cycles of Lake Lahontan. *Geological Society of America Abstracts with Programs* 29 (6): A437.

Reheis, M. C., J. L. Slate, A. M. Sarna-Wojcicki, et al. 1993. A late Pliocene to middle Pleistocene pluvial lake in Fish Lake Valley, Nevada and California. *Geological Society of America Bulletin* 105 (7): 953–67.

Snyder, C. T., G. Hardman, and F. F. Zdenek. 1964. *Pleistocene Lakes in the Great Basin.* US Geological Survey Miscellaneous Geologic Investigations Map I–416.

MINERALS, RESOURCES, AND
MINING DISTRICTS OF NEVADA

Adams, S. S., and B. R. Putnam, III. 1992. Application of mineral deposit models in exploration: A case study of sediment-hosted gold deposits, Great Basin, western United States. In *Case Histories and Methods in Mineral Resource Evaluation,* ed. A. E. Annels, p. 1–23. Geological Society, London, Special Publication 63.

Buchanan, L. J. 1987. Precious metal deposits in detachment terrains, southeastern California and western Arizona. In *Bulk Mineable Precious Metal Deposits of the Western United States,* ed. J. L. Johnson, p. 1–15. Geological Society of Nevada Symposium Proceedings.

Buffa, R. H., and A. R. Coyner, eds. 1991. *Geology and Ore Deposits of the Great Basin.* Geological Society of Nevada Field Trip Guidebook Compendium.

Castor, S. B., and G. C. Ferdock. 2004. *Minerals of Nevada.* Nevada Bureau of Mines and Geology Special Publication 31.

Cline, J. S., A. H. Hofstra, J. L. Muntean, et al. 2005. Carlin-type gold deposits in Nevada: Critical geologic characteristics and viable models. *Economic Geology 100th Anniversary Volume,* p. 451–84.

Cornwall, H. R. 1972. *Geology and Mineral Deposits of Southern Nye County, Nevada.* Nevada Bureau of Mines and Geology Bulletin 77.

Doebrich, J. L., and T. G. Theodore. 1996. Geologic history of the Battle Mountain mining district, Nevada, and regional controls on the distribution of mineral systems. In *Geology and Ore Deposits of the American Cordillera,* eds. A. R. Coyner and P. L. Fahey, p. 453–83. Geological Society of Nevada Symposium Proceedings.

Henry, C. D., J. E. Faulds, D. R. Boden, et al. 2001. Timing and styles of Cenozoic extension near the Carlin trend, northeastern Nevada: Implications for the formation of Carlin-type gold deposits. In *Regional Tectonics and Structural Control of Ore: The Major Gold Trends of Northern Nevada,* eds. D. R. Shaddrick, E. Zbinden, D. C. Mathewson, et al., p. 115–28. Geological Society of Nevada Special Publication 33.

Henry, C. D., and M. W. Ressel. 2000. Eocene magmatism of northeastern Nevada: The smoking gun for Carlin-type gold deposits. In *Geology and Ore Deposits 2000: The*

Great Basin and Beyond, eds. J. K. Cluer, J. G. Price, E. M. Struhsacker, et al., p. 365–88. Geological Society of Nevada Symposium Proceedings.

Hofstra, A. H., and A. R. Wallace. 2006. *Metallogeny of the Great Basin: Crustal Evolution, Fluid Flow, and Ore Deposits.* US Geological Survey Open-File Report 2006-1280.

Hudson, D. M. 2003. Epithermal alteration and mineralization in the Comstock district, Nevada. *Economic Geology* 98 (2): 367–85.

John, D. A. 2001. Miocene and early Pliocene epithermal gold-silver deposits in the northern Great Basin, western United States: Characteristics, distribution, and relationship to magmatism. *Economic Geology* 96 (8): 1827–53.

John, D. A., A. H. Hofstra, and T. G. Theodore. 2003. A special issue devoted to gold deposits in northern Nevada: Part 1. Regional studies and epithermal deposits. *Economic Geology* 98 (2): 225–34.

Kleinhampl, F. J., and J. I. Ziony. 1984. *Mineral Resources of Northern Nye County, Nevada.* Nevada Bureau of Mines and Geology Bulletin 99-B.

Koski, R. A., and J. R. Hein. 2002. Stratiform barite deposits in the Roberts Mountains allochthon, Nevada: A review of potential analogs in modern sea-floor environments. In *Contributions to Industrial-Minerals Research*, eds. J. D. Bliss, P. R. Moyle, and K. R. Long, p. 1–17. US Geological Survey Bulletin 2209.

LaPointe, D. D., and J. G. Price. 2009. *Digging Deeper into the Comstock.* Nevada Bureau of Mines and Geology Educational Series E-48.

LaPointe, D. D., J. V. Tingley, and R. B. Jones. 1991. *Mineral Resources of Elko County, Nevada.* Nevada Bureau of Mines and Geology Bulletin 106.

Ludington, S., S. B. Castor, B. T. McLaurin, et al. 2006. Mineral resource potential of the Piute-Eldorado Tortoise, Crescent Townsite, and Keyhole Canyon Areas of Critical Environmental Concern, Clark County, Nevada. In *Mineral Resources Assessment of Selected Areas in Clark and Nye Counties, Nevada*, ed. S. Ludington, p. B1–B67. US Geological Survey Scientific Investigative Report 2006-5197.

Moore, S. 2002. *Geology of the Northern Carlin Trend.* Nevada Bureau of Mines and Geology Bulletin 111, scale 1:24,000.

Muntean, J. L., and D. A. Davis. 2014. *Nevada Active Mines and Energy Producers.* Nevada Bureau of Mines and Geology Educational Series 54.

Papke, K. G. 1984. *Barite in Nevada.* Nevada Bureau of Mines and Geology Bulletin 98.

Ponce, D. A., and J. M. G. Glen. 2002. Relationships of epithermal gold deposits to large-scale fractures in northern Nevada. *Economic Geology* 97 (1): 3–9.

Poole, F. G., and G. E. Claypool. 1984. Petroleum source-rock potential and crude-oil correlation in the Great Basin. In *Hydrocarbon Source Rocks of the Greater Rocky Mountain Region*, eds. J. Woodward, F. F. Meissner, and J. L. Clayton, p. 179–229. Rocky Mountain Association of Geologists.

Price, J. G., J. L. Muntean, D. A. Davis, et al. 2011. *The Nevada Mineral Industry—2010.* Nevada Bureau of Mines and Geology Special Publication MI-2010.

Radtke, A. S. 1985. *Geology of the Carlin Gold Deposit, Nevada.* US Geological Survey Professional Paper 1267.

Ressel, M. W., and C. D. Henry. 2006. Igneous geology of the Carlin trend, Nevada: Development of the Eocene plutonic complex and significance for Carlin-type gold deposits. *Economic Geology* 101 (2): 347–83.

Rodriguez, B. D., J. A. Sampson, and J. M. Williams. 2007. *Major Crustal Fault Zone Trends and Their Relation to Mineral Belts in the North-Central Great Basin, Nevada.* US Geological Survey Open-File Report 2007-1115.

Sillitoe, R. H., and H. F. Bonham, Jr. 1990. Sediment-hosted gold deposits: Distal products of magmatic-hydrothermal systems. *Geology* 18 (2): 157–61.

Silver, E., R. MacKnight, E. Male, et al. 2011. Lidar and hyperspectral analysis of mineral alteration and faulting on the west side of the Humboldt Range, Nevada. *Geosphere* 7 (6): 1357–68.

Singer, D. A. 1996. *An Analysis of Nevada's Metal-Bearing Mineral Resources.* Nevada Bureau of Mines and Geology Open-File Report 96-2.

Teal, L., and M. Jackson. 1997. Geologic overview of the Carlin trend gold deposits. *Society of Economic Geology Newsletter* 31: 13–25.

Theodore, T. G., A. K. Armstrong, A. G. Harris, et al. 1998. Geology of the northern terminus of the Carlin trend, Nevada: Links between crustal shortening during the late Paleozoic Humboldt Orogeny and northeast-striking faults. In *Contributions to the Gold Metallogeny of Northern Nevada*, ed. R. M. Tosdal, p. 69–105. US Geological Survey Open-File Report 98-338.

Thomason, R. E. 2002. Geology and mineralization of the Florida Canyon Mine, Pershing County, Nevada. In *Gold Deposits of the Humboldt Range: New Discoveries in an Old District*, ed. C. Wendt, p. 61–69. Geological Society of Nevada Special Publication 36.

Tosdal, R. M., ed. 1998. *Contributions to the Gold Metallogeny of Northern Nevada.* US Geological Survey Open-File Report 98-338.

Tosdal, R. M., J. S. Cline, C. M. Fanning, et al. 2003. Lead in the Getchell–Turquoise Ridge Carlin-type gold deposits from the perspective of potential igneous and sedimentary rock sources in northern Nevada: Implications for fluid and metal sources. *Economic Geology* 98 (6): 1189–1211.

Tschanz, C. M., and E. H. Pampeyan. 1970. *Geology and Mineral Deposits of Lincoln County, Nevada.* Nevada Bureau of Mines and Geology Bulletin 73.

Vikre, P. G. 1998. *Intrusion-Related, Polymetallic Carbonate Replacement Deposits in the Eureka District, Eureka County, Nevada.* Nevada Bureau of Mines and Geology Bulletin 110.

MAPS, FIELD GUIDES, AND REGIONAL STUDIES

Abbott, E. W., D. P. Laux, and S. B. Keith. 1991. Geochemistry and ore deposits: Influence of magma chemistry. In *Geology and Ore Deposits of the Great Basin*, eds. R. H. Buffa and A. R. Coyner, p. 503–90. Geological Society of Nevada Field Trip Guidebook Compendium.

Adams, K. D. 2012. Response of the Truckee River to lowering base level at Pyramid Lake, Nevada, based on historical air photos and Lidar data. *Geosphere* 8 (3): 607–27.

Adams, O., A. R. Coyner, R. Cuffney, et al. 1991. Roadside geology and precious-metal mineralization, I–80 corridor, Reno to Elko, Nevada. In *Geology and Ore Deposits of the Great Basin*, eds. R. H. Buffa and A. R. Coyner, p. 1085–1123. Geological Society of Nevada Field Trip Guidebook Compendium.

Anderson, R. E. 2003. *Geologic Map of the Callville Bay Quadrangle, Clark County, Nevada.* Nevada Bureau of Mines and Geology Map 139, scale 1:24,000.

Bachi, C. A., C. F. Miller, F. Calvin, et al. 2001. Construction of a pluton: Evidence from an exposed cross section of the Searchlight pluton, Eldorado Mountains, Nevada. *Geological Society of America Bulletin* 113 (9): 1213–28.

Balini, M., J. F. Jenks, R. Martin, et al. 2014. The Carnian/Norian boundary succession at Berlin-Ichthyosaur State Park (Upper Triassic, central Nevada, USA). *Paläontologische Zeitschrift* 89 (3): 399–433.

Beard, L. S., R. E. Anderson, D. L. Block, et al. 2007. *Preliminary Geologic Map of the Lake Mead 30′ x 60′ Quadrangle, Clark County, Nevada, and Mohave County, Arizona.* US Geological Survey Open-File Report 2007-1010.

Best, M. G., E. H. Christiansen, A. L. Deino, et al. 2013. The 36–18 ma Indian Peak–Caliente ignimbrite field and calderas, southeastern Great Basin, USA: Multicyclic supereruptions. *Geosphere* 9 (4): 864–950.

Best, M. G, R. B. Scott, P. D. Rowley, et al. 1993. Oligocene-Miocene caldera complexes, ash-flow sheets, and tectonism in the central and southeastern Great Basin. In *Crustal Evolution of the Great Basin and the Sierra Nevada*, eds. M. M. Lahren, J. H. Trexler, Jr., and C. Spinosa, p. 285–311. Geological Society of America Guidebook.

Boden, D. R. 1986. Eruptive history and structural development of the Toquima caldera complex, central Nevada. *Geological Society of America Bulletin* 97 (1): 61–74.

Bohannon, R. G. 1983. *Geologic Map and Structure Sections of the Muddy and Northern Black Mountains, Clark County, Nevada.* US Geological Survey Miscellaneous Investigations Series Map I-1406, scale 1:62,500.

Bohannon, R. G., and F. Bachhuber. 1979. First day, road log from Las Vegas to Keystone thrust area and Valley of Fire via Frenchman Mountain. In *Basin and Range Symposium and Great Basin Field Conference*, eds. G. W. Newman and H. D. Goode, p. 579–96. Rocky Mountain Association of Geologists.

Bondi, J. W., D. J. Varricchio, F. D. Jackson, et al. 2008. Dinosaurs and dunes! Sedimentology and paleontology of the Mesozoic in the Valley of Fire State Park. In *Field Guide to Plutons, Volcanoes, Faults, Reefs, Dinosaurs, and Possible Glaciation in Selected Areas of Arizona, California, and Nevada*, eds. E. M. Duebendorfer and E. I. Smith, p. 249–62. Geological Society of America Field Guide 11.

Bonham, H. F., and L. J. Garside. 1974. Road log and trip guide, Carver Station: Tonopah district. In *Guidebook to the Geology of Four Tertiary Volcanic Centers in Central Nevada*, p. 6–13. Nevada Bureau of Mines and Geology Report 19.

Brueseke, M. E., J. S. Callicoat, W. Hames, et al. 2014. Mid-Miocene rhyolite volcanism in northeastern Nevada: The Jarbidge Rhyolite and its relationship to the Cenozoic evolution of the northern Great Basin (USA). *Geological Society of America Bulletin* 126 (7–8): 1047–67.

Burchfiel, B. C., and G. A. Davis. 1988. Mesozoic thrust faults and Cenozoic low-angle normal faults, eastern Spring Mountains, Nevada, and Clark Mountains thrust complex, California. In *This Extended Land: Geological Journeys in the Southern Basin and Range*, eds. D. L. Weide and M. L. Faber, p. 87–106. Geological Society of America Cordilleran Section Field Trip Guidebook.

Burchfiel, B. C., R. Fleck, D. T. Secor, et al. 1974. Geology of the Spring Mountains, Nevada. *Geological Society of America Bulletin* 85 (7): 1013–22.

Camilleri, P. A. 1992. Mesozoic structural and metamorphic features in the Wood Hills and Pequop Mountains, northeastern Nevada. In *Field Guide to Geologic Excursions in Utah and Adjacent Areas of Nevada, Idaho, and Wyoming,* ed. J. R. Wilson, p. 93–105. Utah Geologic Survey Miscellaneous Publication 92–3.

Camilleri, P. A. 2010. *Geological Map of the Wood Hills, Elko County, Nevada.* Nevada Bureau of Mines and Geology Map 172.

Camilleri, P. A., and A. J. McGrew. 1997. The architecture of the Sevier hinterland: A crustal transect through the Pequop Mountains, Wood Hills, and East Humboldt Range, Nevada. In *Proterozoic to Recent Stratigraphy, Tectonics, and Volcanology, Utah, Nevada, Southern Idaho, and Central Mexico,* eds. P. K. Link and B. J. Kowallis, p. 310–24. Geological Society of America Field Trip Guide Book, 1997 Annual Meeting, Salt Lake City. Brigham Young University Geology Studies 42.

Carpenter, D. G. 1989. *Geology of the North Muddy Mountains, Clark County, Nevada, and Regional Structural Synthesis: Fold-Thrust and Basin-Range Structure in Southern Nevada, Southwest Utah, and Northern Arizona.* MS thesis, Oregon State University.

Carr, M. D., and J. C. Pinkston. 1987. *Geologic Map of the Goodsprings District, Southern Spring Mountains, Clark County, Nevada.* US Geological Survey Miscellaneous Field Studies Map MF-1514.

Cashman, P., J. Trexler, W. Synder, et al. 2008. Late Paleozoic deformation in central and southern Nevada. In *Field Guide to Plutons, Volcanoes, Faults, Reefs, Dinosaurs, and Possible Glaciation in Selected Areas of Arizona, California, and Nevada,* eds. E. M. Duebendorfer and E. I. Smith, p. 21–42. Geological Society of America Field Guide 11.

Castor, S. B., J. E. Faulds, S. M. Rowland, et al. 2000. *Geologic Map of the Frenchman Mountain Quadrangle, Nevada.* Nevada Bureau of Mines and Geology Map 127, scale 1:24,000.

Christensen, O. D. 1996. Carlin trend geologic overview. In *Structural Geology of the Carlin Trend: Geology and Ore Deposits of the American Cordillera Road Trip B,* eds. S. M. Green and E. Strusacker, p. 147–56. Geological Society of Nevada Field Trip Guidebook Compendium.

Coats, R. R. 1987. *Geology of Elko County, Nevada.* Nevada Bureau of Mines and Geology Bulletin 101.

Coble, M. A., and G. A. Mahood. 2016. Geology of the High Rock caldera complex, northwest Nevada, and implications for intense rhyolitic volcanism associated with flood basalt magmatism and the initiation of the Snake River Plain–Yellowstone trend. *Geosphere* 12 (1): 58–113.

Crafford, A. E. J., ed. 2000. *Geology and Ore Deposits of the Getchell Region, Humboldt County, Nevada.* Geological Society of Nevada Symposium, Field Trip Guidebook 9.

Crafford, A. E. J. 2007. *Geologic Map of Nevada.* US Geological Survey Data Series 249, scale 1:250,000.

Crafford, A. E. J. 2008. Paleozoic domains of Nevada: An interpretive discussion to accompany the geological map of Nevada. *Geosphere* 4 (1): 260–91.

Crafford, A. E. J. 2010. *Geologic Terrane Map of Nevada.* US Geological Survey Open-File Report 10-4, scale 1:500,000.

Day, W. C., R. P. Dickerson, C. J. Potter, et al. 1998. *Bedrock Geologic Map of the Yucca Mountain Area, Nye County, Nevada.* US Geological Survey Miscellaneous Investigations Series Map I-2627, scale 1:24,000.

Duebendorfer, E. M., L. S. Beard, and E. I. Smith. 1998. Restoration of Tertiary deformation in the Lake Mead region, southern Nevada: The role of strike-slip transfer faults. In *Accommodation Zones and Transfer Zones: The Regional Segmentation of the Basin and Range Province*, eds. J. E. Faulds and J. H. Stewart, p. 127–48. Geological Society of America Special Paper 323.

Ehni, W., and G. Saucier. 1997. Day 3: Elko to Roberts Mountains road log. In *The Roberts Mountains Thrust, Elko and Eureka Counties, Nevada*, eds. A. J. Perry and E. W. Abbott, p. 84–86. Nevada Petroleum Society 1997 Field Trip Guidebook.

Eichhubl, P., and E. Flodin. 2005. Brittle deformation, fluid flow, and diagenesis in sandstone at Valley of Fire State Park, Nevada. In *Interior Western United States*, eds. J. Pederson and C. M. Dehler, p. 151–67. Geological Society of America Field Guide 6.

Ekren, E. B., F. M. Byers, Jr., R. F. Hardyman, et al. 1980. *Stratigraphy, Preliminary Petrology, and Some Structural Features of the Tertiary Volcanic Rocks in the Gabbs Valley and Gillis Ranges, Mineral County, Nevada.* US Geological Survey Bulletin 1464.

Ekren, E. B., P. P. Orkild, K. L. Sargent, et al. 1977. *Geologic Map of Tertiary Rocks, Lincoln County, Nevada.* US Geological Survey Miscellaneous Investigations Series Map I-1041, scale 1:250,000.

Ekren, E. B., C. L. Rogers, and G. L. Dixon. 1973. *Geologic and Bouguer Gravity Map of the Reveille Quadrangle, Nye County, Nevada.* US Geological Survey Miscellaneous Investigations Series Map I-806, scale 1:48,000.

Erickson, R. L., and S. P. Marsh. 1974. *Geologic Map of the Golconda Quadrangle, Humboldt County, Nevada.* US Geological Survey Geologic Quadrangle Map GQ–1174, scale 1:24,000.

Farr West Engineering. 2012. *Esmeralda County Water Resources Plan.*

Faulds, J. E. 1995. *Geologic Map of the Mount Davis Quadrangle, Nevada and Arizona.* Nevada Bureau of Mines and Geology Map 105, scale 1:24,000.

Faulds, J. E. 2005. *Field Trip 1: Geologic Highlights of Southeastern Nevada and Northwestern Arizona, Including the Grand Canyon and Flagstaff, Arizona.* Association of Engineering Geologists Annual Meeting, Las Vegas.

Faulds, J. E., D. L. Feuerbach, C. F. Miller, et al. 2001. Cenozoic evolution of the northern Colorado River extensional corridor, southern Nevada and northwest Arizona. In *The Geologic Transition, High Plateaus to Great Basin: A Symposium and Field Guide*, eds. M. C. Erskine, J. E. Faulds, J. M. Bartley, et al., p. 239–71. Utah Geologic Association.

Faulds, J. E., P. K. House, and A. R. Ramelli. 2000. *Geologic Map of the Laughlin Area, Clark County, Nevada.* Nevada Bureau of Mines and Geology Open-File Report 00-6, scale 1:24,000.

Faulds, J. E., E. I. Olsen, S. S. Harlan, et al. 2002. Miocene extension and fault-related folding in the Highland Range, southern Nevada: A three-dimensional perspective. *Journal of Structural Geology* 24: 861–86.

Faulds, J. E., A. B. Ramble, and S. B. Castor. 2010. *Preliminary Geologic Map of the Searchlight Quadrangle, Clark County, Nevada.* Nevada Bureau of Mines and Geology Open-File Report 10-16, scale 1:24,000.

Faulds, J. E., and A. R. Ramelli. 2005. *Reconnaissance Geologic Map of the Granite Range Fault Zone and Adjacent Areas, Washoe County, Nevada.* Nevada Bureau of Mines and Geology Open-File Report 2005-11, scale 1:50,000.

Felger, T. J., and L. S. Beard. 2010. Geologic map of Lake Mead and surrounding regions, southern Nevada, southwestern Utah, and northwestern Arizona. In *Miocene Tectonics of the Lake Mead Region, Central Basin and Range*, eds. P. J. Umhoefer, L. S. Beard, and M. A. Lamb, p. 29–38. Geological Society of America Special Paper 463.

Finney, S. C., J. D. Cooper, and W. B. N. Berry. 1997. Late Ordovician mass extinction: Sedimentologic, cyclostratigraphic, and biostratigraphic records from platform and basin successions, central Nevada. In *Proterozoic to Recent Stratigraphy, Tectonics, and Volcanology, Utah, Nevada, Southern Idaho, and Central Mexico*, eds. P. K. Link and B. J. Kowallis, p. 79–103. Geological Society of America Field Trip Guide Book, 1997 Annual Meeting, Salt Lake City. Brigham Young University Geology Studies 42.

French, D. E., F. Kleinhampl, M. L. Jensen, et al. 1979. Road log from Ely to Las Vegas via Eagle Springs and Trap Springs oil fields, Lunar Crater, Warm Springs, and Pahranagat Valley. In *Basin and Range Symposium and Great Basin Field Conference*, eds. G. W. Newman and H. D. Goode, p. 637–62. Rocky Mountain Association of Geologists.

French, D. E., R. A. Schalla, W. J. Taylor, et al. 1998. Day 2: Ely to Railroad Valley and return. In *Hydrocarbon Habitat and Special Geologic Problems of the Great Basin*, eds. D. E. French and R. A. Schalla. Nevada Petroleum Society 1998 Field Trip Guidebook.

Frizzle, J. E., W. J. Taylor, J. G. Stemmata, et al. 1996. Field trip guide to the Cenozoic structures and stratigraphy of the White Pine and Grant Ranges, Nevada. In *Cenozoic Structure and Stratigraphy of Central Nevada*, eds. W. J. Taylor and H. Langrock, p. 111–22. Nevada Petroleum Society 1996 Field Conference Volume.

Ganev, P. N., J. F. Dolan, K. L. Frankel, et al. 2010. Rates of extension along the Fish Lake Valley fault and transtensional deformation in the Eastern California shear zone–Walker Lane belt. *Lithosphere* 2 (1): 33–49.

Gans, P. B., and E. L. Miller. 1983. Style of mid-Tertiary extension in east-central Nevada. In *Geologic Excursions in the Overthrust Belt and Metamorphic Core Complexes of the Intermountain Region*, eds. W. P. Nash and K. D. Gurgle, p. 107–60. Utah Geological and Mineral Survey Special Studies 59.

Garside, L., and S. B. Castor, eds. 2000. Road log 1: Interstate 80 eastbound, Reno to Fernley (exit 48). In *Geology and Ore Deposits 2000: The Great Basin and Beyond*, eds. J. K. Cluer, J. G. Price, E. M. Struhsacker, et al., p. 19–29. Geological Society of Nevada Symposium Proceedings.

George, B. E., C. F. Miller, B. A. Walker, et al. 2005. Newberry Mountains dike swarm, southern Nevada: Final, extension-related pulse of the Spirit Mountain batholith. *Transactions of the American Geophysical Union, EOS* 86 (18): V13A-01.

Gonsior, Z. J., and J. H. Dilles. 2008. Timing and evolution of Cenozoic extensional normal faulting and magmatism in the southern Tobin Range, Nevada. *Geosphere* 4 (4): 687–712.

Grier, S. 1983. Tertiary stratigraphy and geologic history of the Sacramento Pass area, Nevada. In *Geologic Excursions in the Overthrust Belt and Metamorphic Core Complexes of the Intermountain Region*, eds. W. P. Nash and K. D. Gurgle, p. 139–44. Utah Geological and Mineral Survey Special Studies 59.

Guth, P. L. 1980. *Geology of the Sheep Range, Clark County, Nevada*. PhD dissertation, Massachusetts Institute of Technology.

Guth, P. L., D. L. Schmidt, J. Deibert, et al. 1988. Tertiary extensional basins of northwestern Clark County. In *This Extended Land: Geological Journeys in the Southern Basin and Range*, eds. D. L. Weide and M. L. Faber, p. 239–53. Geological Society of America Cordilleran Section Field Trip Guidebook.

Henry, C. D., and J. E. Faulds. 1999. *Geologic Map of the Emigrant Pass Quadrangle, Nevada*. Nevada Bureau of Mines and Geology Open-File Report 99-9, scale 1:24,000.

Hinz, N. H., J. E. Faulds, and A. R. Ramelli. 2012. *Preliminary Geologic Map of the North Half of the Fourth of July Mountain Quadrangle, Clark County, Nevada.* Nevada Bureau of Mines and Geology Open-File Report 12-8, scale 1:24,000.

Hinz, N. H., J. E. Faulds, A. R. Ramelli, et al. 2012. *Preliminary Geologic Map of the Ireteba Peaks Quadrangle, Clark County, Nevada.* Nevada Bureau of Mines and Geology Open-File Report 12-9, scale 1:24,000.

Hinz, N. H., and A. R. Ramelli. 2015. *Fire and Ice: Geology of the Mount Rose Quadrangle, Lake Tahoe and the Carson Range.* Nevada Bureau of Mines and Geology Educational Series E–57.

House, P. K., P. A. Pearthree, K. A. Howard, et al. 2005. Birth of the lower Colorado River: Stratigraphic and geomorphic evidence for its inception near the conjunction of Nevada, Arizona, and California. In *Interior Western United States*, eds. J. Pederson and C. M. Dehler, p. 357–87. Geological Society of America Field Guide 6.

Howard, K. A., R. W. Kistler, A. W. Snoke, et al. 1979. *Geologic Map of the Ruby Mountains.* US Geological Survey Miscellaneous Investigations Series Map I–1136, scale 1:125,000.

Jones, A. E., ed. 2000. GSN road log 28: US 50 eastbound, Austin to Eureka. In *Cortez to Eureka Gold Deposits*, eds. K. D. Russell and R. C. Hays, Jr., p. 45–54. Geological Society of Nevada Symposium Field Trip Guidebook 6.

Jones, A. E., ed. 2000. GSN road log 38: Interstate 80 westbound, Battle Mountain (exit 229) to Golconda (exit 194). In *Cortez to Eureka Gold Deposits*, eds. K. D. Russell and R. C. Hays, Jr., p. 81–95. Geological Society of Nevada Symposium Field Trip Guidebook 6.

Jones, A. E., and A. Wallace, eds. 2000. GSN road log 2: Interstate 80 eastbound, Fernley (exit 48) to Golconda (exit 194). In *Geology and Ore Deposits 2000: The Great Basin and Beyond*, eds. J. K. Cluer, J. G. Price, E. M. Struhsacker, et al., p. 29–39. Geological Society of Nevada Symposium Proceedings.

Kleinhampl, F. J., and J. I. Zion. 1985. *Geology of Northern Nye County, Nevada.* Nevada Bureau of Mines and Geology Bulletin 99A.

Lang, N. P., B. J. Walker, L. L. Claiborne, et al. 2008. The Spirit Mountain batholith and Secret Pass Canyon volcanic center: A cross-sectional view of the magmatic architecture of the uppermost crust of an extensional terrain, Colorado River, Nevada-Arizona. In *Field Guide to Plutons, Volcanoes, Faults, Reefs, Dinosaurs, and Possible Glaciation in Selected Areas of Arizona, California, and Nevada*, eds. E. M. Duebendorfer and E. I. Smith, p. 187–214. Geological Society of America Field Guide 11.

LaPointe, D. D., J. G. Price, J. E. Faulds, et al. *"Tuff All Over": Exploring Faulted Volcanic Terrain in the Painted Hills, Virginia Mountains, West of Pyramid Lake.* Nevada Bureau of Mines and Geology Educational Series E–52.

Lee, J., D. Stockli, J. Schroeder, et al. 2006. Fault slip transfer in the Eastern California shear zone: Walker Lane belt. In *Kinematics and Geodynamics of Intraplate Dextral Shear in Eastern California and Western Nevada*, conveners J. Lee, D. Stockli, C. Henry, and T. Dixon, p. 1–26. Penrose Conference Report, Geologic Society of America.

Lisenbee, A. L., and B. Kieffer Rowe. 1996. The White Pine Range detachment fault, Blackrock and Freeland Canyon area, White Pine Range, Nevada. In *Cenozoic Structure and Stratigraphy of Central Nevada*, eds. W. J. Taylor and H. Langrock, p. 89–93. Nevada Petroleum Society Field Conference Volume.

Long, S. P., and J. P. Walker. 2015. Geometry and kinematics of the Grant Range brittle detachment system, eastern Nevada, USA: An end-member style of upper crustal extension. *Tectonics* 34 (9): 1–26.

Lunstrom, S. C., W. R. Page, V. E. Langenheim, et al. 1998. *Preliminary Geologic Map of the Valley Quadrangle, Clark County, Nevada.* US Geological Survey Open-File Report 98-508, scale 1:24,000.

Maldonado, F., and D. L. Schmidt. 1990. *Geologic Map of the Southern Sheep Range, Fossil Ridge and Castle Rock Area, Clark County, Nevada.* US Geologic Survey Miscellaneous Investigations Series Map I-2086, scale 1:24,000.

McGrew, A. J., M. T. Peters, and J. E. Wright. 2000. Thermobarometric constraints on the tectonothermal evolution of the East Humboldt Range metamorphic core complex, Nevada. *Geological Society of America Bulletin* 112 (1): 45–60.

Menges, C. M. 2008. Multistage late Cenozoic evolution of the Amargosa River drainage, southwestern Nevada and eastern California. In *Late Cenozoic Drainage History of the Southwestern Great Basin and Lower Colorado River Region: Geologic and Biotic Perspectives,* eds. M. C. Reheis, R. Hershel, and D. M. Miller, p. 39–90. Geological Society of America Special Paper 439.

Mifflin, M. D., and J. Quade. 1988. Paleohydrology and hydrology of the carbonate rock province of the Great Basin (east-central to southern Nevada). In *Field Trip Guidebook,* ed. G. S. Holden, p. 305–35. Geological Society of America 1888–1988 Centennial Meeting, Denver.

Miller, D. A., and J. L. Wooden. 1993. *Geologic Map of the New York Mountains Area, California and Nevada.* US Geological Survey Open-File Report 93-198, scale 1:50,000.

Mueller, K. J., and A. W. Snoke. 1993. Cenozoic basin development and normal fault systems associated with the exhumation of metamorphic complexes in northeast Nevada. In *Crustal Evolution of the Great Basin and the Sierra Nevada,* eds. M. M. Lahren, J. H. Trexler, Jr., and C. Spinosa, p. 20–34. Geological Society of America Guidebook.

Muntean, T. W. 2012. *Muddy Creek Formation: A Record of Late Neogene Tectonics and Sedimentation in Southern Nevada.* PhD dissertation, University of Nevada, Las Vegas.

Muntean, T. W. 2013. *Preliminary Geologic Map of the Valley of Fire East Quadrangle, Clark County, Nevada.* Nevada Bureau of Mines and Geology Open-File Report 13-6, scale 1:24,000.

Nevada Bureau of Mines and Geology. 1999. *Generalized Geologic Map of Nevada.* Modified by S. L. Tingley from Nevada Bureau of Mines and Geology Map 57, *Million-Scale Geologic Map of Nevada,* by J. H. Stewart and J. E. Carlson, and fault maps by C. M. dePolo, 1998.

Noble, D. C., D. B. Slemmons, M. K. Korringa, et al. 1974. Eureka Valley Tuff, east-central California and adjacent Nevada. *Geology* 2 (3): 139.

Nutte, C. 1996. Cretaceous(?) to early Oligocene sedimentary and volcanic rocks at Alligator Ridge, Buck Mountain–Bald Mountain area, central Nevada. In *Cenozoic Structure and Stratigraphy of Central Nevada,* eds. W. J. Taylor and H. Langrock, p. 13–22. Nevada Petroleum Society 1996 Field Conference Volume.

Page, W. R. 1998. *Geologic Map of the Arrow Canyon NW Quadrangle, Clark County Nevada.* US Geological Survey Geologic Quadrangle Map GQ–1776.

Page, W. R., S. C. Lundstrom, A. G. Harris, et al. 2005. *Geologic and Geophysical Maps of the Las Vegas 30' x 60' Quadrangle, Clark and Nye Counties, Nevada, and Inyo County, California.* US Geological Survey Scientific Investigations Map SIM-2814.

Potter, C. J., R. P. Dickerson, D. S. Sweetkind, et al. 2002. *Geologic Map of the Yucca Mountain Region, Nye County, Nevada.* US Geological Survey Geologic Investigations Series Map I-2755, scale 1:50,000.

Ramelli, A. R., W. R. Page, C. R. Manker, et al. 2011. *Geologic Map of the Gass Peak SW Quadrangle, Clark County, Nevada.* Nevada Bureau of Mines and Geology Map 175, scale 1:24,000.

Reheis, M. C., and T. L. Sawyer. 1997. Late Cenozoic history and slip rates of the Fish Lake Valley, Emigrant Peak, and Deep Springs fault zone, Nevada and California. *Geological Society of America Bulletin* 109 (3): 280–99.

Rigby, J. G. 1986. Road log and trip guide. In *Precious-Metal Mineralization in Hot Springs Systems, Nevada-California,* eds. J. V. Tingley and H. F. Bonham, Jr., p. 2–84. Nevada Bureau of Mines and Geology Report 41.

Robinson, P. T., and J. H. Stewart. 1984. *Uppermost Oligocene and Lowermost Miocene Ash-Flow Tuffs of Western Nevada.* US Geological Survey Bulletin 1557.

Rowland, S. M. 1987. Paleozoic stratigraphy of Frenchman Mountain, Clark County, Nevada. In *Geological Society of America Centennial Field Guide: Cordilleran Section,* ed. M. Hill, p. 53–56. Geological Society of America.

Rowland, S. M., J. R. Parolini, E. Exhner, et al. 1990. Sedimentologic and stratigraphic constraints on the Neogene translation and rotation of the Frenchman Mountain structural block, Clark County, Nevada. In *Basin and Range Extensional Tectonics near the Latitude of Las Vegas, Nevada,* ed. B. P. Wernicke, p. 99–122. Geological Society of America Memoir.

Ryscamp, E. B., J. T. Abbott, J. D. Vervoot, et al. 2008. Age and petrogenesis of volcanic and intrusive rocks in the Sulphur Spring Range, central Nevada: Comparisons with ore-associated Eocene magma systems in the Great Basin. *Geosphere* 4 (3): 496–519.

Sandberg, C. A., J. R. Morrow, and F. G. Poole. 2001. Construction and destruction of crinoidal mudmounds on Mississippian Antler forebulge, east of Eureka, Nevada. In *Structure and Stratigraphy of the Eureka, Nevada, Area,* eds. M. S. Miller and J. P. Walker, p. 23–50. Nevada Petroleum Society 2001 Summer Field Trip Guidebook.

Schweickert, R. A., M. M. Lahren, R. Karlin, et al. 2000. *Preliminary Map of Active Faults of the Lake Tahoe Basin, California and Nevada.* Nevada Bureau of Mines and Geology Open-File Report 2000-4, scale 1:62,500.

Silberling, N. J., K. M. Nichols, J. H. Treadler, Jr., et al. 1997. Overview of Mississippian depositional and paleotectonic history of the Antler foreland, eastern Nevada and western Utah. In *Proterozoic to Recent Stratigraphy, Tectonics, and Volcanology, Utah, Nevada, Southern Idaho, and Central Mexico,* eds. P. K. Link and B. J. Kowallis, p. 161–96. Geological Society of America Field Trip Guide Book, 1997 Annual Meeting, Salt Lake City. Brigham Young University Geology Studies 42.

Smith, E., D. Honn, and R. Johnsen. 2010. Volcanoes of the McCullough Range. In *Miocene Tectonics of the Lake Mead Region, Central Basin and Range,* eds. P. J. Umhoefer, L. S. Beard, and M. A. Lamb, p. 203–19. Geological Society of America Special Paper 463.

Snoke, A. W., K. A. Howard, A. J. McGrew, et al. 1997. The grand tour of the Ruby–East Humboldt metamorphic core complex, northeastern Nevada. In *Proterozoic to Recent Stratigraphy, Tectonics, and Volcanology, Utah, Nevada, Southern Idaho, and Central Mexico,* eds. P. K. Link and B. J. Kowallis, p. 225–69. Geological Society of America Field Trip Guide Book, 1997 Annual Meeting, Salt Lake City. Brigham Young University Geology Studies 42.

Stewart, J. H. 1999. *Geologic Map of the Carson City 30 x 60 Minute Quadrangle, Nevada.* Nevada Bureau of Mines and Geology Map 118.

Stewart, J. H., and J. E. Carlson. 1978. *Geologic Map of Nevada.* US Geological Survey and Nevada Bureau of Mines and Geology Map, scale 1:500,000.

Stockli, D. F., T. A. Dumitru, M. O. McWilliams, et al. 2003. Cenozoic tectonic evolution of the White Mountains, California and Nevada. *Geological Society of America Bulletin* 115 (7): 788–816.

Swadley, W. C., and W. J. Carr. 1987. *Geologic Map of the Quaternary and Tertiary Deposits of the Big Dune Quadrangle, Nye County, Nevada, and Inyo County, California.* US Geological Survey Miscellaneous Investigations Series Map I-1767.

Sweetkind, D. S., and E. A. du Bray. 2008. *Compilation of Stratigraphic Thicknesses for Caldera-Related Tertiary Volcanic Rocks, East-Central Nevada and West-Central Utah.* US Geological Survey Data Series 271.

Taylor, E. 2010. *Characterization of Geologic Deposits in the Vicinity of US Ecology, Amargosa Basin, Southern Nevada.* US Geological Survey Scientific Investigations Report 2010-5134.

Taylor, W. J., and H. Langrock, eds. 1996. *Cenozoic Structure and Stratigraphy of Central Nevada.* Nevada Petroleum Society 1996 Field Conference Volume.

Thorman, C. H., K. B. Ketner, D. M. Miller, et al. 1987. *Field Guide, Roadlog, and Comments on the Geology from Wendover, Utah, to Wells, Nevada.* US Geological Survey Open-File Report 87-0493.

Tincher, C. R., and D. F. Stockli. 2009. Cenozoic volcanism and tectonics in the Queen Valley area, Esmeralda County, western Nevada. In *Late Cenozoic Structure and Evolution of the Great Basin–Sierra Nevada Transition*, eds. J S. Oldow and P. H. Cashman, p. 255–74. Geological Society of America Special Paper 447.

Trexler, J. H., P. H. Cashman, C. D. Henry, et al. 2000. Neogene basins in western Nevada document the tectonic history of the Sierra Nevada–Basin and Range transition zone for the last 12 ma. In *Great Basin and Sierra Nevada*, eds. D. R. Lageson, S. G. Peters, and M. M. Lahren, p. 97–116. Geological Society of America Field Guide 2.

Tschanz, C. M., P. P. Orchid, and F. G. Poole. 1979. Road log from Las Vegas to Ely, Nevada, via Caliente and Pioche. In *Basin and Range Symposium and Great Basin Field Conference*, eds. G. W. Newman and H. D. Goode, p. 597–619. Rocky Mountain Association of Geologists.

US Department of Energy. 2002. *Final Environmental Impact Statement for a Geologic Repository for the Disposal of Spent Nuclear Fuel and High-Level Radioactive Waste at Yucca Mountain, Nye County, Nevada.* DOE/EIS-0250, Volume I Impact Analyses.

Warme, J. E., J. R. Morrow, and C. A. Sandberg. 2008. Devonian carbonate platform of eastern Nevada: Facies, surfaces, cycles, sequences, reefs, and cataclysmic Alamo impact breccia. In *Field Guide to Plutons, Volcanoes, Faults, Reefs, Dinosaurs, and Possible Glaciation in Selected Areas of Arizona, California, and Nevada*, eds. E. M. Duebendorfer and E. I. Smith, p. 215–47. Geological Society of America Field Guide 11.

Webster, G. D., M. Gordon, Jr., R. L. Langenheim, et al. 1984. Road logs for the Mississippian-Pennsylvanian boundary in the eastern Great Basin: Salt Lake City, Utah, to Las Vegas, Nevada. In *Western Geologic Excursions*, ed. J. Lentz, Jr., p. 1–86. Geological Society of America Annual Meeting.

Weimer, B. S. 1987. *Geologic Roadlogs: Reno, Steamboat Springs, Virginia City, Carson City, Wadsworth, Lake Tahoe, Mount Rose Summit, Pyramid Lake.* Nevada Bureau of Mines and Geology Open-File Report 87-4.

Willden, R. 1964. *Geology and Mineral Deposits of Humboldt County, Nevada.* Nevada Bureau of Mines and Geology Bulletin 59.

Willden, R., and R. C. Speed. 1974. *Geology and Mineral Deposits of Churchill County, Nevada.* Nevada Bureau of Mines and Geology Bulletin 83.

Wyld, S. J., and J. E. Wright. 1997. Triassic-Jurassic tectonism and magmatism in the Mesozoic continental arc of Nevada: Classic relations and new developments. In *Proterozoic to Recent Stratigraphy, Tectonics, and Volcanology, Utah, Nevada, Southern Idaho, and Central Mexico*, eds. P. K. Link and B. J. Kowallis, p. 197–224. Geological Society of America Field Trip Guide Book, 1997 Annual Meeting, Salt Lake City. Brigham Young University Geology Studies 42.

Yount, J., and D. D. LaPointe. 1997. Glaciation, faulting, and volcanism in the southern Lake Tahoe Basin. *NAGT Field Trip II*, p. II-1–II-22. National Association of Geoscience Teachers, Far Western Section, Fall Field Conference.

Index

Page numbers in bold include photographs

387

About the Authors

Since mapping the geology of the Roberts Mountains as a college student in the 1970s, **Frank DeCourten** has been fascinated by geology and landscapes of the Basin and Range region. For more than four decades he has taught geology and conducted geological research in and around the Great Basin of northern Nevada. The author of four books and numerous technical papers, Frank has participated in the geology programs at the University of Utah, University of Nevada, and California State University, Sacramento. He has conducted educational seminars and field study programs in the western United States for a broad array of government agencies and scientific organizations. Since 1994, Frank has been professor of earth sciences at Sierra College in Grass Valley, California. He currently lives in Penn Valley, California, with his wife, Becky, and dog, Blue.

Norma Biggar graduated from Antioch College and went on to earn a master's degree at the University of Alaska. She joined a consulting company to evaluate the seismic hazards along the Alyeska pipeline. She stayed with the consulting company for thirty-three years, evaluating seismic hazards in such far-flung places as Iran, Colombia, and Israel. The latest project was on the high-level nuclear waste project in Nevada, on which she worked for fifteen years from her home in Las Vegas. Upon retirement, her attention turned to hiking, dancing, propagating native plants, and compiling *Roadside of Geology of Nevada*.